SHOP *talk*

dee Hobsbawn-smith

For Sheila —
Tootle through
town!
Hugs,
dee xx

The Open-All-Hours Insider's Guide to Finding Great Ingredients in Calgary, the Bow Valley and Beyond

Last Impression Publishing

Calgary, Alberta

Last Impression Publishing
930–30 Avenue NW, Calgary, Alberta T2K OAI
Phone: (403) 289•5718 • Fax: (403) 289•0157
E-mail: lastimpression@shaw.ca

First Edition
April 2008
12 11 10 09 08 — 1 2 3 4 5 6 7 8 9 10

Library and Archives Canada Cataloguing in Publication

Hobsbawn-Smith, Dee
    Shop talk: the open-all-hours insider's guide to finding great ingredients in Calgary, the Bow Valley & beyond / dee Hobsbawn-Smith.

Includes index.
ISBN: 978-0-9784634-0-3

    1. Grocery shopping—Alberta—Calgary Region—Guidebooks. 2. Grocery trade—Alberta—Calgary Region—Guidebooks. 3. Grocery trade—Alberta—Calgary Region—Directories. 4. Calgary Region (Alta.)—Guidebooks. Title.

TX360.C33C34 2008   381'.4564130025712338   C2008-902018-9

EDITING & PROOFREADING: Sandy Gough, Jeremy Drought and dee-Hobsbawn-Smith, Calgary, Alberta.
INTERIOR & COVER DESIGN: Jeremy Drought, Last Impression Publishing Service, Calgary, Alberta.
COVER PHOTOGRAPHY: dee Hobsbawn-Smith in 2007 by Angela Chard, Crystal Image Studios, Calgary, Alberta.

Printed in Canada by Friesens Corporation, Altona, Manitoba.

Contents

Foreword

*"We are food, everything is food, we are connected by food
and the making, producing and sharing of food."*

VANDANA SHIVA
Slow Food's Terra Madre Conference, Turin, Italy, 2006

FIRST MET DEE in her days as a chef and restaurateur. I have come to
know her much better as a chef and the extraordinary investigative
food journalist that she is today. Dee has chronicled the enormous progress
of our city's culinary resources. She has connected us with varied
opportunities—to buy basic ingredients from the farmgate, from farmers'
markets and retailers, good and delicious prepared foods from chefs and
caterers, and essential social services and community outreach programs.

We can learn from her findings in her books, newspaper columns,
presentations, and cooking classes. Dee teaches people—of all ages—how to
cook. Cooking and knowing how to nourish ourselves properly should be
considered as essential as knowing how to read and write.

At my restaurant River Café, we strive to source high quality and delicious
ingredients from local farmers and producers—primarily in Alberta—especially
those practicing sustainable agriculture and responsible stewardship of the
land. Supporting our local food growers and producers is making a commitment
towards better awareness of the culture and production of our food and
understanding food as it relates to nature and the land that sustains us. When
we find a new farmer or grower, chances are dee has already visited them and
discovered first-hand what they do, listened to their philosophy, and can
recount their story.

I am often asked many questions that start with "Where can I buy...?" In
Shop talk, dee has provided a complete and comprehensive answer to finding
the best local ingredients but has gone much further in providing sources
for the cook's tools, quality wine selections, artisanal cheese, handcrafted
breads, spices from around the world, and suppliers of many quality prepared
foods to complement great meals at home.

Food is the most primary element in our lives. This book celebrates real
food as opposed to fast food. We are faced with a huge decline of diversity in
our food chain, a direct result of agricultural and food service monopolies.
Patronize the many independent food producers, purveyors and artisans
featured in this book. They offer us diversity and preserve our choices for
better quality foods. Whether you are cooking your way through *Larousse
Gastronomique*, recreating a family recipe, or hosting a dinner party with a
selection of well-prepared foods, this is Calgary's first definitive guide for
where to find the best ingredients for your table. Get shopping, chopping,

and cooking, and take the time to enjoy the pleasure of delicious food at home with family and friends.

Sal Howell
Proprietor, River Café
Calgary, Alberta
January 2008

Introduction

A COOK IS ONLY AS GOOD AS HER INGREDIENTS. The ingredients available to cooks in and around Calgary have never been so rewarding. We can buy local foods raised in the black-soil fields and gardens around Olds, yoghurt, milk, and cheeses from the windy heights of Fort Macleod, hardy greens from the hillsides of Black Diamond, and lamb, bison, and beef from the plains. We can find imported goods that are at ease in a Moroccan *souk*—glittering pomegranates, heaps of *couscous*, Medjool dates—or ingredients as easily found in a French *marché*—*le puy* lentils, pork bellies, wheels of Cantal, smudges of *chèvre*. We have South Asian sweet shops, with gleaming rows of pistachio and almond delicacies drenched in *rose water* syrup. We spread cultured Alberta butter on *levain boules* and flaky croissants, and buy *molé* sauce or Panang curry paste. And in specialty shops and bakeries we encounter quintessentially prairie flavours, like maple barley cookies or cranberry mustard. There is no one Alberta cuisine any more than there is a defining Canadian cuisine, but there are some damn fine eats, and they have taken root, slowly but persistently, in the land where the chinook wind blows across the hillside.

But you have to know where to look!

To aid cooks and eaters, this book contains details of more than 350 businesses producing or retailing foods in Calgary, the Bow Valley and beyond. For the record, no money changed hands for inclusion in *Shop talk: The Open-All-Hours Insider's Guide to Finding Great Ingredients in Calgary, the Bow Valley and Beyond*.

The idea of a good grocery directory sprang from my food background: my restaurant, *Foodsmith*, presented regional cuisine to Calgarians in 1992 – 94. Finding the good stuff meant hooking up with local growers, driving across town or across the countryside for specialized ingredients. Since, I have put my efforts into classes and onto the page, telling cooks and readers where to find what they need to cook fine fare.

Here they are, the good guys and the hardworking women, catalogued by their efforts and areas of expertise: the butchers, the bakers, the beekeepers and greengrocers, the specialized ethnic retailers, and sellers of beverages and kitchenware. Not to be missed are the growers who offer farmgate sales, the farmers' markets where local produce gleams on shelves, caterers, personal chefs and home meal replacement options (HMRs), and a list of relevant food organizations.

Most of us are immigrants. The influx of new arrivals in Calgary and its outlying districts has had a direct impact on the food culture of the city, as it has impacted every other facet of life. Immigrant parents who are keen to preserve their cultural heritage while helping their children assimilate into their new home are relieved to find food that their kids will recognize. It eases the pangs of homesickness while smoothing the way to integration.

It has not been a sudden thing—the change of the culinary landscape in Alberta.

The population in Calgary has grown by about 200,000 since 1994, and reached one million in 2006. Each year more than 7,000 immigrants arrive in Calgary from overseas. To this influx of new Canadians, add the numbers of migrants from elsewhere in Canada, and we have an annual total of close to 10,000 new faces and mouths to feed. India ranks third in immigration to Canada (behind China and the Philippines but ahead of Pakistan, the UK, Korea and the USA). Muslims now number about 85,000 in Calgary, from all sects—Sunni, Shiia, Ismaili or Ahmadi, the smallest group, also known as Ahmadiyya Muslims. Because the Calgary (and Alberta) economy is presently strong, analysts are predicting that within twenty years, immigrants will account for 60 percent of the population in Calgary and the city will be all the more multicultural a marketplace.

The reality is clear: where people dwell is also where they shop—for food, for clothing, for entertainment. Most frequently, for food! Hidden throughout the city are small enclaves and strip malls, freestanding stores and businesses, each business attempting to cater to the perceived needs of its community. It takes an effort to step outside of our rotes and rhythms to explore the truly vast variety of goods and foodstuffs that reside in our own neighbourhood, let alone those farther afield. The effort is worthwhile.

In a city of more than one million residents, shopping for groceries has evolved, with increasing diversity of choice and dispersion of destination. In a city as widespread and busy as Calgary has become, the daily or weekly task of shopping for groceries comes with the usual urban challenges. Inevitably, the task makes demands on our time and financial resources—as it has always done—but never more so than now, with all of the choices available, the distances we must drive, the congestion, the parking! Italian groceries do not necessarily occupy the same street as African goods, or even the same quadrant of the city. How do we rationalize our choices?

My hope is that shopping for food will continue to evolve into more community-minded expeditions, where shoppers can source all that they desire within a smaller geographic region instead of long cross-town trips for a few diverse ingredients. It is another way to think of local. Locale is the venue. Local is the adverb.

How to Use this Book

With all of this in mind, *Shop talk* is divided into 26 broad categories which are presented alphabetically and include nine for food and drink (Bakeries, Booze, Cheese & Dairy, Chocolates & Sweets, Coffee & Tea, Fishmongers, Greengrocers [Fruit & Vegetables], Meat & Game, and Organics), five for geographic and cultural origins (Asian, East Indian, European, Latin, Caribbean & African, and Middle Eastern), and a spectrum of services (twelve) within the food industry (Chains [both Big & Small], Cooking Schools & Classes, Culinary Tours, Farmers' Markets, Farmgate Sales [largely located in the Bow Valley & Beyond], Gems, Home Delivery, Kitchenware, Local

Producers, Make 'n' Take Meals/HMRs, Personal Chefs & Caterers, and Food Organizations).

Within *most* of these categories, listings are presented geographically, beginning with those businesses which offer city wide service, and then clockwise through Calgary's quadrants (Northeast, Southeast, Southwest, and Northwest). Both city wide and within each quadrant, businesses are presented alphabetically by business name. I say *most* categories because there are always exceptions. Perhaps the potential for confusion is greatest when it comes to presenting our growing list of local producers, some of whom offer what are called farmgate sales. The vast majority of local producers are actually located on farms and acreages, orchards and gardens in or near communities other than Calgary. Some of them welcome visitors to the "farmgate" but many cannot accommodate the retail traffic—yet! With a few exceptions, local producers who entertain farmgate sales are to be found in the Bow Valley and beyond, listed under their home community. All other local producers—those which you cannot presently visit at the farmgate— have some sort of presence in the city either because they provide direct delivery service, have a storefront presence at a farmers' market, or make their produce available via other retail businesses. Thus, local producers are presented alphabetically by major categories and presently include: Booze, Cheese & Dairy, Chocolate & Sweets, Fishmongers, Greengrocers, Meat & Game and a small number of not-to-be-overlooked Others—businesses which did not fit neatly or appropriately into any of our broad categories.

Beyond metropolitan Calgary, in the section we've called Bow Valley & Beyond, city quadrants are replaced by the cardinal points of the compass (Points North, Points East, Points South and Points West). For each cardinal direction, entries are presented in alphabetical order by community name, and within each community, alphabetically by the same broad categories and then alphabetically by business name. Think Russian dolls!

Browse the categories of your interest and get to know the individual businesses within your home quadrant (in town). When heading across town, we hope you can be more aware of the businesses that exist in your destination quadrant and make the most of your trip. When heading out of town we hope you will become more aware of the businesses located in some of the smaller communities you are travelling past or through. Regardless of the direction in which your travel plans take you, *Shop talk* was designed to assist you in planning your grocery shopping, to support your making use of stores and retail outlets which are of closest geographic proximity to your home and to make expeditions farther afield more fulfilling. It is a smart, fuel- and time-efficient approach to shopping for your groceries and for learning more about your own neighbourhood, your own city, the Bow Valley and beyond!

Each business listing includes a précis of who began the business and when, a location address, hours of business, methods of payment [V = Visa, MC = MasterCard, AE = American Express, DC = Diners Club, Debit = your Interac or ATM card and $ = cold, hard cash], house specialties, where else what's available can be found, driving directions to locations out of town, and the preferred means of contact—phone, e-mail, website. Some of these details do vary with season and change over time, sometimes on a whim, so check beforehand if it is a trek.

At the back of the book are three additional resources. These are: 1. a comprehensive series of lists presented according to the major categories, in which businesses with more than one service aspect to the enterprise are appropriately cross-referenced, 2. a master index of business names, and 3. a glossary of mostly lesser known ingredients and culinary terms—set in italics in the body of reviews.

The extent of cross-referenced listings demonstrates the multi-faceted nature of many of the businesses featured in *Shop talk*—a market reality which occasionally served to confound the process of easy classification. However, all businesses have been classified and the location of a business profile is indicated when the name of the business is set in **bold** type. Consult these lists for a complete spectrum of businesses that might provide some or all of what you are looking for. Look up the categories that interest you, study the businesses located within your home quadrant and then read the individual profile for the details.

The master list of business names is the quickest way to find a review of a particular business—assuming you already know the name.

The glossary of ingredients provides more detailed explanations of unfamiliar terms—as an aid to shoppers in asking fewer or perhaps simply more informed questions.

Shop talk is not the *Yellow Pages*. It is not intended to be anything but a personal reflection of where, in 25 years as a curious cook, I have found good places to source good groceries.

Businesses change hours, change locations, change phone numbers, change direction, change hands, and close. Nothing is certain—except death and taxes. Facts presented in this book were as accurate as possible when it went to press. Any mistakes herein are mine, and inadvertently made. Depending upon marketplace receptivity, it is my intention to update the contents of this particular cook's virtual pantry biennially. In the interim, I wish you good shopping, good cooking, and good eating with good friends and loved ones.

Gratitude

MY THANKS GO TO THE MANY PEOPLE who assisted on this project, chief among them my business partner, Jeremy Drought of Last Impression Publishing Service. Jeremy has the many and varied skills I lack—including linear thinking, graphic design, book production knowledge beyond the writing phase—and he is a damned nice guy, with a shared philosophy about the role and relevance of food, especially local and sustainably raised food. We have become good friends as well as colleagues, and that as much as his professionalism and skills has made this book a pleasure to research and to write.

My heartfelt thanks to my family—my wonderful sons, my parents on their Saskatchewan farm, my sister, brothers and aunts—and to my dear friends who have endured my obsessions and jammed pantry with grace, fortitude, appetite and good humour. I love you all. A hug to Jeff Collins, my deep thanks to Sal Howell for her perceptive and inspiring words, and many thanks to my foodie colleagues John Gilchrist and Catherine Caldwell for feedback and support.

Some of this work has appeared in other publications, including the *Calgary Herald* and Calgary's *City Palate*. Thank you to my eagle-eyed editors at these publications, Val Berenyi and Kathy Richardier, for doing your respective jobs so well.

To copy editor Sandy Gough, thank you for your discerning eye and green ink. And to photographer Angela Chard of Crystal Image Studios, oh thank you! Pink has never looked so utterly wonderfully brightly pink!

My gratitude goes to my readers and students who have peppered me with requests for information on sourcing ingredients. To their refrains of "Where? Who?", I can finally respond, "Here!" This book is the "open-all-hours" indispensible reference-resource that can now guide your own culinary exploration of Calgary, the Bow Valley and beyond.

My appreciation to the retailers, chefs and cooks who have been so generous with their time and knowledge, educating me in the nuances and niceties of the many ways there are to cook. It is a big world, and Calgarians reflect much of it on our tables.

To the growers, farmers and ranchers who have fed me, given me a bed to sleep in, toured me around their homes, and shared the largesse of their crops and knowledge, my thanks. Every cook is only as good as her ingredients. In Alberta, we are blessed with many generous and talented food producers who gift us with the finest food to prepare. God keep you all safe, prosperous, happy and well fed.

dee Hobsbawn-Smith
Calgary, Alberta
December 2007

— for my sons Darl and Dailyn —

Asian

IT IS EASY TO LOVE ASIAN FOOD. It offers all that our palates like—hot, sweet, salty, sour—in textures and shapes we have learned to appreciate. We might have begun with egg foo yung and chicken chow mein, but we have progressed to a wide variety of Asian dishes from nearly a dozen cultures, from Japanese sushi to Panang curry.

Ingredients in Asian markets vary in quality as well as in scope. Some Asian stores have pristine produce, while others have wilted herbs and battered vegetables. Some stock live fish, while others have frozen fillets. There is no apparent norm.

The Asian section of Calgary used to stretch just south of the Bow River, from the Chinese Cultural Centre to the Harry Hayes Building. Now, Asian markets are scattered throughout most of the city's quadrants, and the cohesive heart that was Chinatown verges on becoming a cook's ghost town, housing just a few food shops among the dim sum emporia, jewellers, and martial arts studios. Many shoppers prefer to avoid downtown parking problems in favour of shopping the fringes, in other neighbourhoods, where the choices are wider.

NORTHEAST

T&T Supermarket

Established: 1998 • Managers: Victor Wong (PP) & Michael Wu (HHC)

800, 999–36 Street NE	*1000, 9650 Harvest Hills Boulevard NE*
(Pacific Place Mall)	*(Harvest Hills Crossing)*
Phone: 569•6888	*Phone: 237•6608*
Monday–Friday 9:30 am–9:00 pm	*Monday–Thursday 9:30 am–9:00 pm*
Saturday–Sunday 9:00 am–9:00 pm	*Friday–Sunday 9:00 am–9:00 pm*

V, MC, Debit, $

THIS pair are the biggest, "bustlingest" and likely the busiest source of Asian ingredients in the city. Avoid the crowds and shop off-hours: T&T's aisles can be as congested as a Beijing street at rush hour.

The whole world of Southeast Asian ingredients is on display somewhere in T&T, including big and small bags of rice, rice cookers, and portable butane burners, row after row of noodles—fresh in the cooler and dried noodles of all sorts, made from mung beans, rice, wheat, and eggs—sauces, tinned cookies, vinegars, oils, a bakery, a butcher, and a busy fish market. Look for all kinds of Asian pickles, from seaweed to much more prosaic ginger. Be adventurous! Free-range chickens, head-on, feet attached, some birds whole, many cut up. Rows of pork parts, including meaty side ribs. Half a dozen beef cuts, all AA or AAA. This market has the city's widest selection of fish, and by far the largest choice of live fish and shellfish. Tanks are filled with lobster, Dungeness crabs, locally raised tilapia, scallops in the shell, cherrystone or manila clams, mussels, oysters, sea snails, and conch. Whole fish, steaks, and fillets on ice include salmon, eel, carp, catfish, snapper, corvina, striped bass, mackerel, and baby octopus.

Thaw a *durian* fruit if you dare. This pungent Asian fruit is sold frozen for a reason, as its strong aroma when fresh is overwhelming. Wise shoppers collect it last, just before going to the checkout clerk. The city's freshest Asian produce is on display in immaculate wicker baskets, from perfect chive blossoms and *pea tendrils* to *gai lan, gai choy, ya choy, shar li hon* and every green-in-between. Colours continue with red spinach, white ginger, *enoki*, shoe-brown shiitake, and golden *ya pears*. The new location in Harvest Hills has dim sum, Vietnamese sub and sushi stands for ready-now snacks and meals. Pacific Place offers *T&T Gourmet*, a take-out counter just beyond the checkout stands.

- *House Specialties*: Pan-Asian ingredients, fish market, meat market, produce, dry goods.

www.tnt-supermarket.com

SOUTHEAST

Can Fung Oriental Foods & Fresh Meats

Established: 1997 • Owner: Ky Ly, Manager: Huong Lang
215–1 Street SE
Phone: 263•2823
Monday–Saturday 10:00 am–6:00 pm
Debit, $

THIS tiny downtown shop has a wall of former coolers converted into storage shelves, now holding lentils, beans, and mostly rice-based noodles. The herbs alone are worth the jaunt and the parking struggle—sparkling Thai basil mint, cilantro, pennywort, hard-to-find fresh *kaffir lime* and curry leaves. Jewel-like Thai bird chilies, tiny but incendiary, are bright and fresh, and star anise in packets are large and intact. Huge bags of chili flakes and *curry powder* make it clear that the restaurant trade also shops here for spices. Good brands make all the difference in Asian cooking, and there are some good ones here: Kadoya Japanese sesame oil, Koon Chun *hoisin*, Saigon Hot Sauce. The shop's organization might feel a bit haphazard, but it is clean and tidy, and produce is fresh, clean and appealing.

- *House Specialties*: Thai, Chinese, and Vietnamese ingredients, herbs, sauces, and condiments.

Read the Label!

GOOD brands are just as important in food as in clothing. You get exactly what you pay for, so do not succumb to the "cheap food" ploy. When you are stocking your Asian pantry, look for these reliably good brands:

- ABC is my favourite Indonesian *ketjap manis*.
- Doll brand spring roll wrappers can be found in store freezers.
- Kadoya is my preferred Japanese roasted sesame oil. Store it in the fridge.
- Kikkoman is my preferred Japanese *tamari*. It contains some wheat.
- Koon Chun's blue and yellow label is a reliable marker for good *hoisin*.
- Lee Kum Kee Premium, with a gold-edged label, is a stellar oyster sauce.
- Mae Ploy is my favourite Thai-made Panang curry paste.
- Maurukan and Mitsukan are high-calibre Japanese rice vinegars.
- Pearl River Bridge is my preferred Chinese soy, available in a range of flavours and weights, from mushroom to light or dark.
- Rooster brand makes good Vietnamese-style hot chili paste, Sriracha hot sauce, and *sambal oelek*.
- Wing's wonton wrappers are locally made and good for potstickers (fried or steamed dumplings). The square wrappers are noticeably thinner than the round ones.

Hang Fung Foods

Established: 1980 • Owner & Manager: John Chen
119–3 Avenue SE (Opulence Centre)
Phone: 269•4646
Monday–Sunday 9:30 am–7:00 pm
$ only

THIS survivor of downtown life is a doorway into another world through its funky pair of rooms. Walk past the cardboard boxes of *gai lan* and *sui choy* into the rest of the building and find big ceramic pots full of beans and grains, some dry goods and sauces, coolers crammed with noodles and fresh produce, and an odd assortment of kitchenware. More produce is in the rear, along with immaculate mung bean sprouts and herbs, fresh and dried noodles—mostly rice-based, along with a few thick Peking-style noodles and a few fine egg noodles. Some English is spoken here, but not much, so know what you want.

- *House Specialties*: Produce and Asian dry goods.

Hiệp Hòa Asian Foods
Established: 1992 • Owner: Nhan Vo
Bay E, 4710–17 Avenue SE
Phone: 272•4789
Monday–Saturday 9:00 am–9:00 pm, Sunday 9:00 am–8:00 pm
Debit, $

LOOK for fine Vietnamese fare here. The women at the cash register hand-sort Thai basil, filling the air with its spicy camphor-like licorice scent. In addition, find good-looking cilantro and mint, cress, green onions and garlic chives. The eggplant is Asian and elongated, the *bok choy* is tiny and trimmed. The frozen chickens have feet attached, and the pork on display at the meat counter is tidily trimmed. There are chicken gizzards, and a tight and tidy collection of beef: shank, flank, inside round. Find fresh rice noodles and rice rolls, fresh mung bean sprouts, greens, and many fruits. Feel like *dragonfruit* or *lychees*? Or maybe hairy *rambutans* or sleek *mangosteens*, aromatic mangoes and crisp Asian pears. This is a good place to feed your tropical fruit craving. A few kitchen pots and pans are boxed in by a freezer full of spring roll wrappers, tofu, many types of fish, and *durian*. Don't thaw it in public—*durian's* strong scent is best enjoyed privately. Then peruse the dry goods, labeled in Vietnamese—rice paper, lily buds, fish sauce, more, more, more.

• *House Specialties*: Fresh Vietnamese herbs, vegetables, and fruit.

Lucky Supermarket
Established: 2003 • Contact: Linh Nguyen
4527–8 Avenue SE
Phone: 569•0778
Monday–Sunday 9:00 am–9:00 pm
V, MC, AE, Debit, $

THIS concise and well-stocked market is bright, tidy, and comprehensively if not exhaustively stocked. A bright produce area, a fish market with live tanks, a tidy and clean fresh meat market, and a wide range of shelves in-between means I can get all I need for my Asian cooking in one stop. I am particularly impressed by the lovely Asian dishes—plates, bowls, platters—and the noodle collection, fresh and dried, rice, wheat, and alternatives. Whew! Find Philippine bread from *Mang Pedro* (Mr. Peter), Philippine banana ketchup, and coconut vinegar, Thai shrimp pastes and dried prawn crackers, Chinese Koon Chun sauces, Vietnamese fish sauces, and Caribbean condiments. Along the perimeter, find bamboo in water, Vietnamese pickles and bean curd, and the fish market's live tanks filled with swimming tilapia, lobster, oysters, clams, crabs, and slow-moving snails. Nestled on ice next to the tanks are immaculately fresh fillets of pickerel, carp-like buffalo fish, and salmon. In the meat market, a few beef cuts (tripe, flank, short ribs, oxtail, shank) are outnumbered by the classic Asian allegiance to pork. Aficionados can indulge in "the fifth quarter," also called "offal"—lung, ears, tongue, kidneys—or the more usual cuts from the other four. Here, the meat

is tidily trimmed and the counters are clean. If a party is in your near future, maybe a whole beef strip loin, tenderloin, or rib-eye is what you can take home. Add *pea tendrils, durian,* kabocha squash, *taro* or *lychees, jicama* or *bok choy,* and any of a dozen varieties of tea, from chrysanthemum to Earl Grey. It is all here, including herbal medications in a glass case beyond the cashiers.
• *House Specialties*: Vietnamese, Thai, Philippine, and Caribbean ingredients.
www.luckysupermarket.ca

Nha Trang Market
Established: 1982 • *Owner: Dep Huynh*
101, 575–28 Street SE
Phone: 248•3301
Monday–Saturday 10:00 am–8:00 pm, Sunday 10:00 am–7:30 pm
Debit, $

LIKE a magician's trunk, this corner store in Radisson Heights is bigger on the inside than it appears on the outside. Find primarily Thai and Vietnamese ingredients here, including Mae Ploy, my favourite hard-to-find Panang curry paste, frozen lime leaves, and chopped lemongrass, pickles and noodles, dried and frozen fish, and a wide selection of fish sauces. Also find Japanese and Chinese ingredients for sushi, stir-fries, and *sand pots*. The produce is variable in quality, but the frozen banana leaves and jute, the frozen shredded coconut, and grated *cassava,* the *galangal* and *tamarind*—and the amazing mortars and pestles—are worth a look.
• *House Specialties*: Chinese, Thai, and Vietnamese ingredients.

Shun Fat ("88") International Market
Established: 1996 • *Owner: Quang Trinh, Manager: Maria Tung*
3215–17 Avenue SE
Phone: 272•8888
Monday–Saturday 9:00 am–9:00 pm, Sunday 9:00 am–8:00 pm
V, MC, Debit, $

INTERNATIONAL succinctly sums it up. Good-looking produce and fresh herbs—*shiso leaf,* mint, pokey leaf, cress, Thai basil, cilantro—and canned goods, from coconut milk to hot sauce, *nori* and curry paste, and huge bags of dried fungi. Just how big a pot do you need at home to cook one of those 5-pound bags of dried mushrooms?
A side shop inside—*Vinh Khon BBQ* deals in cash only at its own till, selling fresh and barbecued pork and poultry, including feet and bones. The beef cuts in the case include oxtail, tongue, and tripe, but pork rules here.
Teatime can be easily managed here, with dozens to choose from, including chrysanthemum, *oolong,* Yunnan, jasmine. Find fresh and dried noodles, huge sacks of rice, a wondrous array of Chinese sausage, and kitchenware for cooking it all. On the produce shelves, expect to find stalks of *burdock* and heads of Shanghai *bok choy,* rounds of kohlrabi or kabocha squash, and expect the unexpected—fresh purple yams, tiny eggplant, *karela, chayote,* mini

mangoes and okra, *cassava* and *taro*. Banana-leaf-wrapped sausages, too. In the freezer, a wide choice—*kaffir lime leaves*, duck, black-skinned silkie chickens—ideal for smoking or grilling, quail and snails, fish balls—and more unexpected items. Dry goods? Equally diverse! Noodles—rice, fresh and dried, cellophane, wheat, egg, *soba*. Rices, all nice, plus pickled fish, sauces, palm sugar, lentils. An entire row of soy sauces to select from! Pan-Asian is the best word for Shun Fat ("88")'s goods. A cook can spend all day in here.

• *House Specialties*: Pan-Asian ingredients.

Tatak Pinoy Food Store
Established: 2006 • Owners: Doreis & Edmund Pedro
528, 22 Midlake Boulevard SE
Phone: 244•8083
Monday–Friday 10:00 am–8:00 pm
Saturday 10 am–7:00 pm, Sunday 2:00–7:00 pm
Debit, $

IT took an ad in a Filipino-Calgarian newspaper to steer me to this bright but tiny shop. Doreis Pedro and her husband Edmund arrived from Manila in 1996 with three small children, IT skills, and a deep desire to make a better life for their kids. In 2006, as their eldest approached university age, they decided to work just a bit harder and save extra dollars towards post-secondary education for their children. The tidy store, which has become a hub for the city's growing Philippine community, is the result. Here, look for *longanisa* and *tocino* in the freezer, along with frozen stuffed milkfish. Milkfish is the national fish of the Philippines. (I didn't know either!) There is more than milkfish in the freezers: schools of other fish, mostly unfamiliar to me and all imported from the Philippines, along with mackerel, sardines, fish flakes, and desserts from Goldilocks in Vancouver. There is ice cream too—flavoured with *macapuno*, *halo-halo*, mango or *ube*. Jars of fruits and red beans in syrup all attest to the national sweet tooth, as does the sweet banana ketchup and sweet spaghetti sauce. Try the soy sauce spiked with *calamansi*; the sauce leads with acid, not salt. Try too the national fish sauce, which is stronger than the Vietnamese version. Shelves are full of dry goods— noodles of rice and wheat, bread from *Mang Pedro*, a Calgary baker who caters to Filipino clientele, but no rice—perhaps in tacit recognition that the big chains carry ample choices. Despite that, there is much here to choose from for a veritable and authentic Philippine meal.

• *House Specialties*: Philippine groceries, frozen meats and fish, fish sauce and condiments, Goldilocks desserts, ice cream, seasonings, and dry goods.

SOUTHWEST

Arirang Oriental Foods, Transocean Trading Co. Ltd.

Established: 1997 • Owner: Chung Lee
30, 1324–10 Avenue SW
Phone: 228•0980
Monday–Saturday 10:00 am–8:00 pm, Sunday 10:00 am–7:00 pm
V, MC, Debit, $

PRONOUNCING the name is the hardest part. Add a guttural "d" to each "r" as it rolls past your palate, then find this shop and good parking in a small strip mall adjacent to **Community Natural Foods** on 10 Avenue SW in the Beltline. This tidy shop is well organized and easy to navigate despite an absence of English labels. Shop here for Japanese and Korean staples and produce: *miso* and sushi makings—*gari*, short-grain rice, *wasabi, nori* of varying calibre, frozen rainbow-tinted *tobiko*—and a wonderful array of soy sauces and vinegars. Look in the freezer for thinly sliced beef to use in Korean *bulgogi* or Japanese *shabu-shabu*. Japanese rice vinegar is cheaper by the gallon here, and Japanese sesame oil is among the finest made. Korean noodles are made from sweet potato pulp, and Japanese cooks use *soba* and *udon*. Korean and Japanese cooks place big store in pickles like big jars of Korean *kimchee*. Ask before you plunder the refrigerated shelves: many labels are not translated. The coolers hold some produce—herbs, Korean *bok choy*, eggplant—and the shelves have a wide choice of rice cookers for when a pot simply won't do.
* *House Specialties*: Korean and Japanese ingredients like sushi rice, Korean fresh vegetables, and slivered short ribs for *bulgogi* and *shabu-shabu*.
* *Also Available*: Wholesale to some Calgary restaurants.

NORTHWEST

Lambda Oriental Foods & Market

Established: 1977 • Owner: Francis Wan
1423 Centre Street North
Phone: 230•1916
Sunday–Thursday 10:00 am–7:30 pm, Friday 10:00 am–8:00 pm
Saturday 9:00 am–8:00 pm
V, MC, Debit, $

THIS tidy Asian market has been my Westside favourite for decades, being less overwhelming than **T&T Supermarket**, and more comprehensively stocked than most of the others, with the possible exception of **Shun Fat ("88") International Market** on the Eastside. Cardboard boxes of produce at the entrance and a bigger produce section at the rear are framed by a Chinese herbal pharmacy where one can buy a box of tiny herbal Po Chai stomach ache pills for when you've eaten too much! Find 5-pound tins, and little jars too—of Koon Chun's good *hoisin*, oyster sauce, and barbecue sauce—for big and small kitchens. Just inside the door is *Maxima Bakery & Cake House* (cash only). Find good pork buns and egg tarts. At the back is a clean butcher counter (also cash only), called *Fat Kee*, primarily featuring pork, immaculately trimmed. The fish tanks at *King's Seafood Distributors* (another cash-only business) hold a wide selection of live fish, mainly shellfish—the city's best source of lobster and Dungeness crab. Freezers are stocked with imitation crab and fish, *edamame*, squab, small black-skinned silkie chickens, duck legs and whole ducks, and a huge choice of dumplings and dim sum. Vegetarians can choose from a dozen kinds of tofu and even more noodles—fresh, dried, and frozen—made from rice, tapioca, wheat, eggs, buckwheat, or sweet potato. Swish it all down with a drink of ginseng or pennywort, and take home a tin of almond cookies or a dozen egg tarts for dessert. The produce section is prime pickings for tropical fruits, like mangoes, papaya, and starfruit, plus so-lovely lotus root, *pea tendrils*, bitter melon and *lo bok*, stacked in boxes just inside the entrance. Past the cashiers, head for the flags announcing "New Arrival" to find seasonal specials: at Chinese New Year, shelves are heavy on oranges, such as Ponkan Taiwan oranges, and honey tangerines.

• *House Specialties*: Asian produce and dry goods.
• *Also Available*: Wholesale to some Calgary restaurants.

Tops 100 Supermarket

Established: 2006 • Manager: Jimmy Tio
1623–16 Avenue NW (Central Landmark Mall)
Phone: 276•8889
Monday–Sunday 9:30 am–8:30 pm
V, MC, Debit, $

THIS mall has housed several Asian markets, but the current incarnation has, by far, the best produce, as fine and fresh as any greengrocer in the city. Three sides of the store hold fruit and vegetables—Hami melons, perfect mangoes, immaculate *pea tendrils*, many families of *choy, burro bananas, longans, Welsh onions* and pristine watercress. It is all good. Central aisles house Asian sauces—good brands, in big and small sizes, like Kadoya sesame oil, Koon Chun sauces, and many shelves of soy. *Wai's BBQ Centre* sells (cash-only) barbecued pork, duck, and chicken. A fish shop with live tanks is slated to be "coming soon."

• *House Specialties*: Produce.
• *Also Available*: Wholesale to some Calgary restaurants.
www.topssupermarket.net

Bakeries

WE LOVE OUR BREAD. And our pastries and cookies too. Bakeries are one of the two most popular types of food shops in the city and surrounding region. (Meat markets are the other. Some things never change.) This is perhaps because home baking is a dying craft, its practitioners viewed as wizards with magic hands and a knack for exactitude. Fewer home bakers translates directly into more baking businesses, across many cultures.

Baking is highly specialized. In Calgary, you can find Afghani bakers making mahogany brown flatbreads similar to that which residents of Kabul enjoy. Several bakers are Filipino, more familiar with rice flour and purple yam than wheat flour. There are also bakers attending to the business of wedding cakes, the challenges of allergies, the desire for cookies in children of all ages, the timeless allure of pie and the finely turned crust. Artisan bakeries using sourdough starters and handcrafting loaves are emerging, and artists are crafting jewelled sweets worthy of a frame and a gallery.

CITY WIDE

Cakes For All Occasions

Established: 2003 • Owner: Juliette Chabot
City wide
Phone: 870•0572
Hours by Appointment
Cheques, $

CAKES For All Occasions, despite its name, specializes in wedding and Christmas cakes, light and dark, by advance order only. Plan ahead, and call in November for a Christmas cake, and at least a month ahead for a wedding cake. Three generations of women have been involved in this family business at one time or another, in a triple-tier matriarchy built on buttercream, marzipan and batter, and based on creating pleasure. Gisele Santucci and her mother, Juliette Chabot, jointly produce 200 pounds of Christmas cake in each holiday season, with part-time participation by Gisele's daughter Julie. Juliette, a dark-haired pixie of a grandmother, glitters with more energy in her 70s than many mothers with half her years. Her daughter and granddaughter, feminine clones in chocolate-smudged whites, burst with the same channeled focus. Juliette began decorating cakes with her first cake decorating kit, purchased from her father's small-town Saskatchewan store in 1952. Her hobby became a business. Alain, Juliette's youngest son and one of the city's elite "white tablecloth" chefs, is currently in charge of the kitchens at Il Sogno Ristorante. He is the reason for granddaughter Julie's interest in food. *"Mon oncle Alain"* would hang out with his niece, raving about his

9

current culinary craze; she eventually caught the bug and completed a two-year culinary arts program at the Culinary Institute of Canada in PEI. For Christmas, order your *tourtières* in advance.

- *House Specialties*: Wedding and Christmas cakes, *tourtières*, advance order only.

www.cakesforalloccasions.ca

NORTHEAST

Amandine Bakery & Pastry

Established: 1979 • *Owner & Manager: Shotaro Kajita*
3, 2610 Centre Street North
Phone: 276•3532
Tuesday–Saturday 8:00 am–6:00 pm, Sunday 9:00 am–4:30 pm
V, MC, Debit, $

O WNED and managed by Shotaro Kajita, Amandine Bakery & Pastry opened in Dover in 1979, and has 20-plus years logged at its current Northside location. It's a popular neighbourhood haunt—a group of seniors hang out over coffee and sweets once a week. Rustic European-style sweets—Dutch almond cake and apple *kuchen* with crunchy topping—steal the show from the peasant loaves and Sovital breads on the racks. Pastries and layer cakes are immensely popular, and there is frozen puff pastry for home bakers to purchase.

Holiday baking is a big extravaganza here. Come spring, house-made Easter chocolates and Vienna cookies filled with apricot jam are available. For Christmas, elves craft hundreds of *Bûche de Noël*, gingerbread houses, chocolate truffles, and almond rings with marzipan.

- *House Specialties*: Pastries, layer cakes, chocolates.

Byblos Bakery

Established: 1975 • *Co-owners: George, Sal, Slieman & Elias Daklala*
2479–23 Street NE
Phone: 250•3711
Monday–Saturday 9:00 am–5:00 pm, Sunday 9:00 am–4:00 pm
Debit, Cheque, $

F OUR Lebanese brothers—George, Sal, Slieman and Elias Daklala—began the business making white and whole wheat pita in 1975, when, says George, "no one in Calgary knew anything about pita." They added bagels in 1980 and were the city's first bagel-bakers. Filo, tortillas, and *kataifi* are also available on-site.

- *House Specialties*: Pita, *baklava*, bagels, tortillas.
- *Also Available*: On-site at the storefront—also their "damaged pita" outlet—across western Canada, including Ontario, and the USA.

www.byblosbakery.com

City Bakery (Calgary) Ltd.

Established: 1908 • Manager: Paul Wakeling
906–1 Avenue NE
Phone: 263•8578
Tuesday–Friday 8:00 am–5:00 pm, Saturday 8:00 am–3:00 pm
V, Debit, $

C ITY Bakery dates back to 1908, and has racked up more than three decades at its current location. It is now owned by Weston Foods, which purchased it from Fritz Painsi and Hans Werner in 2001. Fig and date bread is sweet, scented, and perfect for breakfast, as are croissants, *stollen* and other familiar European classics. Good dense rye breads, multi-flour, multi-seed sasquatch loaves, baguettes, open-textured crusty breads, and friendly German women behind the counter make this a great stop.
• *House Specialties*: European breads and pastries.
• *Also Available*: Many Calgary and area restaurants.

Latin American Empanadas

Established: 1992 • Owners: George & Liliana Giacalone
826–68 Street NE
Phone: 235•1646
Monday–Friday 10:00 am–6:00 pm, Saturday 10:00 am–5:00 pm
Debit, $

H OMESICK Latinos may weep at the sight of *hahuallas* and *mariquettas*, but everyone loves the *empanadas* baked here, regardless of their backgrounds. Individual rounds of savoury pastry are filled with ground beef, chicken, *verdure*, or seafood, then baked. A few staples are stocked here, including *masa harina*, dozens of varieties of *yerba maté*, canned sweet potato paste, quince paste and *cajeta*.
• *House Specialties*: Latin American *empanadas*.

Melly's Bakery Café

Established: 1993 • Owner: Melly Abesamis
112, 6800 Memorial Drive NE
Phone: 569•1517
Tuesday–Sunday 11:00 am–8:00 pm
V, MC, AE, Debit, $

T HIS little Philippine bakery is crammed with *maja blanka, pan de coco, leche flan*, egg and *ube yema, langka* tarts in bateau shape, mango tarts, and *pandan leaf* cake. Ask! It's all good. Cakes are flavoured with *langka*, mango, *macapuno, pandan leaf* or *ube. Sapin-sapin* cakes are rainbow-coloured, all rice flour-based. Rice flour is the starch of choice, although many dishes have wheat in them. There are breads too: *monay putok* and savoury buns stuffed with chicken or pork. Ask! Ask! Ask! All good things come to those with the will to ask. Stay for a little lunch too, made in a modernized approach to traditional Philippine cuisine. Take a seat while you wait for fried tilapia, or varieties of *adobo*—pork or chicken—with rice.

• *House Specialties*: Philippine baked goods, wedding and birthday cakes.

Rolymie Bakery
Established: 1995 • Owners: Violeta & Renato Barnachea
Bay 5, 5008 Whitehorn Drive NE
Phone: 590•0099
Tuesday–Sunday 11:00 am–7:00 pm
$ only

THIS small shop specializes in *ube* and glutinous rice baking, but also produces and decorates wedding cakes. Ask Renato to bake a wedding cake, and he will build something handsome for you.

• *House Specialties*: Philippine baking.
• *Also Available*: 1071 Knotwood Road East, Edmonton.

The Urban Baker
Established: 2003 • Owners: Tanya Heck & Clark Adams
802 Edmonton Trail NE
Phone: 266•3763
Monday 10:00 am–6:00 pm, Tuesday–Friday 10:00 am–9:00 pm
Saturday 9:00 am–6:00 pm, Sunday 9:00 am–3:00 pm
V, MC, Debit, $

CLARK Adams put in his time as pastry chef in other Calgary kitchens and is finally in his own kitchen. His partner Tanya baked at Belvedere, Wildwood and Murrieta's before they joined forces on this venture. They continue founding baker Whitney Armstrong's dedication to the wood-fired *forno*, producing pizzas and flatbreads, with more savouries to come. The handmade breads, leavened with naturally made sponges and *poolish* in a changing array of flavours, including raisin, roasted squash, cranberry chocolate sourdough and corn rye, are the best bet. The cinnamon buns are yum, not too sweet. The sweets ("All butter all the time," says Tanya) are uncomplicated and home-style (including date squares, butter tarts, bread pudding, muffins and scones); the breads are the best draw, in this baker's opinion. Sixty-five percent of the flour used is organic, locally grown by **Grainworks Inc.** This bakery is venturing into wedding cakes and special-order cakes.

For Christmas, purchase shortbreads, white chocolate bark, gingerbread men or *stollen*, but there's no ordering in advance for Christmas fare.

• *House Specialties*: Artisanal bread, special-order cakes, home-style pastries and individual desserts, one-crust fruit pies and custom-made wedding cakes.

www.urban-baker.ca

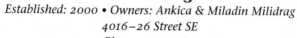

SOUTHEAST

Euro Pastry

Established: 2000 • Owners: Ankica & Miladin Milidrag
4016–26 Street SE
Phone: 273•0087
Tuesday–Friday 9:00 am–7:00 pm, Saturday 9:00 am–5:00 pm
Debit, Cheque, $

A large variety of Croat, Hungarian, and Serbian specialties are baked here, so many in fact that it is best to ascertain which are freshly out of the oven for best texture, flavour, and crumb. Explore sweet and savoury Hungarian *borek* in a snakelike squiggle-pastry filled with sour cherry, spinach, or beef, crepes and either hazelnut, walnut, poppyseed, or apple strudel, *boem*, *shampita*, *plum kifli*, Bosnian *baklava*, and *dobosh torte*.

- *House Specialties*: Croat, Hungarian, Serbian specialties.
- *Also Available*: **Amaranth Whole Foods Market, Community Natural Foods, Crossroads Market** (May–September).

www.europastry.ca

Golden Happiness Bakery

Established: 1990 • Owners: The Chau Family
111–2 Avenue SE
Phone: 263•4882
Monday–Sunday 7:00 am–6:00 pm
$ only

I N its previous location, this bakery had a pig and her piglets of glazed golden dough in the window. At this location, in their place is a towering edifice of cakes. We prefer the pigs, really! The city's best Danish raisin twists (called "nay-nays" by my sons in their very young days) are housed here, along with steamed and baked BBQ pork buns, cocktail buns and coconut buns of tooth-aching sweetness. Dim sum in the freezer is the most recent addition. Troll for red bean, peanut, or sesame sweet rice balls, spring rolls and pork dumplings, mini buns and wonton. The strange blend of East-West baking is evident in tiramisu mousse cake, Florentines, almond cookies, and *palmiers* alongside the cocktail buns and egg tarts, which are far better than their western companions.

Ask for *mooncakes*, shipped worldwide to celebrate the autumnal Moon Festival.

- *House Specialties*: Raisin twists, BBQ pork buns, egg tarts, *mooncakes*.

Günther's Fine Baking Ltd.

Established: 1971 • Owners: Elizabeth & Günther Stranzinger
4306–17 Avenue SE
Phone: 272•0383
Tuesday–Friday 10:00 am–5:30 pm, Saturday 9:00 am–3:00 pm
$ only

GÜNTHER Stranzinger still makes the best apple strudel in town. This Austrian baker and his wife Elizabeth have more than three decades under their hard-working hands, producing impeccable *stollen* (available after Remembrance Day); go ahead, it keeps well for up to three months at room temperature. They produce reliably good whole-grain and multi-grain European classics. Günther dismisses trends, saying that nothing has really changed much as people rediscover grains all over again. "Eat breads made with whole grains and don't worry about Atkins!" His Finnish oat loaf with sunflower seeds is an excellent edible example to follow. Günther's buttercream-filled cakes are not necessarily Atkins-friendly, but there are many reasons to eat baked goods. Cookies are available in dozens of flavours and shapes. Ask about *honigkuchen* or *honig nuss*.

In the last week of November, ask about decorated Christmas tortes and *rouladen*. Günther says it is always nice to call ahead. If you order, you know you will get what you want. I want apple strudel and *stollen*, Santa, take note.

• *House Specialties*: Apple strudel, whole-grain breads, *stollen*, rye breads.
• *Also Available*: **Edelweiss Village, Jan's Meats & Deli, Mueller's European Delicatessen Bakery & Imports, Paolini's Sausage & Meats.**

Jing Jing Bakery

Established: 1990 • Owners: Martin & Grace Yan
Basement, 100–3 Avenue SE
Phone: 265•9588
Tuesday, Wednesday & Friday–Sunday 10:00 am–6:30 pm
$ only

THE sign in the lower-level window at Chinatown's bustling intersection reads "8:00 am hot," but baker-owner Martin Yan alters his hours to match circumstances. When his kids were small, he opened at 9:00 am, and opens at 10:00 am now in acceptance of staff shortages, as is the case in many Calgary businesses. Take the elevator or stairs, the trip is worth it for the city's best cocktail buns. Downstairs, survey shelves filled with many things, including *pandan leaf* roll, chestnut cream roll, or miniature egg tarts by the half dozen. Savouries are good too: the ham and onion buns studded with cheese are substantial, and the BBQ pork buns are worth a bite. Little English is spoken here, so know what you want. Hong Kong-trained Martin reminds me that Asian bakers do not favour butter, and he is currently experimenting with other fats. The odd design of this space encompasses a "basement within a basement," with the production kitchen a half-level down, behind the deck oven and counter; when Martin emerges behind the till, head first, from his kitchen four steps down, it looks a little Phantom-of-the-opera-ish, but it is really just the odd building design.

• *House Specialties*: Hong Kong-style buns and birthday cakes.

Loriz Pilipino Bakery & Convenience Store

Established: 2001 • Owners: Boyie "Riz" & Lorie Liberato
F13, 8330 Macleod Trail SE (Heritage Plaza Shopping Centre)
Phone: 278•8660
Monday–Thursday 10:00 am–8:00 pm, Friday & Saturday 10:00 am–9:00 pm
Sunday 11:00 am–8:00 pm
Debit, $

THIS bakery creates in the Philippine style, so do not expect much Western-style wheat-based baking beyond four types of bread arrayed on the centre shelf. Instead, choose between *pichi-pichi* or *sapin-sapin* coloured with *annatto* and *ube*; both are popular with the city's nearly 30,000 Filipinos. Philippine dough is a little sweeter, says Riz, and the Eastern approach may not coincide with Western experience: butter horns are not what I expect, but twists of dough topped with butter and sugar after baking. For an Asian taste, try *bibingka* or steamed buns filled with chicken or pork *asado*.

The owners have broadened their range to include a selection of pork products—pork loaf, cured pork, pork blood and pork stew—and Philippine cooking ingredients: canned hot peppers, *halo-halo* in syrup, a variety of sausages and rice noodles, coconut juice and milk, sugar cane, *ube*, fish sauce, frozen fish and shrimp paste. For non-cooks, there are frozen choices: *siopao* filled with pork or chicken, wontons or spring rolls.

• *House Specialties*: Philippine dry goods and baked goods.

Manuel Latruwe Belgian Pâtisserie & Bread Shop

Established: 1998 • Owner: Manuel Latruwe
1333–1 Street SE
Phone: 261•1092
Tuesday–Saturday 7:30 am–10:00 pm
V, MC, Debit, $

BELGIAN baker Manuel Latruwe bakes the finest sourdough baguettes, the most delicious sourdough olive baguettes, nut breads, and fresh fruit tarts in the city. Elegant mousses, *ganaches,* and sponges transform "cake" into the sophisticated highlight of a meal. Little mousses have become popular alternatives to traditional tiered cakes for weddings, and his ice cream, voted #1 on the continent by *Gourmet Magazine* in 2002, is addictive. A slow-paced renovation is underway, adding seating for 40, and the owner is applying for a liquor license. "My new focus will be on light lunches and desserts—featuring ice-cream cups and glacé, with a nice glass of wine." It sounds wonderfully civilized to me. Everything is high quality here. At Christmas, luxurious European-style holiday baking is addictive, so book early.

• *House Specialties*: Baguettes, olive bread, mousses and tarts, ice cream.
• *Also Available*: **Mercato**, and some Calgary restaurants.

Nectar Desserts

Established: 2006 • Owner: Rebekah Pearse
Upstairs, 1216–9 Avenue SE
Phone: 263•8486
Monday–Thursday 10:00 am–11:00 pm, Friday & Saturday 10:00 am–1:00 am
V, MC, Debit, $

REBEKAH Pearse opened Nectar Desserts in April 2007 after launching her goods at **Red Tree**. For this chef, dessert, like life, is not always about sweetness. It is about interesting—about tempering sweet with savoury herbal flavours, salt, spice, the prickling heat of *ancho* chilies, even bitterness. But mostly, Pearse says that she just likes to have fun, adding provocatively, "Dessert is all about that moment when you roll your head back and go, mmmm. It's foreplay. You don't eat dessert because you are hungry." Visitors to Nectar Desserts will find a dessert shop and a dessert bar, with daytime counter service that morphs into full—and licensed—service at night. Pearse's intensely flavoured non-dairy, eggless sorbets and ice creams, flavoured with Mexican vanilla, Valhrona chocolate, and local honey, have lustrous texture and mouth feel that match her hedonist's philosophy. Her increasing wholesale business produces signature desserts for other restaurants. Time travel to the 1950s with Red Velvet cake or rum balls, with a side of voluptuous hot chocolate made from Valhrona chocolate. If you want Nectar Desserts at home, arrange a catered event. Ordering in advance is advised for corporate gift giving and private consumption at Christmas, when Pearse tucks treasures into tins: gingerbread men, hazelnut *baci*, vanilla sugar cookies, orange *tuiles* and chocolate macaroons. Her organic fruitcake is pale in tone, loaded with dried fruit and soused in bourbon.

- *House Specialties*: Ice cream, Red Velvet cake, seasonal fruit tarts, lemon curd with lavender meringue, smoky chocolate and sea salt caramel tart.
- *Also Available*: **Mise en Place**, **Red Tree** and some Calgary restaurants, including Flames Central and Tangerine Supper Club.

www.nectardesserts.com

Pies Plus Café

Established: 1987 • Owner: Patrick Cousineau
611, 12445 Lake Fraser Drive SE (Avenida Village)
Phone: 271•6616
Tuesday–Saturday 8:00 am–6:00 pm
Cheque, $

PIE belongs to another era. It's a generational thing. But stalwart bakers like Patrick are striving to bring it back into vogue. And his pies are good enough that he just might succeed. Patrick learned from his dad, a former banker, who decided to make the leap from counting cash to counting piecrusts when he founded the business in Bragg Creek. Everything is made from scratch, and as is true of many things, the simpler you keep things, the better they turn out. These pies are close to flawless. Chocolate banana cream

Sweets for Holidays & Holy Days

SWEETS are intrinsic to festivals. It doesn't matter where we are from, we all eat sweets to celebrate. Sweets have no religion. Sweets have no borders or boundaries either. Even though our cultures have taught us to look for particular tastes and textures when we celebrate, in Canada, we have the opportunity to look in our neighbour's window and on their table to share what they are accustomed to.

North American-style bakeries have become the keepers of the Christmas candle, baking the holiday treats our grandmothers used to make for us. Even though the Christmas season is only two months long, its flour-dusted elves begin their preparations long in advance: some start macerating fruits for fruitcake in autumn, and others make long-keeping classics like *stollen* and *Bûche de Noël* in November. Cookies in particular have become a seasonal indulgence: gingersnaps, shortbreads, cinnamon stars. The occasional baker makes seasonal tarts like pumpkin pie or *tourtière*. Some chocolatiers and candy makers contribute holiday sweets as well; peruse the entries in Chocolate & Sweets for a taste.

Muslims, Hindus, and Sikhs look for *mithai*, sweets to celebrate Eid, the festive conclusion to Ramadan's month-long fasting, and Diwali, the festival of lights and renewal. *Mithai* are available year-round, to celebrate other beginnings—weddings, births, and any event that marks overcoming obstacles or fresh starts. *Mithai* are not baked, having evolved from a culture with little emphasis on baking or wheat. Many are based on milk, adding more meaning to the role and importance of cattle in culture; the phrase, "sacred cow," is no accident. The slowly simmered and thickened paste, similar to fudge, is flavoured with nuts, *ghee* and spices. Some types are made from fresh cheese, or are steeped in sugar syrup. Others are made from chickpea flour, with a taste reminiscent of peanut butter. Most *mithai* are slow and painstaking to make, so many families buy them by the boxful instead of making them at home. Find them in the East Indian section.

Hanukkah (Chanukah) is the Jewish festival of lights, with its own set of foods and traditions. The festival is historically connected to the harvest of the olive, and its oil has a special role in the celebration. Celebrants look for food with a common element of fat or oil to honour the miracle of the menorah that burned for eight days instead of only one: *latkes* are fried in oil, and *sofganiot* are deep-fried. Sugar cookies are cut out in the shape of dreidels and menorahs, and may be garnished with a Star of David.

pie is as good as my grandmother's, and the variations on strawberry, rhubarb, and Saskatoon are all worth having for lunch. Production varies, from 30–120 pies a day, swinging sharply upwards for pumpkin pies (upwards of 1,000, says Cousineau) before the arrival of Christmas. Truth to tell, I never quite get around to eating quiche or pot pie here, no matter how good it looks. I head straight for the real thing. Pie! For lunch!

• *House Specialties*: Fresh seasonal pies from scratch.

SOUTHWEST

Barel's Bakery & Nosh Ltd.

Established: 2003 • Owners: Berel & Rivkah Zipursky
131, 2515–90 Avenue SW (Oak Bay Plaza)
Phone: 238•5300
Monday–Wednesday 9:00 am–6:00 pm, Thursday 9:00 am–7:00 pm
Summer: Friday 8:00 am–6:00 pm, Winter: Friday 8:00 am–4:00 pm
(in December, Friday 8:00 am–2:00 pm)
Sunday 10:00 am–2:00 pm
V, MC, AE, Debit, Cheque, $

LOCATED in what Berel Zipursky calls "Kosher Corner," Barel's Bakery & Nosh Ltd. is a very busy small busy-ness. It is the only nut-free, dairy-free and kosher bakery in North America and is certified as nut-and-dairy-free by the Canadian government. The bagels are Winnipeg-style, baked in a conventional oven, not a wood-burning one. Benchmark six-strand *challah* is seedless, baked separately on clean sheets of parchment paper to help out those with seed allergies. Try an onion *pletzel*, and maybe Berel will tell you about his grandfather's tea and *pletzel* ritual. Then buy hand-shaped pita, 9-grain, four kinds of rye, or sourdough studded with olives and herbs.

Berel left a thriving career as a television producer and videographer to become a baker with heart and hands invested in what he makes. He is a good baker. "If you don't have a good *challah*, the first thing you eat at the Sabbath meal, the whole meal is ruined," he insists. His *challah* is good. So are his cookies, Danishes, and apple strudel.

Expansion has brought in a frozen meat case, all kosher, including custom-cut lamb and veal on request, fowl, and beef or veal, and frozen deli meats from Omnitsky's in Vancouver. Barel's caters, (nut- and dairy-free and kosher), with a range of salads, *knishes* and *borek*, pasta and fish, pick-up only. The next expansion plans are focused on gluten-free baked goods. Zipursky hopes the business becomes the shetl, or village, in a broader sense the community gathering-place. Ask about the school fundraiser program, with cookie dough, cupcakes or in-house doughnuts available.

For Hanukkah, start looking in November for jam-filled *sofganiot*, and *pareve*, thus suitable for serving at a meat-based meal. His *latkes*, made with potato and carrots in the Winnipeg style, are the best this non-kosher cook has ever tasted. If you like variations, all-carrot, zucchini, or stuffed mushroom versions may be ordered in advance. The variants are all North Americanisms, says Berel. His Hanukkah sugar cookies, shaped like dreidels and menorahs, are decorated with sprinkles but no icing, and are made with trans-fat-free oil.

- *House Specialties*: Nut and dairy-free yeasted doughnuts, chocolate chip cookies and brownies, *latkes*, *sofganiot*, sugar cookies, *challah*, 2-crust blueberry-rhubarb or apple pie, deli and kosher meats.

www.barelsbakery.com

Bianky's Bakery
Established: 1997 • Owners: Rami El Gamal & Mack Hosein
121, 1013–17 Avenue SW
Phone: 244•0103
Monday–Friday 8:00 am–6:00 pm, Saturday–Sunday 9:00 am–6:00 pm
V, MC, Debit, $

PLAGUED by multiple name changes in early years, this latest incarnation bakes baguettes in two flavours (sourdough *levain* and multi-grain) whole wheat loaves, and flavoured soudough breads, featuring Kalamata olives, *jalapeño*, Asiago and sun-dried tomatoes and herbs. For your sweet tooth, sample from a wonderful range of *viennoiserie* pastries, including *croissants* and a wide array of petits fours and cookies. Cakes are ornate elaborations in classically elegant style—Opera, Royale, Oblivion de café. Rich, rich, rich.

- *House Specialties*: Breads, baguettes, cookies, tortes.

Brûlée Pâtisserie
Established: 1997 • Owner: Jennifer Norfolk
Lower Level, 722–11 Avenue SW
Phone: 261•3064
Tuesday–Friday 10:00 am–6 pm, Saturday 10:00 am–4:00 pm
Orders taken for pickup Tuesday–Saturday (ring the bell for pickup)
V, MC, Debit, Cheque, $

BRÛLÉE has become a fine tradition, with its current owner holding the vision of high-style European-style *pâtisserie* to the gold standard set by founder Marianne Saunders and maintained by Rosemary Harbrecht. Jennifer Norfolk, who was Harbrecht's lead baker for eight years, is also keeping longer hours, to the relief of the bakery's many fans. In summer, the tarts are exceptional, as are the berry-studded scones laced with white chocolate, and many customers would rather die than be asked to purchase anything but the lavender shortbreads, lemon cream cake, chocolate Diablo or *baci*. The pecan sticky buns alone are worth a trip downstairs. Truth is, this bakery is capable of nearly anything you might desire, and has a resident wedding cake specialist in-house. All the desserts are elegant and delicious, usually decorated with edible flowers, fruit and berries. Some deserts are flourless, thus gluten-free. Bakers can ask for raw slabs of puff pastry from the freezer.

During Christmas, cakes are macerated in booze—brandy for the dark, Grand Marnier for the orange almond. At Easter, Paschal hot cross buns are cinnamon kissed.

- *House Specialties*: White chocolate scones, pecan sticky buns, layer and wedding cakes, seasonal fruit tarts, lemon cream cake and Scotch apricot torte.

www.brulee.ca

Buttercream Bake Shoppe
Established: 2005 • Owner: Kari Richardson

103, 1019–17 Avenue SW	*H6, 4421 Quesnay Wood Drive SW*
Phone: 228•9900	*(Calgary Farmers' Market)*
Tuesday–Friday 9:00 am–5:00 pm	*Friday & Saturday 9:00 am–5:00 pm*
Saturday & Sunday 10:00 am–5:00 pm	*Sunday 9:00 am–4:00 pm*
V, MC, Debit, $	*$ only*

GET your cute cupcakes here, my sweet babycake, complete with a piped-on swirl of icing sweeter than strawberries or sunny kisses. Each week, there are six kinds to thrill and delight your taste buds, with swirly-girly tutu icing toppings. Icings are seasoned with fresh or organic extracts. Cakes are made from scratch, with butter, in four sizes. You could be Goldilocks trying to make up her mind, but cake is waaay more fun than porridge. Kari does wedding and special occasion cakes in custom designs. As if that were not enough fun, you can have your cake, eat it too, and have cookies and chocolates. Investigate German-made chocolates from Coppeneur, in bars and truffles. For culinary spelunkers, venture into the deep tastes of DC Duby's exotic Wild Sweets, from the Vancouver-based molecular gastronomy team that is achieving world renown for their innovative and stunning approach to sweets. Chocolates from **Olivier's Candies** are here too, for those who prefer the familiar. Seasonality is a theme: Mother's Day, Flames playoffs, holidays, they are all good excuses for something sweet. Check out the bath and body care products, all food-inspired, some edible, in six lines that smell, look or taste like a cupcake. Try *Dessert's On Me,* a delectable body butter that smells sweetly of cinnamon sugar.

For Christmas, there is a swathe of seasonal cupcake flavours—eggnog, gingerbread, cappuccino, tiramisu, hot chocolate, candy cane or apple cider, along with a choice of hand-decorated sugar cookies and gingerbread men. Less traditional souls may want white cake (not fruitcake) decorated with fondant snowflakes.

Oooh la la. It's cake. Don't even think about counting the calories. Have a cappo or espresso while you browse, or snag a patio table out front. Advance order and delivery available.

- *House Specialties*: Cupcakes, cakes, chocolates and cookies.

www.buttercreambakeshoppe.com

COBS Bread

Established: 2007 • Managers: Corinna Hyska (KP) & Brad Trent (WTC)

7610 Elbow Drive SW   *236 Stewart Green Way SW*
(Kingsland Plaza)   *(Westhills Town Centre)*
Phone: 253•2999   *Phone: 217•1553*

Monday–Sunday 7:00 am–7:00 pm
Debit, $

ORIGINALLY an ancient building material, "cob" is a mixture of straw, clay, sand and earth from which thick-walled buildings have been made in the UK, Africa, the Middle East and the eastern coast of the USA. Cob is also used to build dome-shaped outdoor ovens, and this Vancouver-based bakery chain has adopted the name, I suspect, to invoke a certain earthy approach to hands-on baking. The invocation holds true for some of the goods this business produces: apricot delight roll or loaf is fibre-dense, sugarless, 50 percent fruit, and makes a wonderful breakfast toast. Cape seed bread is speckled with flax, poppy, sunflower, and sesame seeds. The sweets, including gooey custard-filled teatime-twisted apple custard of mammoth proportions, are sweet to the point of saturation. The *croissants* are fair-to-middling, chocolate Danishes are better and the Mediterranean Scroll is like a vegetable-filled pizza with height. Supplies have been known to run out, so get there ahead of the Saturday crowd.

- *House Specialties*: Handmade *croissants*, Cape seed loaf, apricot delight loaf or roll.
- *Also Available*: 107, 150 Crowfoot Crescent NW (Crowfoot Corner Shopping Centre) and 5, 1941 Uxbridge Drive NW (Stadium Shopping Centre).

www.cobsbread.com

Crave Cookies & Cupcakes

Established: 2004 • Owner: Carolyne McIntyre Jackson
120, 815–17 Avenue SW
Phone: 270•2728
Tuesday–Friday 10:00 am–6:00 pm, Saturday 10:00 am–5:00 pm
V, MC, AE, Debit, $

THREE sisters opened Crave Cookies & Cupcakes: two do all the work. Ain't that the family style? Working sibling Carolyne McIntyre Jackson just grins and eats... well, she eats cake. The rest of us can too. Or we can eat cookies, oh yes, double chocolate pistachio adapted from Carolyne's mom's recipe, as well as five other varieties. If cakes are what you crave, get on with it, have your cake, glitzy or plain, from cupcake to full size. Cakes are special order only, with two days' notice, so plan your cake time. If you need a cake to say "I do," place your order here, groom (or bride) not included in the request. Delivery service for all goods is available for a fee.

Seasonal baking is just that—seasonal, following weather, whim and time of year. Carolyne is a fan of Crave's Christmas-only salted nut bar (shortbread and nuts and butterscotch caramel), but she raves about the seasonal Twix square too (layered shortbread, caramel and chocolate *ganache*). Those squirrel-away, plan-in-advance types may want the "baking bundles" of cookies and squares for Christmas.

- *House Specialties*: Wedding cakes, cookies, cakes, and cupcakes like "Crave-O-Licious"—with blue vanilla icing.
- *Also Available*: 1107 Kensington Road NW.

www.cravecookies.com

Daily Bagel

Established: 2004 • Owner: Kris Frantzen
H6, 4421 Quesnay Wood Drive SW (Calgary Farmers' Market)
Phone: 479•5556
Friday & Saturday 9:00 am–5:00 pm, Sunday 9:00 am–4:00 pm
Debit, $

THE bagels are baked in the northeast, in the Montreal style—first boiled in honey-sweetened water, then baked in a wood-burning oven, for that chewy, dense texture. These bagels taste like it, and are as tightly structured as a choreographed jazz routine. Cinnamon raisin sells out quickly, but the orange and cranberry and whole wheat are equally good. Once you eat the real deal, there is no going back to mass-market bagels. Buy a bagful, or ask the guys to build you a smoked salmon or Montreal smoked meat sandwich. The kicker is more than just the Kicking Horse organic coffee, by cup or pound, but the local products used here, from **Gull Valley Greenhouse** and **Lund's Organic Produce**, as well as **Grazin'Acres**.

- *House Specialties*: Sesame, cinnamon raisin, multi-grain and orange cranberry bagels, flavoured cream cheeses, Montreal smoked meats and Winnipeg cream cheese sandwiches.

www.thedailybagel.ca

Decadent Desserts Inc.

Established: 1983 • Owner: Pam Fortier
831–10 Avenue SW
Phone: 245•5535
Monday–Friday 10:00 am–5:30 pm, Saturday 10:00 am–5:00 pm
V, MC, AE, DC, Debit, $

WHEN she bought it from co-founder Bev Polsky, Pam Fortier gently changed the direction of this Calgary institution, heading away from the rich chocolate constructs that made its name. She made her own name instead. Fortier is a fan of suave, sophisticated, and sleek and her bakery's goods reflect her preferences. She takes a trans-Atlantic approach: French-style rustic tarts, made with fresh fruit, or tangy lemon for lemon lovers, and North American-style butter cakes. Die-hard fans can find a few Polsky-era standards still goin' strong, like Seymours, (pastry wedges topped with nuts and caramel, dipped in milk chocolate), and chocolate pecan pie, but there is much more to sample! For daily desserts, choose an elegant frangipane, a fruit streusel, or a blood orange creamsicle tart if chocolate is too much for you. Fortier, a grad of Dubrulle Culinary Institute's professional pastry and desserts program in Vancouver, specializes in lovely understated wedding cakes in a clean-lined and spare style. She takes a personalized approach to **Chocolaterie Bernard Callebaut** chocolate, using it as a medium for making ribbons, braided tassels, and bows that are edible. Newly ensconced in the Design District across from Mountain Equipment Co-op, Fortier's larger location offers the chance to provide more pre-assembled trays for pick-up, as well as *tchotchkes* suitable for serving cakes and cookies.

For seasonal Christmas sweets, place your orders before mid-December, although the holiday showcase is always full but "first come, first served." Seasonal treats include brandied sour cherry truffle cake, caramel nut tarts, frangipane cranberry apple tarts, and gift-perfect cookie boxes.

• *House Specialties*: Wedding cakes, American-style butter layer cakes, French-style rustic fruit and seasonal tarts, and specialty baking ingredients. Ordering ahead is advisable.

www.decadentdesserts.ca

Glamorgan Bakery

Established: 1977 • Owner: Don Nauta, Manager: Frank Taal
20, 3919 Richmond Road SW
Phone: 242•2800
Monday–Friday 7:00 am–6:00 pm, Saturday 7:30 am–5:00 pm
V, MC, Debit, $

DUTCH baking is front and centre in this European-style bakery. Chief among all the sweets to select from are lacy rolled Florentine cookies filled with mocha cream—they have inspired us for 25 years! Old-style baking includes hard-to-find Parker House rolls, buttercream-filled cakes, fruit strudels and Danishes. Breads too, plain and sliced. I know couriers who plan their routes to include a regular stop for cheese buns from Glamorgan Bakery.

Each year's annual Christmas display in the front window—a stunningly artful gingerbread crèche—is worth the trip to this busy suburban plaza. In December, expect *stollen* and fruitcake, ginger cookies, almond rings, and almond sticks.

• *House Specialties*: Cheese buns, Florentines, Parker House rolls, cakes.

www.glamorganbakery.com

Heritage Bakery & Deli

Established: 1986 • *Owner: Kathy Batorowska*
1912–37 Street SW
Phone: 686•6835
Monday–Friday 8:00 am–6:00 pm
Saturday 9:00 am–5:00 pm, Sunday 9:00 am–2:00 pm
Debit, $

THE Polish baking in this shop has been rounded out with meals to go, so pick up lunch or dinner, including European cheeses, house-made garlic and ham sausage, and schnitzel when you stop by for a cheesecake. Poppy seeds abound: try the rich cottage cheese cake and strudel, cheesecake and crescent rolls (also filled with plum and marzipan). I especially like the Hungarian *palascinta*, also known as *blintzes* to my Jewish friends. Fans of pierogies can try nine varieties, and fans of densely textured dark breads have a plethora of choices, including rye breads made in the style of the Black Forest, the Tyrol, and Russia. Polish preserves are centre stage on the back shelves: select from jars of *musztarda chrzanowa*, pickles, herring, plums or beets, then supplement it with herb *tisane* or noodles.

Christmas baking is available from mid-November. Try *stollen*, two types of *babka*, and hand-decorated gingerbread men and trees.

• *House Specialties*: Poppyseed cheesecake and strudel, cabbage rolls, pierogies in nine types, house-made garlic and ham sausage, schnitzel and *palascinta*.

• *Also Available*: Pierogies, cabbage rolls, and sausages at Pazzer's Pub.

(A) Ladybug Belgian Pâtisserie

Established: 2004 • *Owners: Marie Leclerq & Yves Ghesquière*
H6, 4421 Quesnay Wood Drive SW (Calgary Farmers' Market)
Phone: 689•0244
Friday & Saturday 9:00 am–5:00 pm, Sunday 9:00 am–4:00 pm
Cheque, $

MARIE Leclerq loves her Belgian lace, and wears it on hot days while working with her husband, Yves Ghesquière. Long-time Belgian food professionals, he is a pastry chef, a baker, a *chocolatier*, a candy and ice cream maker; she trained on the savoury side of the kitchen. Her family has a near-continuous history of baking professionally, dating back to 1792 and an ancestor named Petrus. The couple's son, Pierre, is continuing the tradition, doing detail work and working in the *crêperie*, but he laughs and declines a full-on bakery role, says he is just going to bed when his father rises to tend the ovens at 1:00 am. The big booth at the market is filled to capacity: the *crêperie* occupies one end, with a bustling bakery adjacent. One of the couple's biggest successes is frozen raw *croissants*, sold in half dozens. "Oh millions, we make millions!" Leclerq giggles. "But Yves does not want people to buy too many at once, they deteriorate over time, are best within 30 days." The shop's healthy alternatives to *croissants* are "ancient grains" loaves made of *kamut* and *spelt,* available ready-to-eat or frozen. The sophisticated tarts—a meringue *merveilleux* or *sand rose praliné*—are very good, understated and elegant, what Leclerq calls, rather self-deprecatingly, "market baking." In fact, the tarts on display are as stylish as the owner's Belgian lace.

At holiday time, look for Christmas logs in three flavours—raspberry and chocolate, praline, or Black Forest—as well as house-made dark chocolate truffles and scrumptious *orangette.* Customers who wish to pick up any baked goods at A Ladybug Workshop (production location) on 42 Avenue SE *must* order in advance at the **Calgary Farmers' Market** location. Remember to arrange a pick-up time.

- *House Specialties*: Frozen *croissants,* ancient grains breads, crêpes, tarts, mousses, cakes, chocolates.
- *Also Available*: A Ladybug Workshop, 510–42 Avenue SE (advance order pick-up only). In conjunction with **Blush Lane** and **Sunworks Farm**, a new location will open at 10 Aspen Stone Boulevard SW in May 2008.

Lakeview Bakery
Established: 1967 • Owner: Brian Hinton
6449 Crowchild Trail SW (Lakeview Shopping Centre)
Phone: 246•6127
Monday–Friday 8:00 am–6:00 pm, Saturday 8:00 am–5:00 pm
V, MC, Debit, $

THIS bakery has a checkered past. It began as a German bakery, was relocated, stood empty from 1980–1988, and re-opened when the Olympics commenced in early 1988, under the steerage of Brian Hinton. Hinton, his wife Maureen, and their sons Daren and David, purchased the bakery in 1990. After virtually owning the "low-carb" baking market, Hinton has shifted his focus to what he prefers to call "special dietary" or "allergy" baking. His bakers use rice flour, *kamut,* and *spelt,* usually in mixes that are wheat-free and organic. Check out the pie shells, brown and white rice muffins, and rice flour pastries. Wheat-friendly shoppers looking for brownies and butter tarts will still find them, along with cookies and grain bars, cinnamon buns, seasonal pies, sourdough breads, seven-grain breads and flax seed pizza shells.

Christmas baking appears from mid-November each year. Expect *spelt* shortbread, gluten-free rice-flour dark fruitcakes, wheat flour cakes with almond icing, suet-enriched mince tarts and eggnog Nanaimo bar.

- *House Specialties*: Organic baking and "special dietary" baking, using *kamut, spelt* and rice flour.
- *Also Available*: **Amaranth Whole Foods Market,** the **Calgary Co-op, Community Natural Foods** and **Planet Organic Market.**
www.organicbaking.com

Montreal Bagels
Established: 2003 • Manager: Vanessa Siva
103, 8408 Elbow Drive SW
Phone: 212•4060
Monday–Saturday 9:00 am–5:30 pm, Sunday 10:00 am–4:00 pm
$ only

BAGELS, Montreal style, are traditionally boiled in honey water, then baked in wood-burning ovens fueled by birch and apple wood. The result is a dense, chewy, slightly sweet bagel with singed edges and a slightly woodsy-smoky undertone to it. This is NOT a bready, fluffy, airhead bagel. This is the real thing, *bien sûr*. Taste one and you'll get it in the first bite. Expect all the classic flavours in white flour bagels: sesame, poppy seed, blueberry, and cinnamon-rasin, plus multi-grain bagels topped with seven types of seeds, and unadorned whole wheat bagels.
- *House Specialties*: Montreal bagels of white, multi-grain, and whole wheat flour.

Rustic Sourdough Bakery
Established: 1968 • Owner-Baker: Jos Rehli
1305–17 Avenue SW
Phone: 245•2113
Monday 10:00 am–5:00 pm, Tuesday & Wednesday 8:00 am–5:00 pm
Thursday & Friday 8:00 am–6:00 pm, Saturday 7:00 am–5:00 pm
V, MC, Debit, $

FORMERLY known as Chalet Bakery and founded by Norbert Zielka, Jos Rehli changed the name in 2005 when he purchased this booming business. The best cheese Danish in the city is one reason for the Saturday morning lineups. Baker-owner Rehli says it out-sells all his other Danishes, it must be the quark filling. Yum, I have loved it for years. All products are made daily, no advance ordering needed except for large volumes. German crusty buns, dense rye (90-percent and 100-percent rye) breads and buttermilk rye bread have people lined up out the door on Saturday mornings. Of course there are classic European-style cakes filled with cream and buttercream, plus cookies and strudel. They now stock cold cuts and European cheeses— mostly Swiss and Italian, make sandwiches to order, and carry locally made preserves from **Jammin' It Jams & Jellies**, and sauces made in Lethbridge by the Saucy Ladies, in addition to sweet imported mustards, noodles, and sweet or salty licorice.

Christmas baking begins to surface in early November. Ask for German-style *stollen*, European-style cookies (chewy cinnamon stars are primo), sweet yeasted fruit breads—raisins, citrus, dates, cranberries, apricots, and currants— or seasonal soft gingerbread. For fun, gingerbread men decorated as Santa with marzipan faces; for traditions, Christmas logs, pecan and rum tarts. Ask if you do not see what you want.

- *House Specialties*: Swiss light rye sourdough, multi-grain and whole-grain breads in the German style, pound cake, cream-filled cakes, cheese Danish.
- *Also Available*: **Calgary Farmers' Market.**

Simple Simon Pies

Established: 1987 • Owner: Bob Whitworth
H6, 4421 Quesnay Wood Drive SW (Calgary Farmers' Market)
Phone: 205•3475
Friday & Saturday 9:00 am–5:00 pm, Sunday 9:00 am–4:00 pm
Cheque, $

SIMON is still "The Pieman" after more than 20 years of hawking handmade heaven. Owner Bob Whitworth came to Canada from Manchester, and his dulcet British tones can be heard cajoling ladies and lads into a taste of lunch in the best hawker's style this side of...well, Manchester. The pies are pretty good, too, in simple robust styles, available in two sizes for the savoury (individual 4" and big-enough-to-share 9"), and just one size for the sweet (individual 4"). My sons eat two of the 4" shepherds' pies at a time, but I prefer the curried chicken. Try the quiche or the steak pie. Simon is most likely going to have a pie to suit your palate. Fruit pies include the expected assortment of berries, but also a decent pecan and a good rhubarb. Simon recently added a second stall, called *Wish in a Dish*. These hearty meals-to-go are also available in two sizes, and include a starch. Choose from more than a dozen selections, including spicy Sicilian chicken, shrimp Creole, ratatouille, and other meatless options.

- *House Specialties*: Sweet and savoury pies.
- *Also Available*: Home delivery for a fee (September–June), **Crossroads Farmers' Market, Gour-Mart Meat Shop, Master Meats,** and Swifty's Esso in Douglasdale.

www.simplesimonpies.com

NORTHWEST

COBS Bread

Established: 2007 • Managers: Chaela Fasuba (CCSC), Brad Trent (SSC)

107, 150 Crowfoot Cresent NW	*5, 1941 Uxbridge Drive NW*
(Crowfoot Corner Shopping Centre)	*(Stadium Shopping Centre)*
Phone: 239•2666	*Phone: 282•1779*
Monday–Sunday 8:00 am–7:00 pm	*Monday–Saturday 8:00 am–7:00 pm*
	Sunday 9:00 am–7:00 pm

Debit, $
[see SW Bakeries for main entry on p. 21]

Crave Cookies & Cupcakes

Established: 2004 • Owner: Carolyne McIntyre Jackson
1107 Kensington Road NW
Phone: 270•2728
Tuesday–Friday 10:00 am–6:00 pm
Saturday 10:00 am–5:00 pm, Sunday noon–5:00 pm
V, MC, AE, Debit, $
[see SW Bakeries for main entry on p. 21]

Edelweiss Village

Established: 1982 • Owners: Stan & Marianne Kundert
1921–20 Avenue NW
Phone: 282•6600, Toll Free: (800) 559•8655
Monday–Wednesday 9:30 am–7:00 pm, Thursday–Friday 9:30 am–8:00 pm
Saturday 9:00 am–6:00 pm
V, MC, Debit, $

SHOPPING in the Village is like shopping the *strasse* or *platz* in Europe. A bakery, a busy takeout coffee shop, a lunch stop, a gift shop, a bustling deli, and the widest range of European imports in the city make this a slow wander. In the bakery, find apple strudel, marzipan treats, classic German cheesecake or torte and *labkuchen*. In the deli, Swiss cheeses for *raclette* or *fondue* are immensely popular. Sausage hounds will enjoy the selection of *schinkenspeck* and link-style sausages, suitable for *raclette* pan, sauerkraut pot or grill. Elsewhere in the store, find fuel for the *fondue* pot, or a tabletop pan (and pickles!) for the *raclette*, and dress your table in organza from Austria and Germany. There are wonderful Eastern Canadian products and giftware: Brickstone Fine Foods does up brandied cherries, boozy blueberries, cranberries in vodka, or amaretto apricots. Dark Pickle from PEI puts up densely packed East Coast berries, jams, and teas. Chocolate fans will be delighted by a wide—mostly European—selection, including Lindt, Droste, Weinrich, Toblerone, and Hachez in a variety of sizes, flavours, and shapes of bars.

In season, ask for house-made *Bûche de Noël* with marzipan mushrooms, gingerbread whimsies, Dutch-style filled *speculaas*, spicy *pfeffernusse* and German baked products, including *dominosteine* and 3-kilogram Otto Schmidt of Nurnberg tins in a different design each year.

• *House Specialties*: Baked goods, chocolate, European ingredients, deli.
• *Also Available*: Some exclusive imports can be found at **Community Natural Foods** (breads), and **Calgary Co-op** (diabetic chocolate).
www.edelweissimports.com

Lazy Loaf & Kettle
Established: 1989 • Owners: Michel & Helen Labonté
8 Parkdale Crescent NW
Phone: 270•7810
Monday–Friday 7:00 am–8:00 pm, Saturday–Sunday 8:00 am–8:00 pm
V, MC, AE, Debit, $

BREAD is the staff of life, and the 9-grain loaf here is a dense and grainy thing, made without dairy, eggs or fat. Buy sandwiches or buy the whole loaf to take home and make into turkey stuffing, sandwiches, or supper. The house's soups are from scratch, as is the very filling carrot loaf, a winner among the many un-fussy baked goods this kitchen produces. Helen believes that if you provide a good product and are generous with your portions, clients will remember you amid all the other choices. It is true. Corporate catering is a big part of the package here, from soup and sandwiches to sweet trays.

For Christmas, Lazy Loaf & Kettle's Transylvanian-born baker, Albert Balazs, bakes Mexican-style peppery coffee cookies, plus shortbreads, cheesecakes with cranberries or mint, and fruit strudels and *croissants* for lazy holiday breakfasts. Phone ahead for extra quantities.

• *House Specialties*: Breads and sandwiches, *croissants*, carrot loaf with cream cheese icing, soups, scratch-baked goods and corporate catering.
www.lazyloafandkettle.com

Prairie Mill Bread Company
Established: 1997 • Owner: John Juurlink
129, 4820 Northland Drive NW (Northland Plaza)
Phone: 282•6455
Monday–Saturday 6:00 am–6:00 pm
V, MC, Debit, $

FINDING this shop is the hardest part! (It is perched on the southeast corner of Northland and Northmount Drives.) Inside, like a nursery rhyme come to life, the mill that grinds the organic grain that makes the bread is housed in its own glassed-in room in the house that Jack (well, actually his name is John) Juurlink built. (Nursery rhymes never seem to fully translate into real life.) This is toothsome, hearty, full-flavour bread, shaped by hand, made with organic whole wheat and rye; the white flour is unbleached, and no preservatives or oils are added. A rotating roster of specialty breads have a weekly schedule of appearance—apple caramel, apple crunch, apple cheddar, cranberry orange, cinnamon swirl, *jalapeño* cheddar, Mediterranean, multi-grain sourdough, pesto Parmesan, roasted garlic, spinach onion, tomato cheddar. For sweets, try the huge cinnamon rolls, oatmeal cookies and banana bread with or without chocolate. For a true baker's dozen, buy 12 and get the 13th free.

• *House Specialties*: Organic 9-grain bread, Yukon sourdough, cinnamon swirl.

• *Also Available*: **Amaranth Whole Foods Market, Community Natural Foods, Grassroots Northland Farmers' Market, Planet Organic Market,** and **Sunnyside Market, Nutters Bulk & Natural Foods** in Canmore and Okotoks, and online at **<www.spud.ca>**.
www.prairiemillbread.com

Wayne's Bagels

Established: 1997 • Owners: Wayne & Helen Kim
328–10 Street NW
Phone: 270•7090
Monday–Saturday 8:00 am–6:00 pm, Sunday 8:00 am–4:00 pm
V, MC, Debit, $

O**N** the Northside, prowling for good baked goods, when we wandered into Wayne's Bagels on 10 Street NW, it was reassuring to see the wood-burning oven filling the back half of the bakery, a long slanted plank the home of bagels-in-waiting. Chewy and dense is the definition of Montreal-style, Wayne says, not fluffy like New York bagels. Buy one, buy a half dozen, by a dozen—cinnamon raisin smells like fresh-ground cinnamon, multi-grain is studded and textural, sun-dried tomato is flecked with tasty bits. Eat them for breakfast—toasted and smeared with cream cheese, for lunch—loaded with *crème fraîche* and tomatoes, or for supper—sliced into croutons topped with *chèvre*. Here is a chewy bagel that can get you through your day. All of the smoked meat is brought in from Montreal, and the cream cheese is from Winnipeg. On Tuesday's, look for special prices.

• *House Specialties*: Marble rye, energy bagels with vanilla, walnut and almonds, cinnamon and raisin bagels, multi-grain bagels.

Booze

THERE ARE MANY PLACES TO BUY WINE: corner stores and big chains alike have taken a stab at selling us our booze. But what sells booze best is knowledge, offered by thoughtful people who like people. Wine as a game of one-upmanship is not on the list of must-plays. The story—about the grapes, the grower, or tips on food pairings—is most palatable when it is delivered by considerate people. Some wine merchants prefer staff with formal wine training available through the Wine and Spirit Education Trust (WSET) or the International Sommelier Guild (ISG). Others hire wide-open eyes, mouths, hearts and ears, educated in the less formal, more rigorous school of life.

Several local specialty producers—makers of mead, beers and fruit wine are noteworthy. Check listings for Strathmore and Okotoks in the Bow Valley and Beyond.

NORTHEAST

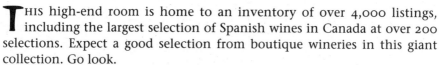

CSN Wine & Spirits

Established: 1993 • Manager: André Kok
1716 Centre Street North
Phone: 296•0240
Sunday–Wednesday 10:00 am–11:00 pm
Thursday–Saturday 10:00 am–midnight
V, MC, Debit, $

THIS high-end room is home to an inventory of over 4,000 listings, including the largest selection of Spanish wines in Canada at over 200 selections. Expect a good selection from boutique wineries in this giant collection. Go look.
• *House Specialties*: Spanish wines.
www.csnwine.com

Merlo Vinoteca Inc.

Established: 1999 • Owner: Franca Bellusci
813–1 Avenue NE
Phone: 269•1338 or 269•1339
Tuesday–Friday 10:00 am–5:30 pm, Saturday 10:00 am–5:00 pm
V, MC, AE, Debit, $

THIS tiny shop is an Italian boutique specialist in limited editions, owned by a discerning palate, Franca Bellusci. You will find her brother Dominic Caracciolo at **Mercato**. In Merlo Vinoteca Inc., look for the unique and hard-to-find small producers: Gaga, Voerzio, Elio Grasso. Get a bottle of grappa for the purist "Grappa Girl" in your life; this spirit is made in northern Italy, in traditional and modern styles. Shelves hold a wide range of *vin santo* and Italian sweet wines. Staff members here mostly have their ISG certification or WSET diplomas. A new location is scheduled to open in 2008.

• *House Specialties*: Italian wines and grappa.

www.teachyourpalate.com

SOUTHEAST

Big Rock Brewery
Established: 1984 • Owner: Ed McNally
5555–76 Avenue SE
Phone: 720•3239
Brewery Tours: Tuesday – Thursday at 1:30 pm
Big Rock Grill: Monday – Friday 11:30 am – 2:00 pm
Big Rock Store: Monday – Friday 8:30 am – 4:30 pm
Grill, Grasshöpper Room, and Loft available for evening and weekend functions
V, MC, Debit, $

ED McNally built Big Rock Brewery, as the Big, Bigger and Biggest little alehouse in Alberta. This farmer, lawyer, and entrepreneur looked hard at the imported beer in his hand in 1984, and began questioning why Canada's top malting barley became cattle fodder instead of a "barley sandwich" in a glass. Over time, he found funding and a brewmaster, built a brewery, and found a market for his high-quality microbrews, brewed under the Bavarian Purity Law of 1516.

Big Rock produces a large—and changeable—line-up of nearly two dozen largers, ales, and stouts, plus a hard cider. Some, like Grasshöpper, Pale Ale, and Black Amber Ale, are available year-round. Others, such as Cold Cock Winter Porter, Springbok, and a new tipple, Espresso Stout, are or have been regular seasonal offerings. One seasonal, McNally's Extra, began as a Christmas specialty in 1986, but is now available year-round. A new listing, McNally's Reserve, comes highly touted. Check it out yourself.

Big Rock Brewery's handcrafted beer is now produced in such big volumes that it no longer qualifies for the term "microbrew," with kegs, tins, and bottles of beer, including Grasshöpper, Warthog, and Buzzard's Breath shipped south into the States. Big Rock Brewery, built on the rock of sound business sense, uses top-calibre ingredients, marketed in a simple, snappy style with eye-catching labels. Go to the source for a meal, to buy Big Rock shirts and caps, for group tours of the brewery, or just for fun.

• *House Specialties*: Ales and lagers.

• *Also Available*: Most Alberta liquor stores and licensed eateries.

www.bigrockbeer.com

Willow Park Wines & Spirits

Established: 1994 • Owner: Wayne Henuset
Wine Buyer: Peggy Perry, Kitchen Manager: Meiko Pennock
10801 Bonaventure Drive SE (Willow Park Village)
Phone: 296•1640
Monday & Tuesday 10:00 am–11:00 pm
Wednesday & Thursday 10:00 am–midnight
Friday & Saturday 10:00 am–1:00 am, Sunday 10:00 am–9:00 pm
V, MC, AE, Debit, $

FIND the largest selection of wines and spirits in Canada. Willow Park Wines and Spirits relies on selection, price and 22 sommeliers on staff to share their knowledge. All this and classes too: a diverse collection of Calgary chefs and visiting chefs present food and wine pairings for up to 30 guests in hands-on classes; tastings can accommodate up to 80. Three-hour classes cover appetizers, wine and spirits classes, and sommelier certification programs conducted by the Master Sommelier Guild of America. Private classes and events (charitable and social) can be booked by phone. The business produces six separate food and beverage TV shows with over 200 episodes that air across Canada and around the world: an Italian series, *Divine Life*, aired in 2007 on City TV, Access and CLT; *Taste! The Beverage Show* airs on Global.

• *House Specialties*: French and Italian wines.
• *Also Available*: 4012 Bow Trail SW.
www.willowpark.net

SOUTHWEST

Bin 905

Established: 1997 • Manager: Geoff Last
2311–4 Street SW
Phone: 261•1600
Monday–Saturday 10:00 am–8:00 pm, Sunday noon–6:00 pm
V, MC, AE, Debit, $

THIS shop stocks many exclusive listings. Like several other stores in town, small handmade artisanal vintages are its stock-in-trade. Manager Geoff Last enjoys "cult wines," and travels extensively to France, California, Spain and Germany to taste and tell, and he nurtures a special interest in biodynamic wines as well. Staff members are all either accredited sommeliers or WSET diploma holders, with knowledgeable, friendly, and thirsty palates. Besides a large collection of premium spirits and imported beers, the store stocks virtually every Belgian beer on the market.

• *House Specialties*: French, Californian, Italian, Spanish, and German small producers of hard-to-find bottles and cult wines, and Belgian beer.
www.bin905.com

Britannia Wine Merchants

Established: 1994 • General Manager: Steve Goldworthy
810–49 Avenue SW (Britannia Plaza)
Phone: 287•3833
Monday–Friday 10:00 am–8:00 pm, Saturday 10:00 am–6:00 pm
Sunday noon–5:00 pm
V, MC, AE, Debit, Cheque, $

THIS shop embraces exclusive or semi-exclusive listings, from big prices to hand-crafted finds. "South African and Argentinian wines are French wines at half the price," manager Steve Goldworthy says. They are made in French styles and aged in French oak. He carries an extensive collection of single malts. Goldworthy likes personable people with a passion for wine, so staff are approachable and believe that the best way to learn about wine is to drink it. On Fridays, check out the in-store tastings. Monthly, an informal festival-style event provides tastes of 15 wines, with good food from some top-line restaurants. It all reflects Goldworthy's belief that a wine store should be a resource, not a place of intimidation.

• *House Specialties*: Wines from Argentina, Spain, Italy, France, South Africa, and British Columbia's Okanagan Valley.

www.britanniawinemerchants.com

The Cellar Fine Wines & Spirits Inc.

Established: 2001 • General Manager: Francois Gaulin
100, 137–8 Avenue SW
Phone: 503•0730
Monday–Wednesday 10:30 am–6:30 pm, Thursday & Friday 10:00 am–8:00 pm
Saturday 10:00 am–6:00 pm, Sunday noon–6:00 pm
V, MC, AE, Debit, $

LOCATED in the stunning and beautiful cellar of the Old Alberta Hotel Building on Stephen Avenue, The Cellar Fine Wines & Spirits Inc. offers wines, spirits, and beers from the affordable to the exclusive. More than 2,500 premium wines are available, plus ports to lay down or open, Bordeaux futures for investers, Burgundy, and Australian bottles. Wine accessories and gifts include German-made Schotts Zweisel titanium zirconium glasses, break-resistant and dishwasher safe—at a fraction of the price of Riedel—in a wide range of styles designed for specific varietals. Beer lovers may enjoy Ritzenhoff's German pilsner and draft glasses. Look at pewter decanters from Royal Selangor of Malaysia, Spiegelau glasses, decanters, and collectible corkscrews. I love my double-hinge waiter pull, but for sheer whimsy, I want the Winemaster by Vacuvin, the Edward Scissorhands of corkscrews, good for the awkward wine geek. For the name alone, buy a Didgeridoonas bag from Australia, its oiled canvas exterior lined with wool will keep wine cool on trips to the outback and back again. The shop hosts wine tastings, a dozen sessions per semester but book ahead to avoid disappointment. Private events are customized: standup, sitdown, formal, casual, with or without cheese or finger foods. For corporate gifting, order by phone or in person. If you are curious, ask a staff person about the ghost said to haunt the building.

• *House Specialties*: Australian wines, ports, Burgundy and Bordeaux, accessories.

www.cellarwinestore.com

J. Webb Wine Merchant • J. Webb Market Wines

Established: 1985 • Owner: Janet Webb

157, 1600–90 Avenue SW	*4580 Quesnay Wood Drive SW*
(Glenmore Landing)	*(Calgary Farmers' Market)*
Phone: 253•9463	*Phone: 685•5218*
Monday–Friday 10:00 am–9:00 pm	*Friday & Saturday 10:00 am–6:00 pm*
Saturday 10:00 am–6:00 pm	*Sunday 10:00 am–5:00 pm*
Sunday 11:00 pm–5:00 pm	

V, MC, Debit, $

J. WEBB Wine Merchant was part of the early trio of shops to open during the Alberta government's first foray into privatization. At the market store, the focus is on value bottles to suit writers' budgets. At the Glenmore Landing location, the budget is up to you. A collaboration with **Richmond Hill Wines**, **Metrovino** and the **Banff Wine Store** means that the four businesses have many exclusive imports, with a common focus on "off-the-beaten-path" wines made by artisanal producers. The specialty bottles are divided among the stores by geographic region. At J. Webb Wine Merchant, expect Californian, and French, along with a rare British Columbian exclusive—Blue Mountain. Classes held year-round for which you can register by phone; information is posted online. In-store weekly tastings are anchored by the "new and unusual" on Saturdays at Glenmore Landing, along with frequently changing "others" at both stores. Spirits fans can explore Armagnacs and cognacs, and upwards of 50 single malts. Staff members are trained through WSET and include a mix of former restaurant sommeliers, including one Master of Wine (MW) candidate.

• *House Specialties*: Californian and French—including a dozen Burgundy exclusives—artisanal producers including British Columbia's Blue Mountain, Italian and Australian bottles, single malts.

www.jwebb.net

Metrovino

Established: 1996 • Owner: Richard Harvey
722–11 Avenue SW
Phone: 205•3356
Monday–Friday 10:00 am–8:00 pm, Saturday 10:00 am–5:30 pm
Sunday noon–5:00 pm
V, MC, AE, Diner's, Debit, Cheque, $

WELL-INFORMED staff and an abiding interest in education make this independent and individualistic store well worth the visit. Harvey has a wide-ranging knowledge of growers, especially the small specialists. He is a dedicated bilingual Francophile and he "holidays" in France during crush, working and picking grapes. He also participates in **The Cookbook Company Cooks'** European cooking camps, and teaches wine education for the International Sommelier Guild (ISG) across North America, and through his own Calgary-based Wine Academy, offering structured classes next door at **The Cookbook Company Cooks.** At Metrovino, the attraction is "families, not factories." Harvey loves things that sparkle, and says, "French Champagne may not go with every food. But it is so captivating that it doesn't matter, it captures you." I for one go willingly, with grace.

• *House Specialties*: Small-production artisanal wines from Southern France and Spain.

www.metrovino.com

Richmond Hill Wines

Established: 1991 • Owner: Gary Jennings
108, 3715–51 Street SW
Phone: 686•1980
Monday–Friday 10:00 am–8:00 pm, Saturday 10:00 am–6:00 pm
Sunday noon–5:00 pm
V, MC, Debit, Cheque, $

IN this shop, staff members are mostly restaurant-trained, some with winery experience, so they can fill you in on wine production, supplying life experience in place of theory. This team likes to educate and runs tastings through the spring. Book a spot after consulting the subscriber list mail-out. There are no spirits here, it is all about the grape, 80–90 percent of which is brought in under a mutually beneficial arrangement with **Banff Wine Store, J. Webb Wine Merchant,** and **Metrovino.** As Jennings says, a relaxed attitude goes a long way towards enjoyment. Look for small-producer labels from Bordeaux, Burgundy, and Australia.

• *House Specialties*: Australian, Bordeaux, and Burgundy wines from smaller producers with many exclusive labels.

www.richmondhillwines.com

Wild Rose Brewery

Established: 1996 • Owner: Michael Tymchuk
4580 Quesnay Wood Drive SW (Calgary Farmers' Market)
Phone: 720•2733
Monday–Saturday 11:00 am–11:00 pm, Sunday 11:00 am–9:00 pm
V, MC, Debit, $

THIS microbrewery makes seasonal beers—bock, barley wines, cherry porters, and seven ales, from dark to light. It is all made on-site, pulled on tap, but is sold in bottles too. Tours can be booked for groups of 10–20 to visit the taproom and sample the goods. A stage serves live music to keep time with the kitchen's beer-beat cuisine. A patio is perched out back, and J. **Webb Market Wines** is next door. Hard to beat.

- *House Specialties*: In the taproom: Alberta Crude Oatmeal Stout, WRed Wheat, SOB (Special Old Bitter), and seasonally Wild Rose Cherry Porter and Barley Wine. In bottles: Industrial Park Ale (an authentic IPA), Raspberry Ale, Brown Ale, and Velvet Fog (a Canadian Wheat Ale).
- *Also Available*: More than 300 Calgary liquor stores, 70+ restaurants and bars, in Calgary, Canmore, and Banff.

www.wildrosebrewery.com

Willow Park Wines & Spirits

Established: 1994 • Owner: Wayne Henuset
Wine Buyer: Peggy Perry Kitchen Manager: Meiko Pennock
4012 Bow Trail SW
Phone: 777•1234
Monday–Thursday 10:00 am–10:00 pm, Friday–Saturday 10:00 am–11:00 pm
Sunday 11:00 am–7:00 pm
V, MC, AE, Debit, $
[see SE Booze for main entry on p. 33]

The Wine Cellar South

Established: 2000 • Owner: Frank Kennedy
600, 9737 Macleod Trail South (Southland Crossing)
Phone: 640•1111
Monday–Friday 10:00 am–9:30 pm, Saturday 10:00 am–8:00 pm
Sunday 11:00 am–6:00 pm
V, MC, AE, Debit, $

FORMER owner Joseph DiAngelis of La Chaumière established the benchmark for Old World wines that still permeates the list of 600 exclusive wines imported by the mother shop, The Wine Cellar in Edmonton. Look for Old World Burgundies, Bordeaux, and Italian listings, then branch across the sea to the US, especially California. Find thoughtful service here: sommeliers on staff are trained via the International Sommelier Guild (ISG.)

For a true "inside Calgary" edge, pick up a bottle with a little Chinook Country local history and colour: Cliff Lede, owner of Ledcor Construction, is a quiet Albertan resident who is also a winery and vineyard owner. His Lede Vineyards, in Napa Valley, produces Sauvignon Blanc, Cabernet Sauvignon, a flagship blend called 'Poetry' (Cabernet, Merlot, and Malbec), as well as Petite Syrah, and claret, the old English name for a Bordeaux blend.

- *House Specialties*: wines from Burgundy, Italy, and California.
- *Also Available*: The Wine Cellar, Edmonton.

www.thewinecellar.ab.ca

NORTHWEST

Kensington Wine Market

Established: 1992 • Owners: Nancy Carten & Richard Lindseth
1257 Kensington Road NW
Phone: 283•8000
Monday–Wednesday 10:00 am–8:00 pm, Thursday & Friday 10:00 am–9:00 pm
Saturday 10:00 am–8:00 pm, Sunday noon–6:00 pm
V, MC, AE, Debit, $

THIS shop has one of Alberta's largest selections of single malt scotch, from cheap 'n' cheerful to rare, from Finlaggan to decades-deep Highland Park. Choices are solid in exclusive Australian treasures, a candidly Canadian collection of national wines is unassumingly large in a so-Canadian self-effacing style, and the pool of Bordeaux is deep. An approachable and knowledgeable staff will help you find what you want, or give you a taste of something new. Most staff are trained via Wines and Spirits Education Trust (WSET) and/or International Sommeliers Guild (ISG.) A small tasting room seats 20 during formal tastings, offered during three sessions annually. Book the space in advance, either online or at the store. Corporate orders and gifting can also be completed online.

- *House Specialties*: Single malts, imported and microbrew beers, Canadian wines, Australian wines, corporate gifts.

www.kensingtonwinemarket.com

Chains (Big & Small)

HAINS MEET NEEDS beyond the kinks or links of fetishists or fence builders. Chains, those ubiquitous, in-every-neighbourhood, sterile, big box shopping experiences, are striving in some cases to fill specific niches, or to be all things to all cooks. They are not, and cannot be. But some do some things well, and others less so.

In matters of convenience, there is no debating that big chains are just that, but not if one factors in parking hassles, sometimes-shoddy or invisible staffing, interminable or self-serve checkouts, and the poor access and road design of suburban malls. Such roads were surely not laid out by anyone who has travelled them.

I have shopped at all of these chains, in many of their locations. I'd bet that all of us have. They fill a niche, there is no denying it, love them or not.

What I like about chains is what everyone else appreciates: convenience, late-night hours, the all-under-one-roof aspect that saves me visits to other shops when I am pressed for time. What I dislike: their institutional feel, impersonal service by people who do not know me, the commodification of food, out-of-season imported produce without provenance, mediocre quality, Cryovac'd cheeses instead of wheels cut to order, insufficient support of local producers and locally grown foodstuffs, nonexistent information about countries of origins and distances foods travel, wildly variable quality and shelf life, especially for produce.

Calgary Co-op

Established: 1956
Head Office: 2735–39 Avenue NE
Phone: 219•6025
City wide and beyond — see quadrant charts
Stores: Monday–Sunday 8:00 am–10:00 pm
8:00 am–6:00 pm Easter Sunday, Thanksgiving, Christmas Eve, New Year's Eve
10:00 am–6:00 pm Boxing Day, New Year's Day
Pharmacy: Monday–Friday 9:00 am–9:00 pm
Saturday, Sunday & Holidays 9:00 am–6:00 pm
Gas Bar: Monday–Friday 5:00 to 6:00 am–10:00 to 11:00 pm
Saturday & Sunday 6:00 to 8:00 am–9:00 to 11:00 pm (times vary with location)
Liquor: Monday–Saturday 10:00 am–10:00 pm, Sunday 10:00 am–8:00 pm
Travel: Monday–Friday 9:00 am–7:00 pm, Saturday 9:30 am–5:30 pm
V, MC, Debit, $

N November 1956, the doors of the first Calgary Co-op store opened, but this local success story really began in 1954. Talk of buying the Alberta Co-operative Wholesale Association retail store in Calgary led to the formation of the co-op. Gordon Barker, one of the founding members, served as chair for more than 30 years. He says, "Calgary Co-op was formed by ordinary people who wanted a business they could rely on when others failed to provide them with the services they needed. Calgary Co-op was formed to serve its members and to be a contributing partner in the community."

Locally owned and operated, Calgary Co-op is one of the largest retail co-operatives in North America, with 413,000 members, 4,000 employees, 23 retail shopping centres, 26 gas bars, 11 travel offices and 16 liquor stores located in Calgary, Airdrie, Strathmore, and Okotoks. That's thinking local!

I drove to the Beddington location to buy cukes and tomatoes grown in Alberta, under the Shirley's Greenhouse label. Elsewhere, in other Co-ops, I can find fine **Paradise Hill Farm** tomatoes from Nanton's Tony and Karen LeGault, and Pic 'n' Pacs from **Gull Valley Greenhouse**. They are good examples of how this prairie-based business walks its talk of "local first," as explained by Brian Lewis, VP of Produce. "We put local first where quality, taste, and food safety meet our standards." He believes that the growing cadre of local-first eaters, dubbed *locavores*, is not too small to be bothered with, and that their dining habits are worth satisfying.

The stores practice target marketing as well: products in one quadrant may not be what other quadrants sell due to differing demographics and different population bases. The key for consumers, Lewis says, is to recall that not all produce is created equal, so be careful of what you are buying and do not buy on price, but for the best-tasting ingredients to make your recipe work. I cannot argue with that.

In the meat department, you can find **Spolumbo's Fine Foods & Italian Deli** sausages, and Alberta AAA beef, but lamb is from New Zealand, for shame. Cooks making stock can find fish bones (*"frames"*) and beef bones in the freezer. At holiday time, fresh, free-range **Winter's Turkeys** arrive. Advance ordering is not necessary, although, as one store manager says, "Latecomers may have the privilege of going without if they don't place an order."

Of the supermarkets I visited, Calgary Co-op had the best supply of organic ingredients. Wheat-free diets can be accommodated with **Lakeview Bakery's** frozen raw rice-flour pies, along with other makes of unsweetened (raw) pies, frozen breads and buns of *spelt, kamut,* and white rice, flavoured with or without cinnamon and raisins, or cheese.

The Beddington store carries a wide range of ethnic ingredients. Find jars of grape leaves (to make dolmades) and *tahini, chana* flour and dried chickpeas, Indian, Indonesian, and Thai seasonings. Bulk bins hold snacks, nuts, and dried fruits, but are devoid of pulses, grains, or dry goods for baking. Calgary Co-op delivers, and offers online ordering.

At the Midtown Market, register for "raw uncooking" classes—potlucks, workshops and lectures—led by Diana Stoevelaar and visiting specialists. Learn "raw uncooking" philosophy and techniques, attend lectures or absorb info on "Spring Cleaning" on the Raw Food Diet.

• *House Specialties*: Local foods.

www.calgarycoop.com • www.picndel.com
www.awesomerawsome.com

NORTHEAST

	P	D	G	W	L	T
Beddington Co-op *8220 Centre Street NE • Phone: 299•4445* ℞: 299•4418, Gas Bar: 299•4380, Liquor: 299•7764	•	•	•	•	•	
Monterey Square Co-op *2220–68 Street NE • Phone: 299•2600* ℞: 299•2606						
North Hills Co-op *540–16th Avenue NE • Phone: 299•4276* ℞: 299•4273, Gas Bar: 299•4277			•			
Taradale Co-op *6520 Falconridge Boulevard NE • Phone: 299•4012* ℞: 299•4016, Gas Bar: 299•4013, Liquor: 299•4020	•		•	•	•	
Village Square Co-op *2520 – 52 Street NE • Phone: 299•5332* ℞: 299•5334, Gas Bar: 299•4377, Travel: 299•4401			•			•

SOUTHEAST

	P	D	G	W	L	T
Copperfield Co-op Gas Bar *15566 McIver Boulevard SE • Phone: 299•4110*	•	•	•	•		
Deer Valley Co-op *1221 Canyon Meadows Drive SE • Phone: 299•4350* ℞: 299•4347, Gas Bar: 299•4351, Travel: 299•2619	•	•	•	•		•
Downtown Co-op Gas Bar *1111–1 Street SE • Phone: 299•4261*	•		•			
Eastfield Co-op Gas Bar *5250–50 Avenue SE • Phone: 299•4443*	•	•	•	•		
Forest Lawn Co-op *3330–17th Avenue SE • Phone: 299•4470* ℞: 299•4467, Gas Bar: 299•4371, Liquor: 299•4372	•		•		•	
Heritage Towne Co-op Gas Bar & Liquor *16 & 76 Heritage Gate SE* Gas Bar: 299•4334, Liquor: 299•4335	•	•	•	•	•	
Macleod Trail Co-op *8818 Macleod Trail SE • Phone: 299•4292* ℞: 299•4289, Gas Bar: 299•4293, Liquor: 299•4288, Travel: 299•4383	•		•		•	•
South Trail Crossing Co-op *4307–130 Avenue SE • Phone: 257•7272* ℞: 257•7243, Gas Bar: 257•7260, Liquor: 257•7255, Travel: 257•7247	•	•	•	•	•	•

LEGEND
P = Propane
D = Diesel
G = Gasoline
W = Car Wash
L = Liquor
T = Travel

SOUTHWEST

	P	D	G	W	L	T
Midtown Market Co-op *1130–11 Avenue SW • Phone: 299•4257* ℞: 299•4255, Liquor: 299•4233, Travel: 299•4231					•	•
Oakridge Co-op *2580 Southland Drive SW • Phone: 299•4355* ℞: 299•5374, Gas Bar: 299•4280, Liquor: 299•5444, Travel: 299•5316	•	•	•	•		•
Richmond Road Co-op *4940 Richmond Road SW • Phone: 299•4490* ℞: 299•4487, Gas Bar: 299•4374, Liquor: 299•5362, Travel: 299•4370	•		•		•	•
Shawnessy Co-op *250 Shawville Boulevard SW • Phone: 299•4426* ℞: 299•4439, Gas Bar: 299•4422, Travel: 299•4130	•	•	•	•		
West Springs Co-op *100, 917–85 Street SW • Phone: 299•4151* ℞: 299•4420, Gas Bar: 299•4407, Liquor: 299•4405	•	•	•	•	•	

NORTHWEST

	P	D	G	W	L	T
Brentwood Co-op *4122 Brentwood Road NW • Phone: 299•4311* ℞: 299•4308, Gas Bar: 299•4312	•		•			
Crowfoot Co-op *35 Crowfoot Way NW • Phone: 299•5353* ℞: 299•5350, Gas Bar: 299•5355, Travel: 216•4500	•	•	•	•		•
Creekside Co-op *12626 Symons Valley Road NW • Phone: 299•4491* ℞: 299•4474, Gas Bar: 299•4424, Liquor: 299•4493	•	•	•	•	•	
Dalhousie Co-op *5505 Shaganappi Trail NW • Phone: 299•4331* ℞: 299•4329, Gas Bar: 299•4332, Liquor: 299•4333, Travel: 299•4400	•		•	•	•	•
Hamptons Co-op *1000 Hamptons Drive NW • Phone: 299•6711* ℞: 299•6713, Gas Bar: 299•6716, Travel: 299•5414	•		•	•		•
Montgomery Co-op *4608–16 Avenue NW • Phone: 299•2602* Gas Bar: 266•2602			•	•		
Rocky Ridge Co-op *11595 Rockyvalley Drive NW • Phone: 299•5450* ℞: 299•5454, Gas Bar: 299•5497, Liquor: 299•5490	•	•	•	•	•	

LEGEND
P = PROPANE
D = DIESEL
G = GASOLINE
W = CAR WASH
L = LIQUOR
T = TRAVEL

Canada Safeway

Established: 1929
Head Office (Calgary): 1020–64 Avenue NE
Phone: 730•3901 Community Relations
Customer Service: (800) 723•3929
City wide and beyond — see quadrant charts
Stores: Monday–Sunday 8:00 am–11:00 pm
Pharmacy: Monday–Friday 9:00 am–9:00 pm
Saturday 9:00 am–6:00 pm, Sunday 10:00 am–6:00 pm
V, MC, Debit, Cheque, $

I shop at Canada Safeway in my northwest neighbourhood. It is convenient, it is open late, it has nearly everything I need, from cat toys to milk and apples for my fruit-loving son. But it can be a frustrating experience when I attempt to obtain provenance or other information—never mind high-quality or locally grown foods—from a large chain with 32 locations in and around Calgary, including Airdrie, Banff, Cochrane, and Chestermere Lake. The kids at the till and in the produce aisles try, but they don't always know where things came from or who grew it, they just have product codes. Everything is standardized to fit 214 stores in Western Canada.

One of the good things about Safeway is the collection of "artisan" slow-fermented breads in a variety of flavours. The crumb and inner structure is fine, not wide-open, and the crust is crisp, dense, toothsome. Try the Calamata Olive, Portuguese Corn, or Jalapeño Cheese Rustica, among others. Swiss Farm Grain is dense and chewy. If you don't see any on the racks, ask. There may be a frozen, partly baked loaf in the back and they bake up in minutes from frozen. Most of the glitzy-looking desserts in the case are prettier to look at than to eat, but the cheese selection is steadily improving, although all cheeses are pre-cut and Cryovac'd.

The meat counters have butchers—available and on-call—who will cut something for you if you do not see what you want, and the meat is all federally inspected. Sausages are made by **Spolumbo's Fine Foods & Italian Deli**. The lamb is Canadian. Nearly 80 percent of Safeway's turkey sales are frozen, but fresh Western Canadian commercially raised turkeys are also available, as are **Winter's Turkeys** free-range birds at some locations. Ask. The business of grocery stores is to sell what people want to buy, so ask for what you want. That includes produce. If you do not see it at your nearby Canada Safeway, say so.

Some locations have a broader range of produce and groceries, organic and conventional, depending, it seems, on their location within in the city. Organic produce at my local Montgomery store is limited and often tired-looking, shelved apart from conventional goods, but my trips to Garrison Woods uncover a clean and crisp collection of greater breadth, in both conventional and organic produce. Scan the natural foods shelves for some organic ingredients, including British Columbia-roasted Kicking Horse coffee beans. Scattered throughout the stores is a relatively new house line, "O," in a growing range of products.

In my search for the best food information, I spoke with Safeway's local VP of Public Affairs, Dave Ryzebol. Safeway puts "local" farther down its list, he says. "Our first responsibility is to provide the safest and best quality foods at the best price." According to Ryzebol, modern consumers do not know where our food originates, even though we eat better than the kings of old. He believes that consumers have learned to want what we want when we want it, as evidenced by winter-grown salads and out-of-season berries from far away. With 214 stores across western Canada, he says that Canada Safeway deals with producers who can fill that scale of supply, something that most local producers cannot hope to provide year-round, and that the company's ordering and supply system is organized accordingly.

All stores have Produce, Deli, Bakery, Meat and Fish, and Floral departments. Most stores have a Pharmacy; many locations are being "lifestyle" renovated to include a Starbucks counter, Gas Bar, and Liquor Store.

- *House Specialties*: Safeway in-house labels, especially their "O" organic line, slow-fermented breads, Kicking Horse coffee beans.

www.safeway.ca

Costco
Established: 1985 • Store Manager: Heather Downey
2853–32 Street NE (Costco North East)
Phone: 299•1610
Monday–Friday 11:00 am–8:30 pm, Saturday 9:30 am–6:00 pm
Sunday 10:00 am–5:00 pm
Additional Exclusive Business Member Hours:
Monday–Friday 10:00 am–11:00 am
AE, Debit, Cheque, $

VEGETABLES are by the big bag; cheeses are likewise packed in large chunks, and eggs are sold by the flat. Everything sold in this chain is based on large-volume consumption, although not all prices are competitive. Do your due diligence if you are shopping for the best financial deals. All beef is AAA, sold in primal cuts and large packs. Look for yourself, but only if you are a member.

Costco
Established: 1985 • Store Manager: Brad Clowes
99 Heritage Gate SE (Costco South)
Phone: 313•7650 or 313•7647
Monday–Friday 10:00 am–8:30 pm, Saturday 9:30 am–6:00 pm
Sunday 10:00 am–5:00 pm
Additional Exclusive Business Member Hours
Monday–Friday 10:00 am–11:00 am
AE, Debit, Cheque, $
[see Chains (Big & Small) NE for main entry on p. 44]

NORTHEAST

	R	S	G	L
Beacon Heights Safeway	•			
20, 1818 Centre Street NE • Phone: 276•3328 • ℞: 276•3313				
Castleridge Safeway	•			
55 Castleridge Boulevard NE • Phone: 293•0255 • ℞: 293•0223				
Northgate Village Safeway	•	•		
399–36 Street NE • Phone: 248•0848 • ℞: 235•4510				
TransCanada Safeway	•	•		
300, 1440–52 Street NE • Phone: 235•1437 • ℞: 235•1414				
Whitehorn Safeway	•		•	
3550–32 Avenue NE • Phone: 291•2035 • ℞: 291•2032				
Gas Bar: 291•2035 Ext. 6				

SOUTHEAST

	R	S	G	L
Bonavista Safeway				
755 Lake Bonavista Drive SE • Phone: 271•1616				
Forest Lawn Safeway				
3301–17 Avenue SE • Phone: 273•2800				
South Trail Safeway	•		•	•
200, 4915–130 Avenue SE • Phone: 257•8510 • ℞: 257•8520				
Gas Bar: 257•8510 ext. 1219, Liquor: 257•8541				
Ogden Safeway	•			
7740–18 Street SE • Phone: 236•1210 • ℞: 279•2220				
South Centre Safeway	•			
11011 Bonaventure Drive SE • Phone: 278•5225 • ℞: 278•8585				

SOUTHWEST

	R	S	G	L
Downtown Safeway	•			
813–11 Avenue SW • Phone: 264•1375 • ℞: 264•1378				
Garrison Woods Safeway	•	•		
2425–34 Avenue SW • Phone: 240•1098 • ℞: 217•1011				
Glamorgan Safeway	•			
3737–37 Street SW • Phone: 698•8222 • ℞: 698•8228				
Glenmore Landing Safeway	•	•	•	
1600–90 Avenue SW • Phone: 255•2755 • ℞: 255•3988				
Gas Bar: 255•2755 ext. 1219				
Mission Safeway	•			
524 Elbow Drive SW • Phone: 228•6141 • ℞: 228•4240				

LEGEND
℞ = Pharmacy
S = Starbucks
G = Gas Bar
L = Liquor

SOUTHWEST – continued:	R	S	G	L
Shawnessey Safeway	•	•	•	
70 Shawville Boulevard SW • Phone: 256•1401 • R: 256•1202				
Gas Bar: 256•1401 Ext. 6				
Southland Crossing Safeway	•			
9737 Macleod Trail SW • Phone: 252•8199 • R: 252•8090				
Westbrook Mall Safeway	•			
1200–37 Street SW • Phone: 246•0003 • R: 240•3223				
West Hills Towne Centre Safeway	•			
200 Stewart Green SW • Phone: 246•4484 • R: 246•0336				
West Hills Fuel Station Safeway			•	
192 Stewart Green SW • Phone: 242•7577				
Monday–Sunday 6:00 am–11:00 pm				
Woodbine Safeway	•			
2525 Woodview Drive SW • Phone: 238•1400 • R: 251•0777				

NORTHWEST

	R	S	G	L
Beddington Safeway	•	•		
8120 Beddington Boulevard NW • Phone: 295•6895 • R: 295•8895				
Brentwood Safeway				
3636 Brentwood Road NW • Phone: 289•1424				
Crowfoot Safeway	•	•	•	
99 Crowfoot Crescent NW • Phone: 239•9000 • R: 239•8839				
Gas Bar: 239•9000 Ext. 6				
Dalhousie Station Safeway	•	•		
5005 Dalhousie Drive NW • Phone: 202•0425 • R: 202•0444				
Hillhurst Safeway	•	•		
410–10 Street NW • Phone: 270•3054 • R: 283•8185				
Market Mall Safeway	•			
3625 Shaganappi Trail NW • Phone: 286•5510 • R: 288•8804				
Montgomery Safeway	•	•		
5048 –16 Avenue NW • Phone: 288•3219 • R: 286•1110				
North Hill Mall Safeway	•	•		
1846, 1632–14 Avenue NW • Phone: 210•0002 • R: 210•0224				
Thorncliffe Safeway	•	•		
5607–4 Street NW • Phone: 730•4955 • R: 730•5080				

LEGEND
R = PHARMA
S = STARBUCK
G = GAS BAR
L = LIQUOR

Costco
Established: 1985 • Store Manager: Rick Firth
11588 Sarcee Trail NW (Costco North West)
Phone: 516•3701
Monday–Friday 11:00 am–8:30 pm, Saturday 9:30 am–6:00 pm
Sunday 10:00 am–5:00 pm
Additional Exclusive Business Member Hours
Monday–Friday 10:00 am–11:00 am
AE, Debit, Cheque, $
[see Chains (Big & Small) NE for main entry on p. 44]

The Real Canadian Superstore
Established: 1979
Head Office: Brampton, Ontario
Phone: (866) 596•7277
City wide and beyond — see quadrant chart
Stores: Sunday–Friday 9:00 am–10:00 pm, Saturday 8:00 am–10:00 pm
Pharmacy & Optical: Monday–Friday 9:00 am–10:00 pm
Saturday 9:00 am–7:00 pm, Sunday 9:00 am–6:00 pm
Liquor: Monday–Saturday 10:00 am–10:00 pm, Sunday 10:00 am–8:00 pm
Gas Bar: Monday–Saturday 7:00 am–11:00 pm, Sunday 8:00 am–11:00 pm
V, MC, Debit, $

THESE superstores are big, they take time to navigate, and staff is hard to locate, but there are good things to find if you spend the time. Take your own grocery bags or pay for the plastic ones before you queue up at the checkout. Do not look in the phone book for phone numbers; they are largely unlisted, but you have them here, in *Shop talk!*

This large business solves the organic issue by producing its own label. As you shop the miles of aisles, keep your eyes peeled for the distinctive green leaf label, on everything from crackers and cookies to pasta and award-winning carrot juice. Carrot and vodka martini, anyone? Bulk bins are filled with as many candy choices as dried beans. Look for wild and *basmati* rice, dry goods for baking, and a good range of dried fruits and pulses, from crystallized ginger to *chana dal* and black-eyed peas.

The produce section is half an acre at least, with some goods in big netted bags and others loose in crates big enough to swim laps in. Some variety, some fluctuation in freshness, with cracked *durian* and dry-looking lemongrass, shimmering *rapini* and *witloof*, immaculate *gai lan* and *ya choy*. The fresh herb selection varies, as does their condition, from wilted to sparkling.

Bargain hunters will find a limited range of large wedges and quarter wheels of imported cheeses that are perhaps what you want for an office or Christmas gathering. The best bet is a goodly collection of Canadian cheddars, some old enough to walk. The meat shelves hold AAA and AA beef and New Zealand lamb (for shame), **Spolumbo's Fine Foods & Italian Deli** sausages. Live tanks contain swimming tilapia, lobsters, crabs and *mollusks*. The freezers stock Canadian whitefish, imported shrimp and prawns, cuttlefish, squid, smelts, beef tongue and kidney. Paw through. Bakers will like the frozen raw puff pastry.

NORTHEAST	Ŗ	G	L	O
Coventry Hills Superstore	•	•	•	•
100 Country Village Road NE • Phone: 567•4219				
Ŗ: 567•4235, Gas: 567•4232, Liquor: 567•4240, Optical: 567•4247				
Sunridge Superstore	•	•	•	
3575–20 Avenue NE • Phone: 280•8222				
Ŗ: 280•8207, Gas: 280•6345, Liquor: 280•8226				
Westwinds Superstore	•	•	•	•
100, 3633 Westwinds Drive NE • Phone: 590•3319				
Ŗ: 590•3335, Gas: 590•3337, Liquor: 590•3340, Optical: 590•3347				

SOUTHEAST				
Deerfoot Meadows Superstore	•	•	•	•
100, 20 Heritage Meadows Way SE • Phone: 692•6219				
Ŗ: 692•6235 Gas: 692•6237 Liquor: 692•6240 Optical: 692•6247				
Mackenzie Town Superstore	•	•	•	
4700–130 Avenue SE • Phone: 257•6537				
Ŗ: 257•6530, Gas: 257•6546, Liquor: 257•6540				
Shawnessy Superstore	•	•	•	
100, 15915 Macleod Trail SE • Phone: 254•3637				
Ŗ: 254•3630, Gas: 254•3601, Liquor: 254•3631				

SOUTHWEST				
Signal Hill Superstore	•	•	•	
5858 Richmond Road SW • Phone: 686•8036				
Ŗ: 686•8035, Gas: 686•8048, Liquor: 686•8043				
Southport Superstore	•	•	•	
10505 Southport Road SW • Phone: 225•6223				
Ŗ: 225•6207, Gas: 225•2711, Liquor: 225•6224				

NORTHWEST				
Country Hills Superstore	•	•	•	
5251 Country Hills Boulevard NW • Phone: 241•4027				
Ŗ: 241•4035, Gas: 241•4045, Liquor: 241•4050				
Huntingdon Hills Superstore	•	•	•	•
7020–4 Street NW • Phone: 516•8501				
Ŗ: 516•8535, Gas: 516•8537, Liquor: 516•8540, Optical: 516•8547				

LEGEND
Ŗ = PHARMACY
G = GAS BAR
L = LIQUOR
O = OPTICAL

The in-house bakery produces mostly simple cakes, big and small, rolls and breads. A far better bet is the ethnic collection of ingredients. Peruse the shelves for Chinese soy sauces and sticky rice, Philippine soy and banana sauces, Thai fish sauces and jasmine rice, Indian curry seasonings and *basmati* rice, glutinous rice starch and tapioca starch, and a reasonable assortment of pulses in bags, in addition to those in the bulk bin collection.

In addition to the to-be-expected staple teas, coffees, honeys, etc., there is a fairly extensive collection of electrical kitchen appliances, with house brands sitting beside name brands: rice cookers, *panini* makers, waffle irons, deep fryers, immersion wands.

• *House Specialties*: Bulk foods, house line President's Choice.

www.superstore.ca

Sobeys/IGA

Established: 1907
Head Office (Alberta): 17220 Stony Plain Road, Edmonton
Phone: (780) 486•4800
Customer Response Line: (866) 486•8570
Calgary Retail Support & Distribution Centre: 7704–30 Street SE
Phone: 279•4483
Store: Monday–Sunday 8:00 am–10:00 pm (most locations)
Pharmacy: Monday–Friday 9:00 am–9:00 pm
Saturday & Sunday 9:00 am–6:00 pm (most locations)
V, MC, AE, Debit, $

THIS old business began in 1907 in Nova Scotia with John Sobey delivering meats. In 1947, at his son Frank's urging, the family expanded from several small stores to a supermarket to keep pace with business and the post-war changes in lifestyle. By 1987, the third generation of Sobeys oversaw the expansion into Ontario. In 1998, IGA was acquired, and with it the business achieved a national presence.

The in-house bakery produces some good-looking fruit tarts, and Pure Decadent Dietary and Organic Cookies are also on the shelves. A tidy fish counter includes live tanks—oysters, clams, mussels, lobster, crabs. The meat counter stocks Alberta lamb, **Spolumbo's Fine Foods & Italian Deli** sausage, Sterling Silver beef, and some tidily stuffed value-added ready-to-cook selections. Noteworthy: raw ready-to-cook stuffed chicken breast, stuffed pork tenderloins, stuffed pork chops. The ready-to-eat collection includes *samosas*, salads, green onion cakes, *naan*, and *couscous* among the wings, pizza, ginger beef, and honey garlic chicken. If you poke through the cheese selection, you will unearth some treats—fabulous cave-aged Swiss *Gruyère*, Spanish *Manchego*, and French *Caprice des Dieux* next to Balderson's Canadian cheddar.

The produce section, some great, some wilted, includes Red Hat cukes and tomatoes grown in Redcliff, Alberta. Choose *habanero*, *serrano*, or *jalapeño* peppers, for your heat quotient.

Sobey's offers home delivery and online shopping.

www.sobeys.com

NORTHEAST	R	S
Country Hills Sobeys	•	
200, 500 Country Hills Boulevard NE • Phone: 226•5500		
R: *567•9302 / Monday–Friday 8:00 am–9:00 pm*		
London Town Square Sobeys		
800, 3545–32 Avenue NE • Phone: 273•5500		
SOUTHEAST		
Deer Point Garden Market Sobeys		
14939 Deer Ridge Drive SE • Phone: 278•2626		
Monday–Sunday 9:00 am–9:00 pm		
Douglas Square Sobeys		
128, 11520–24 Street SE • Phone: 203•0500		
Forest Lawn (former IGA)	•	
5115–17 Avenue SE • Phone: 273•9339		
Monday–Sunday 8:00 am–9:00 pm		
R: *248•8307 or 284•8310*		
McKenzie Towne Sobeys	•	
20 McKenzie Towne Avenue SE • Phone: 257•4343		
Riverbend Sobeys		
100, 8338–18 Street SE • Phone: 279•9070		
Monday–Sunday 8:00 am–9:00 pm		
SOUTHWEST		
Bridlewood Sobeys	•	
100, 2335–162 Avenue SW • Phone: 873•0101		
R: *873•7232*		
Lakeview Sobeys		
6449 Crowchild Trail SW • Phone: 242•7360		
Millrise Sobeys	•	
2000, 150 Millrise Boulevard SW • Phone: 873•5085		
R: *873•5180*		
Strathcona Square Sobeys		
300, 555 Strathcona Boulevard SW • Phone: 242•0644		

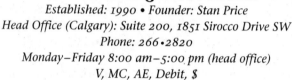

NORTHWEST

	R	S
Royal Oak Sobeys	•	•
125, 8888 Country Hills Boulevard NW • Phone: 239•7344		
R: 239•7455, Canada Post, at 319–8888 Country Hills Boulevard NW: 375•0140		
Monday–Friday 9:00 am–9:00 pm, Saturday 9:00 am–6:00, Sunday 10:00 am–5:00 pm		
Tuscany Sobeys	•	
2020, 11300 Tuscany Boulevard NW • Phone: 375•0507		
R: 375•0577		

SOUTHWEST

Sunterra Quality Food Markets

Established: 1990 • Founder: Stan Price
Head Office (Calgary): Suite 200, 1851 Sirocco Drive SW
Phone: 266•2820
Monday–Friday 8:00 am–5:00 pm (head office)
V, MC, AE, Debit, $

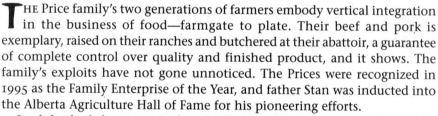

THE Price family's two generations of farmers embody vertical integration in the business of food—farmgate to plate. Their beef and pork is exemplary, raised on their ranches and butchered at their abattoir, a guarantee of complete control over quality and finished product, and it shows. The family's exploits have not gone unnoticed. The Prices were recognized in 1995 as the Family Enterprise of the Year, and father Stan was inducted into the Alberta Agriculture Hall of Fame for his pioneering efforts.

Look for fresh free-range turkey. At the West Market Square location, find whole fresh poultry from Prince Albert and Brome Lake, plus frozen duck breasts and frozen beef bones for stock or soup-making. The fish market is there as a courtesy, but it is not of the same calibre as the meat counter.

If you wanna grab 'n' go, there are many choices and each location has an in-house chef, so ask for substitutions if you need to. Otherwise, peruse the ready-to-cook meats (marinated chicken, lamb or beef, stuffed chicken breasts, skewers of pork, beef, chicken) with or without vegetables. Take dinner home with your groceries, ready to re-heat and eat in a changing array to forestall repetition or boredom: lasagna, ribs, chops, turkey breast, salads, and a supporting selection of cooked vegetables and starches.

I was surprised by what I didn't find here in my quest for organics. But I loved that the staff offered to track down whatever I needed: **Bles-Wold Yoghurt**, **Cochrane Coffee Traders** organic coffee beans.

The deli counter and meat shelves carry a strong collection of **Valbella Meats/ Valbella's Deli & Café** sausages and *pâtés*, and the cut-to-order cheese counter has a limited but strong range: try black-waxed Chèvre Noir, Quebecois goat cheddar with luscious crystalline structure, or "drunken" goat cheese from Murcia, Spain.

I am surprised that this local store is not a stronger advocate for local produce. Most of its produce comes north from California via a direct purchase program, but local fare is rarely in sight, other than for the excellent house-raised meats that are the business's *raison d'être*. Pricy but pretty berries, including hard-to-find gooseberries, and costly tropicals—mangoes and papayas—take centre stage. Toss together California salad greens, bags of *mâche* or arugula, with tiny perfect grape tomatoes. In autumn, discover a good selection of winter squashes, including kabocha and butternut. Cooks in a hurry may like the pre-sliced stir-fry vegetable packets. Plastic-bagged fresh herbs do look fresh, but soggy mung bean sprouts and bashed-up eggplant strike a discordant note in what is otherwise a well-tended produce patch.

For sweet teeth, there is chocolate from all over the globe. Try Swiss Toblerone, Italian Daniel, American Ghirardelli, Belgian Saxon, Belgian-Canadian **Bernard Callebaut**, or Canadian Rogers. The bakery is strong too: good fruit pies, good breads, including a crusty 9-ancient-grains round, and a fussy collection of cakes and sweet slices in the European style.

At the TransCanada Tower location, book ahead to attend demonstration-style cooking classes, beginning with wine and culminating in dinner. Call for catering arrangements. Sunterra delivers, and offers online ordering too.

• *House Specialties*: House-raised meats, HMRs, in-house chefs.
• *Also Available*: Commerce Place and Lendrum Shopping Centre, in Edmonton.

www.sunterramarket.com

Sunterra Marché
Manager: Barry Bischoff
855–2 Street SW (Bankers Hall +15)
Phone: 269•3610
Monday–Wednesday 6:30 am–6:30 pm, Thursday–Friday 6:30 am–8:00 pm
Saturday 9:30 am–5:00 pm

THIS is a busy lunch spot for "to-go" meals and "ready to cook" dishes as well. Browse the produce stand and meat market for makings, including raw marinated meats for dinner, then grab a salad at the bar, or try freshly baked lunchtime pizza or "big pan" sautéed dishes and baked goods brought in from other Sunterra kitchens.

Sunterra Market
Manager: J.V. Finlayson
1851 Sirocco Drive SW (West Market Square)
Phone: 266•3049
Monday–Saturday 8:00 am–9:00 pm, Sunday 9:00 am–8:00 pm

THIS Westside spot is half retail and half full-service seated restaurant. It offers groceries to catering, with an in-house bakery and a strong meat market, large deli, and takeout.

Sunterra Marketplace & Sunterra Grocery Delivery

Manager: David Jannard

803–49 Avenue SW (Shops of Britannia Plaza)

Sunterra Marketplace

Phone: 287•0553

Sunterra Grocery Delivery

Phone: 287•0553

Fax: 287•0569

Monday–Saturday 9:00 am–9:00 pm, Sunday 9:00 am–8:00 pm

E-mail for Grocery Delivery: shop@sunterramarket.com

THE original spot, this retail market feels more crowded than the other locations. Look for the meat department, deli, produce and, currently, a lunch-only chef's station serving hot lunches to go, including soups, *panini*, pasta, and "big pan" sautéed dishes. No sit-down space. The city-wide grocery delivery service is coordinated out of this location.

Sunterra Village Marché

Manager: Tony Columbo

450–1 Street SW (TransCanada Tower +15)

Phone: 262•8240

Monday–Friday 6:00 am–8:00 pm

A huge and busy spot, this is a blend of restaurant, deli, take-out and meals to go, all spread over 2 storeys. Look for lunches to go, an in-house bakery that supplies the muffins and scones to all of Sunterra's locations, deli goods, and a small meat counter stocked with signature marinated raw meats.

Sunterra Petit Marché & Sunterra Catering-Calgary

Manager: Troy Overby

401–9 Avenue SW (Gulf Canada Square +15)

Sunterra Petit Marché

Phone: 263•9756

Monday–Friday 6:30 am–6:00 pm

Sunterra Catering-Calgary

Phone: 263•9759

Fax: 263•9644

Monday–Friday 7:00 am–6:00 pm

Saturday & Sunday, By Request

E-mail: calgarycatering@sunterramarket.com

THIS very small spot produces all of the firm's catering, and also serves breakfast and limited lunches. Look for soups, sandwiches, salad bar, and crepes, and a hot "carved" lunch—served either as a sandwich or as a full meal. You won't find the "big pans" visible in other Sunterra spots, nor meat market or produce stand. This is the location you phone for all catering orders, and either where you come to pick them up or from where they are delivered.

Cheese & Dairy

AFTER A VISIT TO SALTSPRING ISLAND, driving home through Rogers Pass with a cooler crammed with British Columbian cheese, I began to wonder why some foods don't travel across provincial borders. Is it provincial protectionism, I speculated, or something less sinister?

On Saltspring Island, I had visited two of my favourite Western Canadian cheese makers—Moonstruck, where high-butterfat certified-organic Jersey milk is converted into funky-rinded, flavourful blue and surface-ripened cheeses by Julia and Susan Grace; and Saltspring Island Cheese Company, where former Toronto specialty food retailer David Wood makes mostly-fresh goats milk cheeses. Moonstruck is not available in Alberta; Wood's cheeses are.

Wanting food to travel while being committed to eating locally is one of those contradictions that make humans so unpredictable. We really do want it all. Eating local is both a blessing and a curse: a blessing, because food so literally and evocatively represents its roots; and a curse, because if I cannot get it here, I must go there if I want to have some. I learned many years ago to travel with a cooler.

Canadians consumed 12 kg of cheese per capita in 2006, less than half of French consumption, although my trip single-handedly raised the national average by at least a point. I eat British Columbia cheeses because they are good, and they fit on the second ring of my outwardly expanding eating pattern, from local to regional, national and beyond. I and my stomach like variety as much as we enjoy Alberta's fledgling artisanal cheese industry: **Fairwinds Farm** in Fort Macleod is slowly stepping into *la grande chèvre* shoes vacated by Virginia Saputo when she closed Natricia Dairy in Ponoka; **Sylvan Star Cheese Farm's** award-winning Gouda belongs on every Albertan cheese eater's radar.

Regulations governing supply and demand saw the implementation of a Canadian milk production quota in the 1970s. Quota is a controversial, complicated issue. It evolved from supply-side market forces dictating that consumer demand constantly outstrip supply by dairy farmers' cows to keep milk prices stable for the cows' keepers. The quota itself has become a valued commodity, as scarce as hens' teeth, and costly. According to Julia Rogers, head of Cheese Culture, an Ontario-based consulting and education cheese business, acquiring dairy milk production quota costs $25,000 per cow being milked, and is strictly regulated, with each province allocated a set percentage. But there is no quota to be had. Since its issuance, it mostly passes from family hand to family hand, and is rarely sold.

Milk processing is controlled by yet another quota, one that limits the amount of fluid milk pasteurized and converted into yoghurt, sour cream, cheeses of specific types, ice cream, butter, and powder. A third cheese quota governs importation from foreign countries, and is noticeable on our plates when importers trim their summer list to stockpile for the winter season. The permission to engage in business has become a valuable commodity in its own right.

To further complicate: quota applies only to cows' milk. There are not yet such regulations controlling sheep or goat milk, perhaps because, as Rogers comments, there are few dairy sheep and goat herds in Canada, and each animal produces a fraction of what cows yield. Smaller potatoes, perhaps, but for cheese makers like Wood, dealing exclusively in goat and sheep milk has removed one hurdle in his bid for his cheeses to cross the Great Divide.

It has never made any sense that a cheese that is good to eat in Vancouver without a federal license cannot be consumed across the border in Alberta.

The major issues in federal inspection are the requirement for HAACP certification, (a gate-to-plate tracking system that ensures food safety, wholesomeness and security) that includes temperature and time tracking during processing to eliminate contamination risks, packaging and labeling compliance, stringent building requirements, and the presence of a federal inspector in-house, either all the time or for a certain number of hours daily.

None of this begins to address the underlying issues of how our animals are kept, why raw milk is no longer safe to consume (after thousand of years of being a dietary staple!), or why raw milk cheeses are legally required to be aged for a minimum of 60 days. For such a simple food, the leap from milk to cheese, from farmgate to plate, is fraught with complexities.

SOUTHEAST

Say Cheese Fromagerie Inc.
Established: 1998 • Owners: Bill & Joan Tough
1235–26 Avenue SE (Crossroads Market)
Phone: 262•7530 or 819•6706
Friday–Sunday 9:00 am–5:00 pm, with extended Christmas and summer hours
V, MC, Debit, Cheque, $

BILL and Joan Tough are deeply devoted to their *fromage*. They opened their shop after a trip to Europe whetted their appetite for cheese, bread and wine. Choose from among 350 varieties, including over 20 blues, and a raft of cheddars—from crystalline Canadian six-year-old Simcoe Lake to Scottish Drumloch made from high-fat Guernsey milk. *Vacherin Mont d'Or* is another perennial favourite with clientele.

Canadian-made *Chèvre Noir*, a goat's milk cheddar, is a customer favourite, as are *Bleu Bènèdictin* and *Oka*. Joan prefers French Roquefort as her "desert island survival cheese." Don't forget to check the sale shelf for Bill's ready-to-eat-now deals. Joan is both knowledgeable and thoughtful, with insights into the cheese industry, a healthy regard for safety, and a commitment to offering good value. Customers are contributing favourite cheese recipes for a forthcoming charity cookbook based on cheese.

• *House Specialties*: Seasonally varying supply, featuring Canadian cheddars and a wide French and European selection.

Springbank Cheese Company

Established: 2005 • Owners: Adrian & Carie Lee Watters
304–10816 Macleod Trail South (Willow Park Village Shopping Centre)
Phone: 225•6040
Monday–Wednesday & Friday 10:00–7:00 pm, Thursday 10:00 am–8:00 pm
Saturday 10:00 am–6:00 pm, Sunday noon–4:00 pm
V, MC, AE, Debit, $
[see NW Cheese for main entry on p. 58]

SOUTHWEST

Janice Beaton Fine Cheese

Established: 2000 • Owner: Janice Beaton
1017–16 Avenue SW
Phone: 229•0900
Monday–Thursday 10:00 am–6:00 pm, Friday 10:00 am–7:00 pm
Saturday 9:00 am–6:00 pm
V, MC, Debit, $

JANICE Beaton and her team of *fromage* fanatics know whereof they speak. Specialists in the arcane, the obscure, and the artisanal (but only if it is really good cheese), they are keen supporters of raw milk cheeses, Slow Food, and the quality of life that bespeaks support of authenticity. All cheeses are cut to order, and "May I taste first, please?" is always an option.

Try the local goods: baguettes and weekends-only walnut pecan loaves from **Manuel Latruwe Belgian Pâtisserie & Bread Shop**, **Sylvan Star Cheese Farm's** award-winning Gouda from Sylvan Lake and **Fairwinds Farm** *chèvre*. From farther afield, ask for *Brie de Meaux*, France's most famous raw milk brie, suave Swiss raw milk cave-aged *Gruyère*, David Wood's Saltspring Island cheeses or Chaput's lovely goat's milk cheeses. Other great suggestions are Quèbecois *Riopelle*, specialties from Neal's Yard, the UK's leading *affineurs*, or Spanish *Valdeón*.

But this is more than just a cheese shop (and kindly refrain at this time from all Monty Python jokes...) Look for locally made charcuterie—**Valbella Meats/Valbella Deli & Café's** fine air-dried *landjaeger*, garlic rings, black *chimneysticks* or *pâtés*, **Cunningham's Scotch Cold Smoking** fish and *pâté*— and condiments, like **Brassica Mustard** and Palette Fine Foods' cheese-friendly conserves.

Top-line local produce has a special place here too—expect **Hotchkiss Herbs & Produce** greens in season, and **Gull Valley Greenhouse** tomatoes in season. Buy cheese books, serving utensils, and their house signature cheese crackers and seeded flatbreads, or Janice's mom's Nova Scotian oatcakes. For simple *fondue*, buy the house blend of cheeses, grated and ready to melt on your stove. Corporate and private consumers can catch the cheese of the month, order catering, gift boxes or baskets, or arrange "tours of the cheese case" for He Who Has it All. Frequent classes address cheese, cheese-wine

pairings, cooking with cheese, and related topics. But be warned: good cheese comes very dear.
- *House Specialties*: Artisanally made small production raw milk cheeses, local charcuterie and condiments, classes, catering.
- *Also Available*: 1249 Kensington Road NW.
www.jbfinecheese.com

Matterhorn Imports
Established: 1985 • Owner: Silvia Carr-Peterer
Rear Entrance, 3405–26 Avenue SW
Phone: 612•5579
September–May: Wednesday 1:00–4:00 pm, Saturday 10:00 am–4:00 pm
Cheque, $

THIS hole-in-the-wall shop is accessed from the back lane, and keeps hours as restricted as its street presence. Look for the red door with the Swiss flag, and the window with shutters in the alleyway.

Silvia Carr-Peterer specializes in Swiss cheeses, as did her business-founding parents, Elsbeth and Ruedi Peterer. For *fondue*, she mixes together *Gruyère* and *Vacherin*, and is pleased that her display cases include other suitably stellar Swiss choices like *Bleuchâtel* and *Appenzeller*, the latter available in three styles defined by their age: classic, aged three to four months; *sur choix*, aged even longer; extra, aged for six to eight months.) Find *raclette* grills and *fondue* pots for loaning, and for a change of taste, buy some soft French goats' milk cheeses and blue cheeses. The shelves have a few condiments, vinegars, chocolate and jams.
- *House Specialties*: Swiss cheeses.

Springbank Cheese Company
Established: 2005 • Owners: Adrian & Carie Lee Watters
Sweetgrass Market, 873–85 Street SW (West Springs Village)
Phone: 240•3441
Wednesday–Friday 9:00 am–7:00 pm, Saturday & Sunday 9:00 am–5:00 pm
V, MC, AE, Debit, Cheque, $
[see NW Cheese for main entry on p. 58]

NORTHWEST

Janice Beaton Fine Cheese
Established: 2000 • Owner: Janice Beaton
1249 Kensington Road NW
Phone: 283•0999
Tuesday–Thursday 10:00 am–6:00 pm, Friday 10:00 am–7:00 pm
Saturday 9:00 am–6:00 pm, Sunday 11:00 am–6:00 pm
V, MC, Debit, $
[see SW Cheese for main entry on p. 56]

Springbank Cheese Company

Established: 1989 (in Calgary) • Owner: Tom Hemsworth
2015–14 Street NW
Phone: 282•8331
Monday–Friday 8:30 am–7:00 pm, Saturday 9:00 am–6:00 pm
Sunday noon–5:00 pm
V, MC, AE, Debit, Cheque, $

THREE generations of the Hemsworth family are part of the package at Springbank Cheese. The stores are named for Springbank Snow Countess, the Holstein cow famous to residents of Woodstock, Ontario. (My Woodstock-born Smith grandmother used to tell tales about this cow to her grandchildren!) Springbank Cheese is affiliated with shops in Cowichan, British Columbia, and in Woodstock, Ontario where the business began in 1960. The coolers here hold a wide general selection of 320 varieties, led by Ontario-made 7-year-old cheddars, Quèbecois curds, global blues, and Canadian versions of European classics.

At the southeast store, ask about booking a spot at one of the tastings and client education events: these seminars accommodate 10–12 people. Otherwise, the ample sample tray is always out, and a dedicated curious cook could conceivably taste everything in the case, given time and stomach capacity.

Some cheeses are cut to order, some are vacuum wrapped. I would start with my favourite category, the blues, and they alone would take weeks to work through! Check it out: Irish Cashel, Bavarian, France's classics—*St. Agur, Fourme d'Ambert, Bleu d'Auvergne, Bresse* and *Roquefort*—Spanish *Valdeón*, Italian *Gorgonzola Cremosa* or inordinately young and mild *Dolcelatte*, Canadian *Ermite*, or *Bleu Bènèdictin*, English Stilton or Shropshire. The collection of cheddars is just as impressive, but I'll take the blues. Ask about corporate gifting.

- *House Specialties*: Old cheddars from Canada, imported cheeses from around the world.
- *Also Available*: 304–10816 Macleod Trail South, (Willow Park Village Shopping Centre) and Sweetgrass Market, 873–85 Street SE (West Spring Village) in June 2008.

www.springbankcheese.ca

Chocolate & Sweets

A S A YOUNG WOMAN IN VANCOUVER, I often walked past a tiny park on Vancouver's Fairview Slopes. This whimsical spot, called Choklit Park, always smelled like dessert, not surprising since it was home to Vancouver's Purdy's Chocolates. As an adult, living far from Vancouver, I still remember that park and its smells when I eat a Purdy's Georgia Brown or Hedgehog. (Olfactory memory is the most accurate and accute we possess.) In Calgary, there are many spots to find good chocolate, sweets, and desserts. But I have yet to find another chocolate park.

There is a distinct correlation between passion, love, and chocolate. Chocolate combines fat and sugar with melt-in-the-mouth allure and an appealing snap that can make a grown woman's knees weak. And it contains phenylethylamine, that notorious brain chemical that is responsible for the euphoric feelings that accompany being in love.

You can spend a little or a lot on chocolate, but if you buy the really good stuff, a little goes a very long way. Chocolate's quality is determined by ingredients that directly impact taste and flavour: cocoa butter is responsible for the luxurious mouth-feel as chocolate melts; percentages of cocoa mass or cocoa liquor affect the smoothness of the chocolate and absence of grit, as well as the intensity of flavour; added vegetable oils can make chocolate waxy or chalky in texture, with slower melting ability.

Pragmatists would say that chocolate melts at the exact same temperature as our bodies, and they would be right, but that oversimplifies the pleasure of eating really good chocolate. Cooks intent on creating memorable moments for someone special can far exceed red cardboard hearts filled with mediocre chocolates.

NORTHEAST

Chocolaterie Bernard Callebaut

Calgary International Airport, Departures Level D
Terminal Building, 2000 Airport Road NE
Phone: 717•1983
Monday–Sunday 7:00 am–9:00 pm
V, MC, AE, Debit, $

[see SE Chocolates & Sweets for main entry on p. 60]

SOUTHEAST

Chocolaterie Bernard Callebaut

Established: 1982 • Founder: Bernard Callebaut
Head Office & Café Chocolat: 1313–1 Street SE
Phone (Office): 265•5777 • Toll Free: (800) 661•8367 • Phone (Café): 266•4300
Monday–Wednesday 8:30 am–6:00 pm, Thursday & Friday 8:30 am–9:00 pm
Saturday 9:00 am–6:00 pm, Sunday noon–5:00 pm
V, MC, AE, Debit, $

BERNARD Callebaut chocolates, now available at a city near you, are recognized worldwide as a leading name in the realm of edible art. Not only that, but one bite is simply not enough. Callebaut, born into a Belgian chocolate-making family, arrived in Calgary in 1982 intent on converting Cowtown into a chocoholic's paradise. He has succeeded: award-winning Callebaut chocolates shops are now located across the continent, all serving fabulous chocolates made in Calgary, all better even than the Belgian originals. To wit: Bernard Callebaut is the only North American chocolate maker to be awarded the Grand Prix International Artisan Chocolatier in Roanne, France, receiving that accolade in 1998.

All chocolate used and sold at Callebaut shops is specially formulated to Bernard Callebaut's specifications. The slabs and *callets* bear the founder's first and last names to differentiate it, and is, according to marketing manager Peter Grobauer, of a higher calibre than bulk Callebaut chocolate available elsewhere. The higher price a shopper pays for Bernanrd Callebaut chocolate is reflected in higher ccoca content, regulated cocoa butter content, and unflinching control over sourcing of beans.

At a Callebaut shop, the long glass counter is all about chocolates, shaped and dipped, filled and rolled, truffled and trumped. Look for classic copper-coloured boxes filled with chocolate and truffles, or choose your favourites. Mine are: Bernard—two discs filled with egg cream, *rhûm*, seashells of hazelnut and white chocolate—my sons' preferred treat for years, or a dozen or more truffles. Cooks and dessert queens can buy *couverture* slabs, *callets,* or cocoa. Solid chocolate letters make ideal gifts, and the ice cream bars dipped in chocolate rival any anywhere else.

At Christmastime, cherries from the Okanagan in classic *griotte* style, dipped in chocolate after months of maceration, are hugely popular, as are Santas in suits of chocolate, on a racing motorcycle, or on a sleigh. Stampede fans may prefer the Western themes that emerge in July. At Eastertime, bunnies and spring eggs appear.

A tour of the production plant at the main shop—from behind glass windows, unfortunately—is like Charlie in the chocolate factory. Call ahead for a guided tour, or drop in to stroll the long hallway, read the placards, and absorb the images for a self-guided lesson in chocolate harvesting and chocolate-making. After the lesson, go upstairs to the café and store and the all-encompassing aroma of chocolate.

The main office location now has Café Chocolat, where one can sip hot chocolate beverages while ensconced on chocolate-toned stools. Or order online if you just cannot wait. Ahhhh... If that is too messy, opt for eye candy: chocolate computer screensaver-wallpaper is available for ordering.

The factory in Calgary is entirely powered by wind, and the business has an environmental policy that includes reusing and recycling, as well as sourcing organically where possible and where it does not adversely affect the quality of the finished chocolates. All this so you can have your chocolate and feel good about it too.

- *Also Available*: Banff, Edmonton, Lethbridge, and Red Deer in Alberta, Victoria, Vancouver, White Rock, Nanaimo, and Kelowna in British Columbia; Saskatoon and Regina in Saskatchewan, Winnipeg, Manitoba, London and Oakville in Ontario, and four US locations.
www.bernardcallebaut.com

Chocolaterie Bernard Callebaut
Unit 318, 100 Anderson Road SE (Southcentre Mall)
Phone: 271•4100
Monday–Friday 9:30 am–9:00 pm, Saturday 9:30 am–8:00 pm
Sunday & Holiday Mondays 11:00 am–5:00 pm
[see SE Chocolates & Sweets for main entry on p. 60]

Les Truffes au Chocolat
Established: 2002 • Owners: Ralph Buchmuller, Wally Marcolin & Rick Jeffrey
226, 10816 Macleod Trail South SE
(Willow Park Village)
Phone: 225•9399
Monday–Wednesday 10:00 am–6:00 pm, Thursday noon–8:00 pm
Friday 10:00 am–6:00 pm, Saturday 10:00 am–5:00 pm
V, MC, AE, Debit, $

RALPH Buchmuller studied chocolate-making in Europe, and prefers to use all Lindt, all the time. A stunning collection of very good truffles ranges from apple cider to *zabaione* fillings. Buchmuller's truffle specialists also produce several other items—chocolate-coated pretzels, wafers, golf balls, and only in Cowtown, chocolate coated "saddle" potato chips, created to honour the Saddledome. Online orders are taken, including private labels and a sugar-free chocolate bar called Castle Mountain. Cooks on the hunt can choose from *callets* or bars. The latest development is O Trios bars, fortified with omega-3—not that such good chocolate needs help, or justification. Subscribers to the e-mailed newsletter are eligible for monthly draws.

At Christmas, indulge guests and clients with liqueur-marinated cherries or cognac-marinated grapes, truffle trees, chocolate bark, or hot chocolate powder.
- *House Specialties*: Handmade truffles and candy from **Olivier's Candies**.
- *Also Available*: 265, 315–8 Avenue SW (Bankers Hall).
www.lestruffes.com

Olivier's Candies

Established: 1909 • Owners: Wally Marcolin, Rick Jeffrey & Ralph Buchmuller
1316–9 Avenue SE
Phone: 275•5195
Monday–Saturday 10:00 am–5:30 pm, Sunday 11:00 am–5:00 pm
V, MC, Debit, $

FROM truffles to sponge toffee, the sweet teeth of Calgarians have found something delectable to eat since 1909, when Gaspard Olivier founded this landmark Calgary business. The store was bought in 2002 by Rick Jeffrey and Wally Marcolin, who are committed to making sweets the old-fashioned way, without preservatives. Candy lovers can crunch old-style brittle, hard candy or dipped ginger. Chocoholics can choose among domestic chocolate or Belgian Belcolade—made from beans grown in Ghana, or sugar-free **Bernard Callebaut** containing *maltitol*.

Seasonal specialties include Easter eggs and chocolate hearts or Christmas candy canes. The company offers "how-to" open houses on making candy canes, an ideal gift for He Who Has It All. Tours are available too. Kids in candy stores…. For grown-up kids at work, ask about chocolate or candy corporate logos, foil-wrapped or bagged. Fun has no age limit. In late 2007, the business merged with **Les Truffes au Chocolat**.

- *House Specialties*: Ginger in dark or milk chocolate, coconut or peanut brittle, and truffles from **Les Truffes au Chocolat**.
- *Also Available*: Some items at **Canada Safeway, Calgary Co-op, Sobey's/ IGA**.

www.oliviers.ca

SOUTHWEST

Chocolaterie Bernard Callebaut

847–17 Avenue SW   *5571 Signal Hill Centre SW*
(Uptown)   *(Signal Hill Centre)*
Phone: 244•1665   *Phone: 217•1700*
Monday–Wednesday 9:00 am–6:00 pm, Thursday & Friday 9:00 am–9:00 pm
Saturday 9:00 am–6:00 pm, Sunday noon–5:00 pm
V, MC, AE, Debit, $

A123, 1600–90 Avenue SW (Glenmore Landing)
Phone: 259•3933
Monday–Wednesday & Saturday 9:30 am–6:00 pm
Thursday & Friday 9:30 am–9:00 pm
V, MC, AE, Debit, $
[see SE Chocolates & Sweets for main entry on p. 60]

Diabetic Depot & Bakery

Established: 2002 • Owner: Brenda Hill
3905–17 Avenue SW
Phone: 240•4486
Monday–Friday 10:00 am–6:00 pm, Saturday 10:00 am–5:30 pm
Sunday noon–5:00 pm
V, MC, Debit, $

BRENDA Hill, like millions of other Canadians, loves a diabetic. When her husband Craig was diagnosed as a type 2 diabetic, Hill, a scratch cook, initiated changes in how her family ate. In 2002, driven by her desire to help her husband eat a healthier diet, Hill began Diabetic Depot & Bakery. A small retail area in the storefront carries sugarless ingredients and foods. Find good dressings, sugar-free and low-carb baked goods, pasta, snacks, sweets, sauces, and sugar-free over-the-counter pharmaceuticals. Only a few aspartame-based products are in the store, although sugar-free Belgian chocolate containing *maltitol* is available.

The heart of the business is the bakery in the back. It offer choices that focus on low carbs and high fibre, producing cookies, cheesecakes, pies, cakes, muffins, butter tarts and pie crusts. Instead of wheat flour, Diabetic Depot & Bakery uses a specially formulated low-carb and high-fibre "bake mix" that is primarily soy-based. Sugar is replaced with sorbitol, a fruit-derived sugar alcohol.

Dessert is a touchy topic for many diabetics. They get tired of being told what they can and cannot have. Resentment and non-compliance are short steps behind deprivation. Many diabetics, both type 1 and type 2, prefer to factor frequent desserts into their lives and live with the consequences rather than give up sweets. The truth is that diabetes is a serious disease and elevated blood sugars have serious health implications. Higher blood sugars make blood more viscous resulting in the heart having to work harder to pump blood through arteries. Blood pressure can become elevated and peripheral circulation is compromised. Other outcomes can be heart disease, blindness, kidney disease, nerve damage and foot problems, Alzheimer's and dementia. Diabetics take longer to heal from cuts and bruises, and some men suffer from erectile dysfunction. "There is no magic pill," Hill says from her attic office above her bakery. "It is about tweaking your lifestyle, not re-inventing it. We choose good carbs low on the Glycemic Index (GI), so we eat pasta maybe once a month, and our bread intake is a fraction of what it was. We choose wild rice, and we mostly avoid "white' or refined foods, such as potatoes, bread, and rice."

Hill is an outspoken critic of current medical advice on managing diet for diabetics. She disagrees with the assertion that a diabetic can eat virtually whatever he wants, as long as he keeps an eye on the size of the portion. "Choosing wisely is the crux of the matter," she says. "People hear what they want to hear. They remember that they heard their doctor say that they can eat anything. They don't remember the portion control part. Then, when their sugars are high, they think they can just 'dial up' (increase their insulin) or take a magic pill."

Her husband has been able to set aside two kinds of medication since the store opened. The store deals in education and information too, selling books that support good choices, identifying and managing "good versus bad" carbohydrates, and the importance of physical activity. A diabetic I know opted to give up sweets when he was diagnosed, but many diabetics do not want to feel excluded. This store offers an alternative.

- *House Specialties*: Sugar-free and low-carb ingredients for diabetics, sugar-free Belgian chocolate, house-made high-fibre/low-carb baked goods using a soy "bake mix."
- *Also Available*: 147, 1829 Ranchlands Boulevard NW.

www.diabeticdepot.com

Fiasco Gelato

Established: 2004 • Owner: Matt Wilson
736–17 Avenue SW
Phone: 229•2503
April 15–September 30: Monday–Sunday 10:00 am–midnight
October 1–April 14: Monday–Thursday 10:00 am–9:00 pm
Friday & Saturday 10:00 am–10:00 pm, Sunday 11:00 am–9:00 pm
V, MC, Debit, $

MATT Wilson really likes *gelato*. I mean, he REALLY likes *gelato*. He likes it so much, in fact, that when he decided to make *gelato* in Calgary, he went first to Italy to learn how to make the real thing. All is made in-house—in over 50 varieties, including non-dairy *sorbetto*, and lean *gelato*, made with low-fat milk but no eggs. Batches are small, and turnover is high, so freshness is a sure thing. Seasonal favourites make waves for those diehard fans who love their ice cream year-round: Thanksgiving pumpkin is succeeded by Christmas candy cane. Among the most popular flavours are mango *sorbetto* and *tartuffo gelato*. My kind of ice cream. *Gelato*, I mean. Maybe I'll go to Italy, learn how to make it....

- *House Specialties*: Gelati and *sorbetto*, in popular flavours that include *tartuffo* and mango.
- *Also Available*: 207–10 Street NW and **The Urban Baker**.

www.fiascogelato.com

Jammin' It Jams & Jellies

Established: 2005 • Owners: Brenda & Brian Lerner
H6, 4421 Quesnay Wood Drive SW (Calgary Farmers' Market)
Phone: 255•4396
Friday & Saturday 9:00 am–5:00 pm, Sunday 9:00 am–4:00 pm
V, MC, Debit, $

JAM-MAKING is one of those skills that most home cooks have abandoned, along with the traditional jam-making copper pot that hung in the kitchen or wash shed. But fortunately for us, the jams and jellies made by Brian and Brenda Lerner are particularly yummy. I am partial to the pear and ginger jam, but there are many others to sample, including a crystal-clear highbush cranberry jelly. Don't ignore the savoury jellies and jams—red pepper jelly is wondrous with eggs, pork, in glazes for shellfish, and melted into bean pots or braises. Diabetics might like the sugar-free preserves sweetened with Splenda. For variety, try the wine jellies, especially a spectacularly coloured port jelly, and chutneys.

- *House Specialties*: Jams and jellies—low-sugar raspberry-mango or mango jam, highbush cranberry jelly, red pepper jelly, pear-ginger or fresh fig jam, some Splenda-sweetened preserves.
- *Also Available*: **The Urban Baker**.

Les Truffes au Chocolat

Established: 2002 • Owner: Ralph Buchmuller
265, 315–8 Avenue SW (Bankers Hall)
Phone: 269•1010
Monday–Wednesday 10:00 am–6:00 pm, Thursday & Friday 10:00 am–8:00 pm
Saturday 10:00 am–5:30 pm
V, MC, AE, Debit, $
[see SE Chocolate & Sweets for main entry on p. 61]

Lewis Chocolates & Candies

Established: 1993 • Owners: Brady & Sherry Lewis
224, 315–8 Avenue SW (Bankers Hall)
Phone: 262•2566
Monday–Wednesday 10:00 am–6:00 pm, Thursday–Friday 10:00 am–8:00 pm
Saturday 10:00 am–5:30 pm
V, MC, AE, Debit, $

CO-OWNERS Sherry and Brady Lewis tasted hundreds of chocolates after they decided to make the family habit of chocolate gift-giving into the family business. Ultimately, they settled on Belgian-made Callebaut chocolate, including a *maltitol*-sweetened sugar-free version. Buy either at their shop, in *callets* of white, milk, and semi-sweet, and expect a drier texture from the sugar-free version. If you want moulded chocolates, choose from cowboy hats to ballet slippers, in an array of 10,000 shapes and sizes.

Hand-crafted chocolates include mint "smoothies" in square shapes (they make over 100 pounds daily!), chewy caramels and clusters and cream centres. For events, maybe you need party favours—chocolate of course—and bags of nuts or ginger dipped in chocolate. Corporate logos rendered edible means you can put your money where your client's mouth is. For messy and magnificent fun, rent a chocolate fountain, just once.

- *House Specialties*: Chocolate fountain, boxes of house-made chocolates, mints smoothies, moulded chocolates and corporate logos.

www.lewischocolate.com

Manon's Leonidas

Established: 2004 • Owner: Ghislaine Cleiren
815–49 Avenue SW (Shops of Brittania Plaza)
Phone: 214•5414
Monday–Saturday 9:30 am–5:30 pm
V, MC, AE, Debit, Cheque, $

THERE is Belgian chocolate beyond Callebaut, I am told, and the proof—imported filled chocolates and truffles from Belgium—is here at Manon's in Brittania. Newly arrived *Les L's* truffles enrobed in dark chocolate are deeply scented and flavoured—passionfruit in particular verges on perfume in its intensity. Peruse the chocolate case for other choices. Manon is my personal favourite, a praline with coffee and hazelnut in white, milk, or dark. Cleiren says that Manon's makes an equally stunning ice cream, but alas, she cannot import ice cream due to quota restrictions. So Foothills ice cream it is. Quick, someone phone the government…again…about this quota stuff. After you have chosen your repertoire of filled or formed or dipped sweets, buy a few chocolate *callets* to bake with, then perhaps order a gift "basket" of chocolates packed in some lovely tableware—plates, bowls, and cups of European origin.
• *House Specialties*: Belgian filled chocolates, baking *callets*, ice cream, gift baskets.

www.leonidas.ca

My Favourite Ice Cream Shoppe

Established: 1981 • Owner: Joseph Yoon (since 2002)
2048–42 Avenue SW
Phone: 287•3838
April 1–September 30: Monday–Sunday 10:30 am–10:30 pm
October 1–March 31: Monday–Sunday 11:00 am–9:00 pm
V, MC, Debit, $

THE ice cream at this long-time landmark sweets shop is made by Foothills and Nestlé, and the most popular is Rolo Rolo. Kids' taste in ice cream is inexplicable—triple tornado and over the rainbow, or candyfloss? Most of us grow up eventually and so, for the adults, there are dozens of other slightly more sedate ice creams, sorbets and frozen yoghurts. Every time I go into this shop, I end up with chocolate and peanut butter, or Kahlua fudge supreme. If you don't want a cone, have a chocolate-covered banana on special occasions, and the milkshakes, floats, sodas, and malts for everyday. The piano is still there—tinkle its ivories for free ice cream—and so is the magical calliope pony. Some of the city's best people-watching can be done from the old red benches out front.
• *House Specialties*: Foothills and Nestlé ice cream cones, people-watching.

www.myfavouriteicecream.com

Tutti Frutti

Established: 2005 • Owners: Debbie & Henry Mandelbaum
H6, 4421 Quesnay Wood Drive SW (Calgary Farmers' Market)
Phone: 889•5969
Friday & Saturday 9:00 am–5:00 pm, Sunday 9:00 am–4:00 pm
$ only

IT is not just the **Fratello Coffee Co.** beans or the city's best *gelato* that bring me back to this stall on every trip I make to the farmers' market. It is the Mandelbaums, a charming pair of Colombians who fit so gracefully into the farmers' market community, and it is Debbie's meltingly good cookies. I adore the *guava* paste rolls and the chocolate fudge or *cajeta* wrapped inside tender dough. Debbie's amazing market-made *gelato* has an equally melting texture that makes the most of its clear flavours. Ice cream this good is like a really fine set of favourite clothes this girl never wants to outgrow. Thirty choices are rotated through the case, with only 18 available at a time. Some of the best are dairy-free. Like Debbie, I lean toward the Italian chocolate, for its sensual mouth-feel, but the hazelnut and the sour cherry should not be missed. Don't take my word for it. Try all 30, a few at a time, in a house-made sugar cone, or in a cup. If you want *gelato* to go, ask Debbie to pack some into a styro box in one of two sizes; if you don't eat it, it has a good chance of getting home before it melts.

Non-dairy fruit-based tropical flavours include Henry's favourite soursop, as well as *tamarind, guava,* or passionfruit. In a local collaboration that makes the most of both, the Mandelbaums use **Pearson's Berry Farm & Gordo's Foods** blackcurrants in black currant *gelato* that is as intense-tasting as its colour. Yeow! And of course, blue *gelato* (blue cotton candy) for the junior set, all of whom inexplicably gravitate to blue ice cream. They outgrow it, thank goodness.

NORTHWEST

Amato Gelato

Established: 2002 • General Manager: Dino Falvo
2104 Kensington Road NW
Phone: 270•9733
Monday–Thursday 10:00 am–11:00 pm, Friday & Saturday 10:00 am–midnight
Sunday 11:00 am–10:00 pm
Debit, $

THIS family business sells the family *gelato*: Mario's, which originated on Granville Island in Vancouver in 1963, long before the beneath-the-bridge market spot was anything but a construction zone. In Calgary since 2001, this family spot in West Hillhurst can accommodate take out or eat-in, indoors or on the patio, where summer basil and tomatoes grow in planters along the perimeter. It is worth the trip for some of the city's best stuff: 20

sorbettos are non-fat and non-dairy—how is that for having your cake and eating it too? If you prefer tofu, try a tofu-based *gelato*, and take home some sugarless *gelati* if you love a diabetic. Sample an Italian beverage or biscotti, cookies, brownies. But don't miss the *gelato*.

This Italian ice cream contains skim milk and low concentrations of sugar and fat, and has less air too. Somehow that makes it thicker. I don't understand, but there are some things that are best left a mystery, and *gelato* is one.

• *House Specialties*: Gelati and *sorbetto*.

• *Also Available*: Select Banff, Canmore, and Calgary restaurants.

www.amatogelato.com

Chocolaterie Bernard Callebaut

1123 Kensington Road NW   *826 Crowfoot Crescent NW*
(Kensington Gate)   *(Crowfoot Centre)*
Phone: 283•5550   *Phone: 374•1800*
Monday–Wednesday 9:00 am–6:00 pm, Thursday & Friday 9:00 am–9:00 pm
Saturday 9:00 am–6:00 pm, Sunday noon–5:00 pm
V, MC, AE, Debit, $

125, 5403 Crowchild Trail NW
(Crowchild Square)
Phone: 286•2008
Monday & Tuesday 9:30 am–6:00 pm, Wednesday–Friday 9:30 am–8:00 pm
Saturday 9:30 am–5:30 pm, Sunday noon–5:00 pm
V, MC, AE, Debit, $
[see SE Chocolates & Sweets for main entry on p. 60]

Diabetic Depot & Bakery

Established 2002 • Contact: Angela Frey
147, 1829 Ranchlands Boulevard NW
Phone: 547•5555
Monday & Wednesday 10:00 am–6:00 pm
Tuesday & Thursday–Saturday 10:00 am–5:00 pm, Sunday noon–5:00 pm
V, MC, Debit, $
[see SW Chocolate & Sweets for main entry on p. 63]

Fiasco Gelato

Established: 2004 • Owner: Matt Wilson
207–10 Street NW
Phone: 283•1229
April 1–October 14: Monday–Sunday 10:00 am–10.00 pm
V, MC, Debit, $
[see SW Chocolate & Sweets for main entry on p. 64]

Coffee & Tea

ESPRESSO IS A STYLE OF ROASTING, not a type of bean. Most espresso is blended with beans from a variety of geographic regions, each expressing its own *terroir*. Coffee blenders look for characteristics similar to those desired by winemakers: earthiness, acidity, floral or fruity/citrus notes, chocolate or caramel tones, nuttiness, roundness, smoothness, and tang. Some add cheap *robusta* beans to *arabica* beans, for added oil content at lower cost. Roasters have a wide latitude in terms of the degree of roastedness, from the lighter end roasts preferred by Italians, to dark French, and thence to a near-black high-sheen gloss.

There are many ways that roasted beans can be made to suffer at the hands of the brewer or *barista:* using stale beans or grinding beans too far in advance, grinding to the wrong consistency for the type of machine, using too much or too little coffee, using inaccurate tamping pressure, not leveling coffee in the basket, temperature and type of water.

For the best espresso, store beans at room temperature in an airtight, dark container. Invest in a burr grinder—to control texture—and grind just before you make your coffee. Coffee is *hygroscopic,* so on a humid day, it takes longer to issue from the espresso maker, and tastes bitter, acidic, and sour. Compensate by adjusting the grind carefully: too coarse, and the water passes through too rapidly, so ensuing espresso tastes thin; too fine, and very little water makes it through. Pack the grounds evenly into the basket. Use pure carbon-filtered water, not distilled, hard, or treated water: each imparts its own taste, as it does to fine single malt. The optimum water temperature is 93°C.

Crema is the much sought after grace note, thick and dense enough that a puff of breath does not budge it. Look for a characteristic "mouse tail" as coffee issues from the machine, and time the extraction: 20–25 seconds is ideal. Drink up. Then read up: details abound on coffee trivia, and caffeine geeks gather online at many forums, including <www.coffeegeek.com>.

As with coffee, brewing fine tea is no less simple an affair, and tea drinkers take their beverage as seriously as do wine connoisseurs and coffee hounds. Tea comes from an evergreen shrub, *Camellia sinensis*. Drinking tea originated at least 4,000 years ago in China, spreading to Japan, and eventually to India via the British. Different methods of processing result in the major categories: *black, green, oolong, white.*

Slightly assertive and astringent, Darjeeling is the most sought-after *black* tea. *Green* tea leaves are steamed and dried without any fermentation, making a yellowish tea, grassy and tasting closely like its plant of origin; Gunpowder is a popular example. *Oolong* occupies the middle ground, its leaves partially fermented; Formosa *oolong* is the best-known of its type. *White* tea refers to the first-picked, youngest leaves.

Alternative drinks are called *tisanes,* made from plants other than tea: fruit, herbs or spices, *yerba maté,* or the current crowd pleaser, *rooibos.*

Yerba maté, traditionally sipped from a gourd, is bitter-sweet and alfalfa-like. It is a serious stimulant.

Tea is sensitive to heat and light, so store it in an airtight tin. Purists opt for loose tea, and a strainer with which to filter it after it steeps because teabags often contain "sweepings" of stems, broken leaves, and dust.

To make tea, first heat the teapot with hot or boiling water. Empty it, add the loose tea, then pour boiling water over the leaves. Let steep, strain and pour.

Instead of including the many coffee bars in the city and area, herein are details of tea and coffee shops where loose tea, bean sales and roasting form a significant part of the business.

CITY WIDE

Big Mountain Coffee Roasters

Established: 2003 • Owners: Wade Semograd & Georgina Christou-Semograd
Mailing Address: 7680–11 Avenue SW, Calgary T3H 4B4
Phone: 244•6864 • E-mail: bigmtn4@telus.net
Hours by Appointment
Cheque, $

THIS small-batch roaster has great beans, available at more than a dozen good coffee bars and eateries as well as at some retail locations. Purchasing preference goes to organic and fair-trade single estate producers using sustainable practices. Espresso is a house specialty.

- *House Specialties*: Small-batch roasted beans—organic, fair-trade, sustainable—using a Canadian broker and local packaging and single-origin beans. Try the Espresso Pi, one of my favourites; it is a dark blend rendolent of chocolate.
- *Also Available*: **Amaranth Whole Foods Market, Bumpy's Café, Calgary Co-op, Community Natural Foods, The Cookbook Company Cooks** and **Planet Organic Market.**
www.bigmountaincoffeeroasters.ca

tnik teas

Established: 2004 • Owner: Nicole Schon
Phone: 605•1074 • E-mail: nik@tnik.com
Monday–Sunday 9:00 am–9:00 pm
V, MC, Cheque, $, Canadian Tire $

NICOLE Schon likes to make her own rules, and tea embodies all the things she loves. "The ritual of making tea forces you to reflect on what a wonderful world we inhabit," she says. She sources her teas through Ethical Tea Participation (ETP), packages and delivers without a minimum charge. Loose tea—*white, black, green, oolong*, plus *rooibos*, herbal and fruit infusions, *yerba maté* and samplers—is packed in tins of 1, 2, 8 and 16 oz. Her genmaicha, or popcorn tea, is exquisite. Host a tea party, buy tea accessories like the wonderful tea infusion stick, or just buy a cuppa. Buy a customized sampler pack of 7 varieties ("The Daisy," 2 oz. tins), wedding gifts of artisan flowering teaballs, and clear glass tea pots so the recipient can watch the teaball unfurl into a flower. For heavy-duty durability, buy a cast iron teapot. They are prettier than they sound, as tough as a tank, and will become family heirlooms. *Rooibos* is the hot seller, caffeine free, high in antioxidants, and tastes fantastic, iced or hot.

- *House Specialties*: Loose teas and accessories.
- *Also Available*: Private labels for spas.

www.tnik.com

NORTHEAST

Ten Ren Tea & Ginseng Co. (Calgary) Ltd.

Established: 2000 • Manager: Amy Chen

800F, 999–36 Street NE (Pacific Plaza Mall)   *1017, 9650 Harvest Hills Boulevard NE*
Phone: 207•8888   *Phone: 374•1866*
Monday–Sunday 10:00 am–7:30 pm   *Monday–Sunday 10:00 am–8:00 pm*
V, MC, Debit, Cheque, $

BRIGHT green plastic leaves dangle from the ceiling to honour the tea shrub in this tiny Eastside shop. Poke through tea alternatives such as dried ginseng alongside many brands of tea—loose leaf by the gram, in bags, or in tins, with *black, green, white* or *oolong*, being the most popular choices. Ten Ren's Chinese zodiac teapots are elegant works of art (or in Pacific Plaza, go next door to Utsuwa-no-Yakata for costly tiny Yixing tea pots in purple, yellow, red or green clay, handthrown in Taiwan.) In house, peruse other cups and glass tea pots, strainers and baskets. Just once, have a bubble tea to go.

- *House Specialties*: Oolong, green, white and black teas.
- *Also Available*: Toronto and Vancouver shops.

www.tenrentea.com

SOUTHEAST

Fratello Coffee Co.

Established: 1985 • Co-owners: Russ, Jason & Chris Prefontaine

4021–9 Street SE
Phone: 265•2112 or (800) 465•7227 • Espuccino Imports: 263•3224 or (800) 944•2545
Monday–Friday 8:30 am–5:00 pm
V, MC, Debit, $

THIS roasting business has grown from being soley a supplier to restaurants—Espuccino Imports is that wholesale arm—to a booming enterprise with a retail presence. Here, you can buy a Gaggia, or you can buy coffee beans (ten pound minimum). In the back, 210-pound batches of beans are computer-monitored in immense roasters, filling the air with the heavy scent of roasting coffee. The Prefontaine family has invested in top-of-the-line equipment, like the Butterfly, a multi-thousand dollar espresso maker with computerized digital control over each shot pulled. They deal in fair-trade, organic, location-specific, decaffeinated, espresso and blends of beans. One of my overall favourite beans in the city is Fratello's Blackjack espresso blend. As a result of sourcing coffee-growers, the business has made an 8-year commitment to assist the Ethiopian village of Belo. Fratello's team places a premium on educating coffee bar clientele, providing training in how to store, grind and make the best coffee possible.

- *House Specialties*: Fair trade, organic, location-specific, decaffeinated, espresso and blended beans, custom and house roasts, office coffee service and education.
- *Also Available*: House roasts and custom blends at many Calgary coffee bars, including: Caffe Beano, Good Earth, Purple Perk, and **Tutti Frutti**.

www.fratellocoffee.com

Tea Affair

Established: 1997 • Owner: Sam Pruthee
207, 2835–23 Street NE
Phone: 228•3655
Monday–Friday 10:00 am–6:00 pm
V, MC, Debit, Cheque, $

SAM Pruthee's business originated as a virtual shop. Like a good business will, it has grown from a computer-powered place, into a wholesale and retail North American business. Tea Affair has an organic herbal infusion line as well as *rooibos* and *green, black, white* and *oolong* teas, and a comprehensive collection of blends and single estate varieties (like a wine varietal that is single-vineyard), available as loose tea or in bags.

- *House Specialties*: 450 teas and infusions.
- *Also Available*: **The Cookbook Company Cooks, Community Natural Foods, Lazy Loaf & Kettle, Oolong Tea House,** and Wild Ginger.

www.tea-affair.com

Tea Trader

Established: 1994 • Owner: Ted Jones, Manager: Paulie Duhaime
Upstairs, 1228A–9 Avenue SE
Phone: 264•0728
Tuesday–Saturday 10:00 am–5:00 pm
V, MC, AE, Debit, Cheque, $

TED Jones says he has tracked the trends, and tells me that in response to requests by tea-drinkers for organic teas, estates have to-date responded with few selections. Jones says that *terroir* is as influential on tea as it is for food and wine. For example, Darjeeling, raised in the harsh environment of northern India's Himalayan mountains, provides a small, highly-prized harvest of delicate muscatel-flavoured tea. Assam, grown on the river plains to the east, tends to be black, strong and malty in flavour.

Tea Trader carries infusions and teas of every colour—all loose. Glass pots are ideal for flowering teas, and there are many steeping options: tea balls, tea tongs, paper filters, strainers, over-cup strainers, tea socks of unbleached cotton. Loose tea in the pot still produces the best tea, says Ted. Fine porcelain and bone china tea cups are stocked for tea grannies of all ages. Caledon Ginger Chai, a blend of *rooibos* and honeybush with added spices, is named for a South African town situated on the Garden Route—a scenic modern coastal version of a spice road. Other best-sellers include five *black* teas, each blended to honour the personality of one of Alberta's Famous Five (Nellie McClung, Irene Parlby, Emily Murphy, Louise McKnney and Henrietta Edwards) who in 1927 required the Supreme Court of Canada, and subsequently, the British Privy Council, to address the issue of women as persons.

- *House Specialties*: Exclusive Tea Trader blends, including the "Famous Five" *black* teas, Caledon Ginger Chai and Alberta Clipper *black* tea.
- *Also Available*: River Café.

www.teatrader.com

SOUTHWEST

Blends Coffee Roasters
Established: 1995 • Owner: Rudy Peters
4806–1 Street SW
Phone: 452•5525
Monday–Saturday 9:00 am–4:00 pm
V, Debit, Cheque, $

RUDY Peters has been involved in the coffee business since 1987. His current location is a small house on the west side of the train tracks. At the time of writing, there is no seating, so sampling is a stand-up only experience.

Peters was influenced by his maternal grandmother, an immigrant from Eastern Europe who roasted coffee in Edmonton. The only sibling in a large family who took an interest in her daily afternoon coffee-drinking ritual, Peters made a habit of conversing with her over a freshly roasted cupful.

Blends began in Canmore, which is now a separate and primarily wholesale entity. Blends beans are largely sourced from fair-trade and/or organically certified plantations as well as from some wholly owned women's cooperatives in Colombia. Peters prides himself on cultivating relationships with coffee brokers to ensure that he obtains only the best green beans. In Colombia alone, there are 16 varieties of *arabica* beans to choose among, and beans— *arabica* or *robusta*—are not created equally.

As well as roasting for commercial clients, Blends provides coffee brewers and thermal carafes for professional office coffee service. The business custom roasts to order for individuals as well; taste some of the shop's 21 coffees, in medium or dark roasts, from Antigua to Zimbabwe, in medium and dark blends, as well as several organic and/or Swiss water decaffeinated choices.

- *House Specialties*: Bre-X, Blue Nile or Broken Wheel dark blends; Blue Pacific or Mexican Tango medium blends.
- *Also Available*: Central Blends, 203–19 Street NW and Bullet Cappuccino Bar, 2–728 Northmount Drive NW.

Bumpy's Café
Established: 2005 • Owner: John Evans
Lane Access, 1040–8 Street SW
Phone: 265•0244
Monday–Friday 6:30 am–4:30 pm, Saturday 7:30 am–4:00 pm
V, MC, Debit, $

THINGS at Bumpy's are done well—baking and "from scratch" meals and coffee. Evans uses locally roasted **Big Mountain Coffee Roasters** beans, in a light Italian-style espresso. The beans are available for purchase, along with beans from 49th Parallel Coffee Roasters, the original owners of *Caffè Artigiano*, a caffeine stop of renown in Vancouver (with a location recently opened in Calgary at 100, 332–6 Avenue SW, Centrum Place). Sample the two espressos on offer—one from each roaster—and ask about single origin roasts. The current focus is Ethiopian Harrar or Sidamo, but that is bound to change. Fortunately, there are many good beans to try. Krups' inaugural Calgary Cup of Excellence went to Bumpy's in 2007.
- *House Specialties*: House-made sweets, meals, latté art, single origin espressos.
www.bumpyscafe.com

Phil & Sebastian Coffee Co.
Established: 2006 • Owners: Phil Robertson & Sebastian Sztabzyb
H6, 4421 Quesnay Wood Drive SW (Calgary Farmers' Market)
Phone: 612•2266
Friday & Saturday 9:00 am–5:00 pm, Sunday 9:00 am–4:00 pm
MC, Debit, $

PHIL Robertson and Sebastian Sztabzyb began their coffee company in 2006, hanging their sign at the Calgary Farmers' Market in March of that year. They sell ethically traded and single origin coffee beans, a changing roster that is sourced from three highly regarded specialty roasters in Vancouver, Denver, and Chicago. A cool Clover coffee maker makes one cuppa joe at a time, and is it ever good! A few carefully chosen coffee accessories and makers, like an affordable burr grinder, and a stainless plunger that will never break on a patio's stone floor, are arranged on the side shelves, but the coffee is the draw. Coffee geeks immersed in the making of the city's best have had an effect: I line up and wait with all the other fans of fine coffee at the guys' market booth for the city's best espresso.
- *House Specialties*: Ethically traded small-batch roasted beans, single-origin beans, Clover coffee maker, espresso, latté art.
www.philsebastian.com

Steeps, The Urban Teahouse

Established: 1999 • Owner: Emily Jakl
880–6 Avenue SW (Mount Royal Village)
Phone: 209•0076
Monday–Thursday 9:00 am–11:00 pm, Friday 9:00 am–midnight
Saturday 10:00 am–midnight, Sunday 10:00 am–11:00 pm
V, MC, AE, Debit, $

THIS tea retreat, one of several in a small Western Canadian chain, has a mountain of teas, all loose, and a counter full of house-made sweet treats. Personal experience advises that the house chai is ideal with either carrot or coconut cake. All varieties are stacked in tins in groups by the window. Walk around the tower to choose what you wish to try regardless of whether you are drinking "in" or taking your tea leaves home. Currently, the most popular teas are *rooibos*, fruit and spice infusions, *matcha*, and house chai. Order tea online, and it will be shipped to your kitchen door. Renovations have brought better lighting so readers can now see the print in their books. This spot has become a popular business meeting destination and a hangout for laptop writers.

- *House Specialties*: Loose tea in 200 varieties, *matcha* for the morning, chai for cold-weather comfort, ice tea smoothies for warm weather.
- *Also Available*: Edmonton and Vancouver.

www.steepstea.com

TotaliTea The Tea Boutique

Established: 2003 • Owners: Carol & David Pidhirney
336, 315–8 Avenue SW (Bankers Hall)
Phone: 266•6567 or 240•7828 (at CFM)
Monday–Wednesday 10:00 am–6:00 pm, Thursday & Friday 10:00 am–8:00 pm
Saturday 10:00 am–5:30 pm
V, MC, AE, Debit, $

THE smartest part of this smartly designed tea shop is the "sniffing corner," shelves of tea in tiny glass jars that give prospective shoppers an opportunity to sniff before they buy. Be warned that some *black* teas, like wine, have a "closed" nose and do not reveal their nature until steeped and tasted. Carol says that most of her clients are serious fans of good tea, and she is pleasantly surprised at the growing number of youthful clients. The leading teas of our time—*rooibos*, chai, *matcha*, *green*, *oolong*—are all available. Learn how to brew it, including water temperature: many teas do not like boiling hot water, and lose their fragrance. It takes no longer to make good tea than an inferior cupful, and the staff here are happy to help you learn how to make the most of what you buy.

- *House Specialties*: Loose teas in a variety of blends.
- *Also Available*: **Calgary Farmers' Market** and select restaurants including Saint Germain.

www.totalitea.com

NORTHWEST

Cadence
Established: 2001 • Owner: Alexander Czarniecki
6407 Bowness Road NW
Phone: 247•9955
Monday–Friday 7:00 am–4:00 pm, Saturday & Sunday 8:00 am–4:00 pm
Debit, $

O so Negro fair trade beans roasted in Nelson, British Columbia, are the backbone of this kitschy and busy Bowness landmark. Good coffee, good baking, hearty breakfasts, good lineups; be patient. "Road Rider," a light-to-medium blend, is a tip of the hat to long-lived Bow Cycle and its many cycling patrons just up the road. The blend is also known as "Fresh Tracks" in the winter, a nod to Canada Olympic Park, a ski hill just a short cross-country climb away. It's all about neighbourhood. "Prince of Darkness," dark blend is very dark and oily. It may plug your house coffee mill, but is it ever good.

- *House Specialties*: Oso Negro beans in light and dark blends, hearty breakfasts and lunch, featuring good baking.
- *Also Available*: Local distributor for Oso Negro beans in what staff call their "offsite coffee" program to other shops and offices.

www.cadencecoffee.com

Oolong Tea House
Established: 2004 • Owner: Emily Jakl
110–10 Street NW
Phone: 283•0333
Monday–Thursday 10:00 am–11:00 pm, Friday & Saturday 10:00 am–midnight
Sunday 10:00 am–11:00 pm
V, MC, Debit, $

T he aim of the game: offer as many teas as possible. This mellow teahouse boasts a "Great Wall of Tea" offering 138 varieties of loose tea. That's a lot of sipping. Most popular: *matcha, yerba maté*, jasmine Dragon Tears, and *oolong*. There's more: *white, black, green, rooibos*. All teas served in-house (or on the cozy hidden back patio) arrive in a French press. Shop or browse for tea accessories (clear glass pots, sieves, strainers, tea balls). If a nosh is what you need along with your tea, try an Anahata snack bar in a variety of flavours and densities, made by local cook Lisa Krasnow. Vegan homemade soup or house-made baked goods include *matcha* cupcakes and *samosas*. For something more substantial, have a **Simple Simon's** pie.

- *House Specialties*: Loose teas, from *black* to *yerba maté*.

www.oolonghouse.com

Planet Coffee Roasters
Established: 1999 • Owner: Al Jetha
101, 83 Bowridge Drive NW
Phone: 288•2233
Monday–Friday 6:30 am–5:00 pm, Saturday 6:30 am–5:00 pm
Sunday 6:30 am–3:00 pm
V, MC, Debit, $

VICTORIA Roasters roast this small business's good beans and blend them too, in the city's north, but the shop is on the way west, where Highway 1 rolls toward Banff. En route to elsewhere, try the smooth dark-roast Angel's espresso. It smells right, and tastes better on the road. At home, Angel's high oil content may plug your coffee grinder. Be patient.
• *House Specialties*: Planet's best blends are Angel's dark blend and Planet medium Italian espresso.

The Roasterie
Established: 1985 • Owner: Lech Wojakowski
314–10 Street NW
Phone: 270•3304
Monday–Sunday 8:00 am–midnight
Debit, $

OWNER Lech Wojakowski has spent more than two decades roasting 8-pound batches of beans on-site all day, six days a week. He prefers to source fair trade shade grown beans. His house espresso sits close by an equally popular blend named for its client, Buchanan's Chop House. Roasterie beans are used in a handful of Vietnamese noodle houses for their specialty dark French drip iced coffee poured over sweetened condensed milk. Wojakowski's house espresso is among my favourites in the city. He also brings in "monsoon" beans which have been subjected to a super-premium process of drying, alleged to reproduce the environmental conditions to which beans would have been exposed in the hold of a sailing ship as they were transported to ports around the world.
• *House Specialties*: House-roasted coffee beans, specializing in dark roasts, monsoon coffee and fair trade shade grown.
• *Also Available*: Buchanan's, Vietnamese pho houses.

Tea s Collection

Established: 1997 • Owner: Jenny Lam
192, 1623 Centre Street North (Central Landmark Plaza)
Phone: 276•7778
Monday–Sunday 10:30 am–6:00 pm
$ only

IN a chat over tea, Jenny speaks more Chinese than English, so take a translator or simply smile frequently. This tiny shop, lined with geraniums and gifts of plants, carries the city's most costly teas, including fragrant, sweet and floral Dragon Ball that has forever altered my perception of jasmine tea. Engraved tins contain *black, green, oolong, semi-green* and *white* teas.

The term *gongfu* denotes any skill developed through greatly detailed practice—painting, martial arts, or tea-making. *Gongfu* tea service uses small, unglazed teapots made of shades of purple clay from Yixing, in Jiangsu province in China, with tiny cups in proportion to the pot. The pots may look like childrens' toys, but are highly prized, hand-thrown by master potters. Because the clay is slightly porous, each pot becomes impregnated with flavour; a tea drinker with wide-ranging tastes may have a collection of pots, one for each type of tea consumed.

Tea leaves (never teabags!) can be re-used several times (perhaps as many as four or five), and the size of pot dictates the number of tea drinkers. Jenny is adamant that tea be made in small quantities, and that the leaves remain in contact with the water for seconds, not minutes, for tea that is never bitter. She empties the pot immediately after she fills my cup, and makes a fresh potful—using the same leaves—when I am ready for more.

- *House Specialties*: Premium loose Chinese teas and Jiangsu Yixing purple clay teapots.

Cooking Schools & Classes

FOR THE MOST PART, we no longer learn to cook at our mother's apron. Instead, many of us learn to cook as adults. As a society, we are now into the third generation of eaters who did not learn to cook at home. This has many ramifications beyond taking cooking classes as adults. Refer to the sections detailing Make 'n' Take Meals/Home Meal Replacements (HMRs), and Personal Chefs and Caterers.

Often, the impetus to learn how to cook comes from a major change in life circumstances—when we marry, or separate, or when we have babies. When there are kids in the nest, home cooking is more important, more affordable and more attractive than the alternatives—sitting in restaurants, the trough of a fast food drive-thru, or collecting home meal replacements (HMRs) from the store.

Cooking schools rarely survive as stand-alone businesses. Schools are symbiotic creatures, more likely to thrive as adjuncts of food-focused businesses. (Consult our lists for cross-referenced businesses offering classes as additions to their major lines of operation.) A school is an expensive space to equip and run: teaching fees, food costs, support staff, the capital cost of equipment that meets city health standards, tools—from knives to mixers—it all adds up. A hood vent and make-up air system, for instance, the innocuous inverted stainless steel box suspended above every professional stove that fries food, is an object that runs into five digits to purchase and install.

It is a testament to the significance of food—and its complexity—in our lives that a cooking class can be much more than an opportunity to improve our knife skills. A class may be a social event, a learning milieu, a team-building or bonding experience for business colleagues, a practice ground for new techniques, or a parent-free Saturday for kids.

Some classes are moveable feasts offered by chefs-to-go. Some feature instruction by television personalities or out-of-town specialists, while others rely on local talent. There are a variety of choices for those looking to improve their relationship with their stove. Here are some of the educational options.

SOUTHWEST

Talisman Centre

Established: 2006 • Director of Food & Beverage: Kim Randall
2225 Macleod Trail South
Phone: 233•8393
Hours by Appointment
V, MC, AE, Debit, $

A LL the classes presented at the Sears Nutrition Kitchen (named to honour the business that donated the handsome kitchen equipment) are personalized and custom-tailored, but all fit a 3-hour hands-on format. Clients can choose from a broad range of ethnic and technical bases—couples cooking, French dishes, knife skills, Thai, appetizers. The roster of chef-instructors includes Talisman Centre's executive chef Sacha Fritz and several other local chefs. A complimentary pass to the centre's facilities (swimming pool, gym and courts), is included with each class. For team-building corporate or private events, book one month in advance for 10 to 35 participants. Onsite catering is also available.

• *House Specialties*: Custom-tailored ethnic classes and team-building.

www.talismancentre.com

NORTHWEST

Antoinetta's Cooking School

Established: 2005 • Owner: Antoinetta Terrigno; Class Coordinator: Andrea Iapaolo
201–10 Street NW
Phone: 283•5553
Classes by Appointment
Corporate Classes: Monday–Friday 2:00 pm–5:00 pm
Private Classes: Sunday 11:00 am–3:00 pm
V, MC, AE, Debit, $

A N offshoot of the popular Kensington restaurant, Osteria di Medici, this hands-on learning opportunity is based on the owner's latest cookbook, *Italian Cooking: Classic Recipes* (Osteria di Medici, 2005). Menus focus on Molise, located in southern Italy. Dishes include regional specialties, such as *Mozzarella di Bufala*, cured meats, and seasonal vegetables. All classes are custom-designed, but follow a meal format, and can accommodate from 4 to 15 guests. Book classes by phone.

• *House Specialties*: Custom-tailored classes in regional cuisine of Molise, Italy.

www.osteria.ca

SAIT Polytechnic Adult Continuing Education

Established: 1916 • Contact: SAIT Registration Office
Coordinator of Children's Classes: June McKinnon
1301–16 Avenue NW
Phone: 284•7248 (SAIT) or 210•4015 or (800) 284•7248 (SAIT)
Registration: Monday–Thursday 8:15 am–4:30 pm, Friday 9:00 am–4:30 pm
V, MC, Debit, $

SAIT Polytechnic is the nation's first publicly funded technical institute, dating back to 1916, with more than 150,000 alumni distributed in countries around the world, including this writer (culinary apprenticeship program, 1985 graduate). In addition to demanding full-time technical programs, SAIT also offers continuing education classes to the public at large. Most classes are scheduled in the evenings, as single sessions or as a series of sessions. Some classes run weekends.

Adults can select from a wide range of cooking (and wine education) options, including baking and knife skills, tastes of Tuscany or Thailand, or meal-centric theme menus for high holidays. Food and wine professionals can update and upgrade their skills in specific areas, attain apprenticeship standing or acquire sommelier training and standing through the International Sommelier Guild (ISG). Summer kids' classes, "Summer at SAIT Culinary Boot Camp," are taught by chef Desmond Johnston, co-owner of **Brasssica Mustard** in his day job. The kids' classes are week-long programs that cover Professional Cooking or Baking and Pastry Arts. Register online, by fax, mail, or in person at Customer Service in Heritage Hall on campus.

• *House Specialties*: Adult continuing education, summer camp classes for teens 13–17 years old.

www.sait.ca

Culinary Tours

KNOW THY CITY. Then eat thy view. The city's population of 738,184 in 1994 grew to 933,495 in 2004, and crossed the one million threshold in 2006. At least 7,000 out-of-country immigrants arrive annually, plus those who are drawn, moth to a blazing economy, from within Canada's boundaries.

Where to shop? Where to eat? What to buy? Who to trust?

Several culinary tourism businesses have arisen, eager to tell residents and visitors all about where to find the good stuff across Calgary.

Alternatively, take a self-guided tour from the pages of *Shop talk*. It is, after all, open-all-hours!

CITY WIDE

Acquired Tastes Food Tours
Established: 2006 • Owner: Karen Anderson
Phone: 968•2783
Hours by Appointment
Cheque, $

ACQUIRED Tastes Food Tours moves through the entire city's burgeoning food scene with personalized or established 6-hour tours. The owner, Karen Anderson, a people-oriented Slow Food activist with a big heart, started the business in February 2006, and takes small groups of clients by executive van or by foot through an entire day's dining and shopping delights. One tour departs from the **Calgary Farmers' Market**, returning hours later after a movable feast city wide. Another, pedestrian style and rain-or-shine, starts at a tea house, then winds slowly through the Beltline's burgeoning foodie destinations in and around Designer Avenue (11 Avenue SW). Anderson hands out copious pages of notes and ideas, along with restaurant recommendations and pantry-stocking tips. Everywhere, clients receive samples and snacks, and in some places, on some tours, lunch. It is, after all, all about eating well.

• *House Specialties*: Culinary tours on foot or via executive van.
www.calgaryfoodtours.com

SOUTHEAST

International Avenue Business Revitalization Zone
"Around the World in 35 Blocks"

Established: 1997 • Executive Director: Alison Karim-McSwiney
4015–17 Avenue SE
Phone: 248•7288
Weekend Tours: Hours by Appointment
Cheque, $

ALONG the International Avenue Business Revitalization Zone (BRZ) on the Eastside, 35 to 40 percent of the business is food-related. It makes for a worthwhile tour. The BRZ is captained by Executive Director Alison Karim-McSwiney. Since 1997, 14 times a year, she takes a bus full of 40 shoppers on a tour along the culturally diverse stretch of 17 Avenue SE. The tours are conducted on weekends, their timing depending entirely on Karim-McSwiney's busy schedule, and can only be booked by phone.

"We take a school bus, and play off the fact that 17 Avenue is another world to some of the city's residents," says Karim-McSwiney. Each tour vicariously covers the globe, visiting businesses within a few blocks of 17 Avenue SE, showcasing the exotic foods and authentic lifeblood of the city's east side. Food-loving participants are exposed to sights, tastes, and sounds different from their norm, not hard in an enigmatic district that hosts a Ferrari dealership but no truffle oil, a German sausage-maker with a smokehouse and curry ketchup, the city's largest Vietnamese shop with a mind-blowing sauces and condiments aisle, fragrant green olive oil, and olive oil soap, at a Middle Eastern market. During the 3-hour tour, guests sample, meet the manager, and absorb the smells of far-away markets, with music and cultural background. A current initiative is the "new building" fund of the International Avenue Arts & Cultural Centre, showcased by an annual gala at the Metropolitan Centre.

• *House Specialties*: 17 Avenue SE culinary bus tours.
www.internationalavenue.ca

Olympic Plaza Cultural District's First Thursdays

Established: 2001 • General Manager: Meg Van Rosendaal
205–8 Avenue SE
Phone: 294•7455, Ext. 1465
11:00 am–2:00 am on the first Thursday of each month
$ only

THE Olympic Plaza Cultural District's General Manager, Meg Van Rosendaal, has been researching her neighbourhood since 2001, laying the groundwork for self-guided walking tours of the inner city on the first Thursday of each month. Her on-the-hoof research generates e-mail listings that send her guests into hotel lobbies, restaurants, art galleries, and music venues. First Thursdays are intended to explore the rich variety of cultural experiences to be enjoyed in the inner city—between 1 Street SW and 3 Street SE, from 6 Avenue south to the train tracks, there are nearly 60 restaurants, 30-plus arts groups, and many stores. That's the Cultural District. Discover it on foot, on a mostly free self-guided downtown tour that lasts as long as you do. Each month's changing roster of 30–45 participating destinations and events, a few of which do charge an on-site fee, are detailed in a monthly email. Van Rosendaal personally leads a walking tour she calls a "first foray," and will conduct personalized tours upon request and booked in advance. She says that many Calgarians believe the myth that the city has no culture or festivals; First Thursday proves otherwise.

First Thursday is not just about food. Each month, between 300–1,500 walkers can enjoy a variety of activities: take in a serenade at Cantos, learn about the history of the Sandstone City's rebirth after the 1885 fire, sip wine at PiqNiq, or mingle and martini at the Auburn Saloon, second home to some of Calgary's most esteemed writers. To be included in the e-mail listing, each business must offer a "First Thursday" discount or special feature.

• *House Specialties*: Downtown walking tours of cultural and culinary sites.
www.firstthursdays.ca

East Indian

MY FAVOURITE FLAVOURS AND FOODS have been South Asian, also called East Indian, for several decades, the enduring remnant of my vegetarian phase that began in Eastside Vancouver. When I arrived in Calgary in the early 1980s, sourcing ingredients was a challenge, with only a few far-flung spots carrying mustard oil, *basmati* rice, lentils or the many spices that build the layered flavours of this complex cuisine.

This year, what I observe—in addition to growth—is a gradual relocation of many Indian food shops northward into Castleridge, from their former concentration along 17 Avenue SE. Currently, the northeast quadrant is the city's most culturally diverse region for curious cooks to peruse, and Castleridge Plaza in the NE is the hot spot, an octopus-like, rapidly spreading cross-cultural shopping centre that foodies ought not to miss.

East Indian cuisine runs the gamut from meat to sweets, with shops opening to fill every niche, feeding Hindus, Sikhs, and Muslims from a variety of countries. It is all proof that the Silk Road conveyed more than silks; spices and ingredients are multi-ethnic and borderless. Their commonality stretches beyond the actual borders of India, to Pakistan, Africa, the Euphrates valley, as well as central and Southeast Asia. It is a global community, and flavours have travelled to reflect that truth. This section's listing of dry goods, produce, and sweets shops selling *mithai* for holy days and festivals can be augmented by a perusal of Meat & Game, for meats to round out the East Indian feast table.

NORTHEAST

A-1 Spice & Movie Centre

Established: 1993 • Owner: Kuldeep Dhada
96, 55 Castleridge Boulevard NE (Castleridge Plaza)
Phone: 285•2446
Monday–Sunday 9:00 am–8:00 pm
V, MC, AE, Debit, Cheque, $

THIS shiny-clean small space is tidily tucked full. Stroll past the full movie counter of Bollywood hits and find tall shelves of pans and cooking implements, including a stack of *tawas*. Shelves hold a deep range of spices, a wide collection of bagged *basmati* rice and countless jars of pickles. The spice shelf has an entire row devoted exclusively to chilies: an unfortunately named "very hot chilly" sits beside Kashmiri red chilies, cayenne, hot chili flakes and *très épicé* chili paste. Across the aisle, pickles run the gamut from oil-packed lemon, eggplant, ginger, garlic or mango to brined green chili pickle. And of course, chili and pickle meet midway, in red chili-stuffed pickle. Beautiful tiny, round eggplant, *garam masala* made with whole spices, frozen *chapattis, tandoori paste,* a raft of chutneys, *wadi,* soy and chickpea flours, snacks. This store is like the magician's trunk: walk in, and it unfolds about you. Don't forget to choose a Bollywood movie before you go out the door.

• *House Specialties:* Dry goods and spices, Indian produce.

Al-Noor Halal Meat & Grocery

Established: 2005 • Owner: Naseer Chaudrhari
810, 5075 Falconridge Boulevard NE (Castleridge Plaza)
Phone: 293•0888
Monday & Wednesday–Sunday 10:00 am–9:00 pm, Tuesday noon–7:00 pm
V, MC, Debit, $

PAKISTANI ingredients in this bright and clean shop include high-quality Shan-brand spice blends and Rooh Afza, a beverage infused with *rose water* and *pandanus.* Beyond beverages, find *jaggery,* and keynote spices like cumin, coriander, cardamom, and chili. Dry goods include *pappadam* and Pakistani *basmati* rice. Bulk dried fruit, and a wide array of pulses from *chana* to lentils, *ghee* and mustard oils, and Chinese salt. In the freezer, you can spot *halva, Halal* beef patties and *samosa* wrappers. A clean, tidy meat counter sells fresh *Halal* meats—beef, lamb, goat, chicken—but be prompt, because it closes at 6:00 pm, before the rest of the shop.

• *House Specialties:* Pakistani ingredients and *Halal* meats.

APNA Punjab Groceries & Movies

Established: 2002 • Owner: Gurdeep Kalkat
300, 5075 Falconridge Boulevard NE (Castleridge Plaza, south side)
Phone: 590•1611
Monday–Sunday 9:00 am–9:00 pm
V, MC, Debit, $

THE big yellow "Fruiticana" sign above the store is a useful landmark when navigating the narrow and confusing lanes of this multi-address plaza that keeps growing new arms. (Look out for the *Bhatia Cloth House* where you can shop for luscious silks in colours like rainbows smudged in puddles!) Once inside APNA Punjab Groceries & Movies, you will find gorgeous produce: firm purple garlic, impeccable ginger, baby eggplant to convert any non-aubergine fan, the lizard-like gourd called *karela,* and maybe, if you are as fortunate as I was on my last visit, a sociable small boy willing to explain how to cook his favourite vegetables! The north side of the store is devoted to dry goods: bakers will be glad of BIG bags of coconut across from "snack row," and *couscous* (labeled "khush-khush") bears testament to the roving border-crossing nature of ingredients. Find Darjeeling tea, lentils and beans, many big bags of many types of rice stacked under every produce shelf. Scents are part of the experience—breathe in the sharp aroma of dried licorice root, and a waft of herbs and spices. In the freezers: **Thumbs Up Foods'** Serenna's product line, vegetables, and *paneer* in blocks or cubes.

• *House Specialties:* Produce, Indian dry goods.

www.fruiticana.com

Bangla Bazaar

Established: 2003 • Owner: Siddiqui Mohamed
6, 3915 Edmonton Trail NE
Phone: 230•4426
Monday & Wednesday–Sunday 10:00 am–10:00 pm
V, MC, Debit, $

A LMOST on the Westside, this small shop is chockablock, crammed and jammed full—with rice, spices, and spice blends, frozen vegetables, *samosas* and snacks, dried lentils and beans, chutneys and curry pastes. At the meat counter, all meat selections are *Halal* and freshly cut—beef, lamb, goat and chicken. In the freezer, find finned fish from Bangladesh—*rahu, pabda, kingfish.*
• *House Specialties*: East Indian and Bangladeshi dry goods, frozen fish and *Halal* meats.

Bombay Sweet House

Established: 1998 • Owners: Gopal & Deepak Taneja
Bay 82, 55 Castleridge Boulevard NE (Castleridge Plaza)
Phone: 590•1393
Monday–Sunday 10:30 am–10:00 pm
V, MC, Debit, $

N O one I know makes Indian sweets for Eid or for Diwali. They all buy them, and half the city buys Bengali-style *mithai* here. My favourite is the crumbly, not-too-sweet carrot *halva*, which I eat by the handful, palming them like a pony from my fingers, straight out of the paper bag, while I wander the plaza. But you can get others too: sticky-yummy *gulab jamun* in *rose water* syrup, the only-slightly-less-sticky *jalabis* and sweet *burfi* in a dozen flavours, *kheer* redolent of cardamom, crunchy *laddu*.

The plaza is worth a trip. A whole globe co-exists here, including Bombay Silk & Designer Boutique, for armfuls of rainbow silk and saris, located a few steps from Bombay Sweet House. The sweets shop is among my top two favourites of the type in the city. You can sit down and eat lunch, but most people seem to come in for desserts to go.

Nirvana's kitchen, where the sweets are made, is close by. From the sweet shop, I am guided by a cousin of owner Gopal Taneja, through a labyrinth of alleys, down halls, through a kitchen, more labyrinths, and upstairs. I could be in Bombay. In the kitchen, one man is standing beside a stove, slowly stirring simmering milk within a huge wok. Five others are gathered at a table, rolling, shaping and cutting cashew flowers garnished with gilt silver. Enormous pots of *gulab jamun* sit in tubs of syrup, absorbing the floral scent of *rose water*. Inside the walk-in fridge, tray after tray of sweets wait. Gopal says the business sells over five thousand pounds of *mithai* for Diwali. Like many other fans, I am happy to eat *mithai* year-round.
• *House Specialties*: Bengali sweets, including carrot *halva*, *gulab jamun*, *kheer*, and *laddu*.
• *Also Available*: Nirvana Sweet House & Restaurant, 1009, 5075 Falconridge Boulevard NE (Castleridge Plaza).

Desi Bazaar

Established: 2000 • Contact: Manjit Dhanan
143, 5120–47 Street NE (West Winds Business Centre)
Phone: 590•5544
Monday–Friday 10:00 am–9:00 pm, Saturday 11:00 am–9:00 pm
Sunday 11:00 am–7:00 pm
V, MC, Debit, $

THIS octagonal space, tucked into the apex of two arms of a strip mall, is a bit hard to find, but is worth the careful hunt. Manjit Dhanan's family patiently answer questions and provide insights into cooking as they identify *methi* and *wadi* to novices and pros alike. The vegetables are self-serve from their cardboard cases in a tidy walk-in cooler at the rear, and the dry goods shelves—rice, lentils, herbs, spice blends—are highlighted by a garish one-pound tin of Madras curry, labeled, "By appointment to His Excellency the Governor of Bombay, established 1883." That's history!

• *House Specialties*: Indian dry goods, herbs and produce.

Lahore Foods & Halal Meats

Established: 2001 • Owner: Nazir Shad
13, 4525–52 Street NE
Phone: 590•7736
Monday–Sunday 10:00 am–9:00 pm
V, MC, AE, Debit, Cheque, $

THE multiple signs on the exterior of the windows inform shoppers that *Halal* meats are butchered twice-weekly. Choose from Alberta beef, lamb and goat, or British Columbia poultry. The store has the distinctive odour of a butcher shop, and the meat counter at the rear is chronically busy. But the shelves leading inward are stocked too, with dry goods from Nazir's homeland of Pakistan—rice, *ghee*, lentils and beans, *kheer*, hot sauces, and a frozen array of *Halal* meats and snacks, from burgers to chicken strips.

• *House Specialties*: Pakistani ingredients and *Halal* meats.

OK Food & Produce

Established: 1987 • Owner: Laddie Boparai

1023, 5075 Falconridge Boulevard NE	*1, 3250–60 Street NE*
(Castleridge Plaza)	*(Temple Plaza)*
Phone: 293•1186	*Phone: 293•1168*
Monday–Saturday 10:00 am–9:00 pm	*Monday–Wednesday 10:00 am–8:00 pm*
Sunday 10:00 am–8:00 pm	*Thursday–Saturday 10:00 am–9:00 pm*
	Sunday 11:00 am–7:00 pm

V, MC, AE, Debit, $

ONE location is around the corner from The Bhatia Cloth House in Castleridge Plaza, and the other is in nearby Temple. Make sure you know what you want when you shop at either—English translation is sparse and sketchy. Dry goods predominate: lentils, dried herbs, spices, and rice from many lands, including Sri Lanka, Bangladesh, and the Caribbean. The fresh produce is variable, and some frozen fare includes minced ginger and *paneer* cubes. For a good measure of extra atmosphere, choose a Bollywood movie from the shelves on the way out.

• *House Specialties*: East Indian and Pakistani dry goods.

Sabzi Mandi Eastern & Western Groceries
Established: 2005 • Manager: Rabia Samnani
5401 Temple Drive NE
Phone: 280•6797
Monday–Sunday 9:00 am–9:00 pm
V, MC, Debit, $

THE name, *Sabzi Mandi* means "vegetable market," but this is more of a supermarket than a greengrocer. It is huge, and sterile, and fairly plain, so don't look for frills or service, or anyone to carry your groceries to the car. In these rows of shelves, a shopper will find "Canadian" (i.e., not *Halal*) meats, and a good array of spices and rice, especially top-line Tilda *basmati*. There is *ghee*, and mustard oil, and coconut oil, and sunflower oil, and almond oil. One of the highlights is the bagged pulses in great variety: moth beans, *azuki* beans, *moong*, *chana*, pigeon peas, lima, romano, *urad*, and rainbow-coloured assortments of lentils. For cooks less inspired by lentils, there are Indian packets of sauces and spices in a variety of brands. In the freezers, look for whole meals or snacks, including *jalapeño paneer* "poppers," proof that fast food is a global event. Despite the name, the produce is not inspiring.

• *House Specialties*: East Indian dry goods, sauces and spices.

Thumbs Up Foods
Established: 1996 • Contact: Serenna Ramji & Fauzia Kanji
335, 7 West Winds Crescent NE
Phone: 250•9558
Monday–Wednesday 11:30 am–3:00 pm, Thursday 11:30 am–6:00 pm
Friday 11:30 am–5:00 pm
V, MC, $

CALGARIANS who have not yet found Thumbs Up Foods' line of Serenna's Indian foods are in for a wonderful surprise. This business began in 1996, quarterbacked by sisters Serenna Ramji and Fauzia Kanji, and Fauzia's husband Amin. The bulk of their business is wholesale, with most of their production exported to the US, but local shoppers can go direct to the source or to many other Indian shops. At the shop, find *roti* and *masala roti*, both made with 80 percent whole wheat flour, available fresh on Thursdays and Fridays, frozen the rest of the week. The city's yummiest *samosas*, frozen *samosa* wrappers, delectable butter chicken paste, and good *tamarind* chutney are available in this outlet too. In keeping with the spirit of the times, buy what Serenna calls "ready meals"—frozen single servings of *aloo moong*, *aloo gobi* and *aloo mutter*. The business migrated to Westwinds Business Park in July 2006.

- *House Specialties*: *Samosas, tamarind* sauce, "ready meals," *samosa* wraps, *roti*, butter chicken paste.
- *Also Available*: **A1 Spice & Movie Centre, Dalbrent Spice Rack,** and **OK Food & Produce.**

www.thumbsupfoods.com

SOUTHEAST

Calgary Sweet House & Restaurant
Established: 1980 • *Owners: Haseeb & Safa Gowralli*
8, 5320–8 Avenue SE (Penbrooke Plaza)
Phone: 272•7234
Wednesday–Sunday 10:00 am–7:00 pm
V, MC, AE, DC, Debit, $

CALGARY Sweet House & Restaurant makes some of my favourite *mithai*. The shop opened for business in 1980. The shop's current owners (since 2007), Haseeb and Safa Gowralli, are Muslims. Haseeb's grandfather left Peshawar in 1890, settling in Trinidad. Safa comes from Indonesia. Haseeb's childhood memories are multicultural—a Welsh Anglican priest, Hindu neighbours. He holds a degree in computer sciences from the University of Calgary, and is the former administrator of the Calgary Islamic School. His wife, Safa, came to Canada in 1987, and worked as a breeder and trainer of horses. They have seven children, and work hard to merge work life and family time. Over a cup of chai, twin daughters perched on his knees, Gowralli painstakingly explains the slow process of making *gulab jamun*. "Kitchen chemistry is like Einstein's definition of insanity," he says, laughing. "You have to learn why, or you will make the same mistake over and over."

The shop's clientele are Arabs, Caucasians, Sikhs, Hindus, and Muslims, he says. "It doesn't matter where we are from, we all eat. Sweets have no religion."

Mithai boxes—for Eid, Diwali, weddings, festivals, births—can be filled with dozens of choices of handmade sweets. Line up slices of *burfi, ras gullah, ras malai, petisa, peda, laddu* or a horde of *halva*. It is all good, all rich, all eye-candy for giving and sharing.

- *House Specialties*: East Indian sweets, including *burfi, halva,* and *petisa.*

Fairmount Spiceland

Established: 1975 • Owner: Chhotu Muhammad
7640 Fairmount Drive SE (Astral Plaza)
Phone: 255•7295 or 273•1546
Monday–Thursday & Saturday 10:00 am–6:00 pm, Friday 10:00 am–7:00 pm
Sunday & Holidays 11:00 am–4:00 pm
V, MC, AE, Debit, Cheque, $

THIS store is the mother lode. It has migrated several times during its history, but its newest location is just as well stocked as its previous incarnations, even if it is smaller. Rudy Kotadia and his dad began the business to fill the gap for ethnic and Indian spices, from *asafoetida* to *methi* and beyond. Now his cousin, Chhotu, is my preferred vendor of Indian products and knowledge.

Rudy patiently taught me about Asian vegetables: *karela*, which looks like a cucumber crossed with a gecko, but is really a bitter melon; *drumsticks*, which a cook cuts into lengths and squeezes out the tender flesh after cooking; *guvar*; *tindoora*; *toria*. Fresh curry leaves, all those vegetables, a wealth of spices and spice mixes, a mind-boggling array of *basmati* rice, pastes and pre-packaged meals, *chapattis*, *lentils*, *dal*, dried beans, flicks for family fun after dinner, it's all here. For an Indian look at pickles, experiment with lemon, ginger, lime, mango, cauliflower, turnip, chili, and gooseberry—all of them great with curries, *biryani*, and other roundly spiced dishes from the Indian palate. South African-made jams worth trying are made from tomato, melon, ginger, or apple. Caribbean, Indian, and South African cooking is all covered here. Go shopping, then go home and cook.

• *House Specialties*: East Indian dry goods, spices and produce, Caribbean and South African dry goods and staples.

SOUTHWEST

Raja Foods Grocery & Halal

Established: 2003 • Owner: Raja Ikramullah
239–12 Avenue SW
Phone: 205•4733 or 234•8832
Tuesday–Sunday 11:00 am–midnight
Debit, Cheque, $

A small and unprepossessing take-out counter at this Westside spot produced one of the best *naan* I have enjoyed in Calgary, beside a stellar vegetable *samosa*. "*Mazedar khana*," the owner, Raja, translates for me: "Good tasting!" Before emmigrating to Canada in 1995, he was a restaurateur in Karachi. His store shelves carry a modest supply of cooking ingredients, focused mostly on Pakistani dry goods—rice and spices—along with *atta* durum flour for *roti*, Queen of Sheba's *injera* for Ethiopian customers, and dried lentils and beans. A few *Halal* meats are available on request, three days a week only.

• *House Specialties*: Indian and Pakistani rice and spices.

NORTHWEST

Dalbrent Spice Rack

Established: 1985 • Owner: Amir & Norbanu Sorathia
132, 3604–52 Street NW (Dalbrent Professional Building)
Phone: 289•1409
Monday–Saturday 10:00 am–7:00 pm, Sunday 11:00 am–5:00 pm
V, MC, Debit, $

MOSTLY dry goods line the shelves of this long-lived Northwest shop, in flavours that cross boundaries and attract neighbours from diverse global backgrounds. On one visit, I see a Jamaican cook looking for meat seasoning and dried beans; on another visit, a Pakistani family needs a *masala*, and on a third stop, a Lebanese woman in a headscarf is searching for cumin seed among the spices. If cooking is not on the agenda tonight, buy dinner to go at Saffron next door (Bay 136), owned by the same family.

• *House Specialties*: East Indian, Middle Eastern, and Caribbean herbs and spices.

www.saffrontakeout.ca

European

THE FIRST FLUSH OF IMMIGRANTS into Alberta was of white faces from Europe. In 1881, nearly 90 percent of Albertans claimed British or French heritage, with later arrivals from Iceland, Germany, Russia, central, eastern and northern Europe. In the 1940s and '50s, waves of settlers from the Mediterranean basin—Portugal, Greece, Italy—arrived. Post-1960s immigrants came from warmer climes, principally Hong Kong and India, and more recently, the Middle East and Africa, from Lebanon south to Sudan.

Those earliest settlers brought with them their nations' foods, and seeded the uncut prairie soil with simple, uncomplicated dishes that became the backbone of Canadian home cooking.

The Italian influence waned over the past two decades as other immigrants outnumbered them, although the current popularity of Italian fare is a good omen for an increase in the good ingredients that define Italian cooking.

In Calgary, delis and smokehouses filled with the sounds and smells of Krakow, Berlin, and Amsterdam are tucked into out-of-the-way places. This is not strip mall shopping, and many of these businesses do not accept credit cards. Welcome to the Old World.

NORTHEAST

Italian Store

Established: 1958 • Owner: Sera Duros
5140 Skyline Way NE
Phone: 275•8222
Monday–Saturday 9:00 am–5:00 pm
V, MC, Debit, $

SERA Duros is the central scion in the family business, *Scarpone's Great West Italian Importers*, now celebrating five decades of business. Her mom, Christina, is still working the floor, and her dad, Alberto, is the coolest guy in the store, says Sera. Sera's husband, their two adult children, and her sister and brother-in-law are all on board. The business has several divisions: Scarpone is the house label; Great West is the wholesale moniker; the Italian Store is the retail division. Duros, conscious of the double-edged sword inherent in blending retail and wholesale, admits that the store can offer "very competitive" prices because of their direct buying.

The cheese counter sells 2-year-old Italian parmesan, grated or in chunks, cows' milk *bocconcini* made in Ontario, Greek cheeses, and seasonal treats that include "pricey" *Mozzarella di Bufala* at Christmastime. The deli stocks meats from Canmore smokehouse extraordinaire, **Valbella Meats/Valbella's Deli & Café**, and Italian meats from Italy. The store has a limited range of fresh produce, sticking to what the on-site kitchen uses: fresh herbs and greens, anise, peppers, zucchini.

Look for fresh pizza dough every day but Monday, then prowl the angled rows for olive oil, rich balsamic vinegar, coffee beans, and bulk nuts. Sweet lovers can indulge in *gelato*, or espresso with house-made olive oil biscotti. Italian rice, grown mostly in the Po valley, is available, in the classic Italian choices of a*rborio, carnaroli, vialone nano.*

Pasta choices include frozen stuffed—with squash or lobster—and dried, in numerous artisanal and commercial brands. Jars of house-made tomato sauce make supper simple, and house-made bread is hot and ready after one o'clock. Even easier, try lasagna—frozen or oven-ready, breaded veal with tomato sauce and cheese, house-made traditional hot and sweet pork sausages, specialty calamari—available on Fridays, thin-crust pizza—made daily, eggplant parmigiana—made fresh once-weekly, then frozen, stuffed peppers and cabbage rolls—Italian-style, all sell like hotcakes.

- *House Specialties*: Fresh Italian deli products, house-made baked goods, preserves, dry goods, oils and home meal replacements (HMRs).
- *Also Available*: **Calgary Co-op, Canada Safeway, DinoRosa's Italian Market, Sobey's/IGA,** and **Sunterra Quality Food Markets.**

Italian Supermarket Ltd.

Established: 1963 • Owners: Filomena, Gina & Emilio Di Gaeta
265–20 Avenue NE
Phone: 277•7898
Monday–Friday 9:00 am–7:00 pm, Saturday 9:00 am–6:00 pm
Sunday 10:00 am–5:00 pm
V, MC, Debit, $

THIS family operated business, established in 1963, was purchased by Emilio's parents in 1972, and has been at the current location since 1983. Emilio, personable and chatty, is grooming his son to become the third generation behind the counter. "He's got some of his grandfather in him, he can sell snowballs to Eskimos," he says of his son Marco.

This great day-in-day-out Italian market offers good selections at reasonable prices, and the family takes a traditional approach and style. The business is not big but it bustles, and its owners like to pass on both information and traditions. Emilio will advise the deep-pocketed about the "Cadillacs" of olive oil, then just as impartially point a budget-minded shopper to less costly options.

He knows that his customer base has changed, and immigrants are happy to find their familiar flavours, so he stocks products from Poland and Croatia as well as cheeses from around the globe. Diehard Italians can sift through several types of rice, then sort through in excess of 50 types of olive oils, then peruse 140 linear feet of pasta selections—fresh, frozen and dried— olives in bulk, house-made sausages, veal shanks and scaloppini. In-season, look for California grapes and juice for home winemaking. The wood-burning pizza oven operates on Saturdays, with hot lunches available six days a week, either sit-down or "to go," offering half a dozen changing items, made by Marco's grandmother, Filomena, who also bakes the bread.

The house specialty is the "other" family business. In 1989, it was difficult to find good fresh frozen pasta, locally or from other cities in Canada, Emilio recounts. So the family bought an interest in Delizia's Pasta Ltd., a small pasta-making business that was struggling because of language and cultural barriers. "The recipes were bang-on, but the language barrier cost the Asian owners business," recounts DiGaeta. He bought half the business, brought in his wife, Lina, to look after placing orders with suppliers and taking orders from clients. Sales doubled in one year. The ravioli is very good. I especially like the squash, and asparagus with mascarpone. A variety of types, including cannelloni and gnocchi, are available, frozen, on-site only, and on the menus of some of Calgary's leading restaurants.

- *House Specialties*: House-made pasta, Italian dry goods, cheeses, meats, lunch café.
- *Also Available*: Pasta on menus of many fine local restaurants including the Calgary Tower and Hyatt Hotel.

www.italiansupermarket.com

Lina's Italian Market & Cappuccino Bar

Established: 1994 • Owner: Lina Castle
2202 Centre Street North
Phone: 277•9166
Monday–Friday 9:00 am–7:00 pm, Saturday & Sunday 9:00 am–5:00 pm
V, MC, Debit, $

LINA and Tom Castle head up 39 staff at this very busy market. In 2007, Lina was honoured with an Immigrants of Distinction Award. She arrived in Canada at age 16, and she is still moving at teenage speed. The business is no longer a simple, small Italian village *mercato*, but has grown into a sleek, immaculate, brightly lit European-style bastion, bustling, and high-ceilinged. The store is many things: modern-style deli carrying dry goods and tableware, greengrocery, bakery, and cappuccino bar with a wide range of products made on the premises. If you get past the stacked boxes of *panettone* without succumbing, you are a more rigorously disciplined shopper than I. Get past them, and succumb to in-store baked goods: tiramisu, Sicilian *cannoli*, tortes and tarts of seasonal fruit on Italian cream, nut tarts, fine Florentines and biscotti. Baskets hold bunches of buns, *ciabatta*, baguettes and *focaccia*.

The full shelves hold tools: cannoli-making tubes, blow torches, measuring apparatus, and silicone-tipped hand tools. Need a new java maker? Lina stocks the city's most comprehensive collection of stovetop Moka-style espresso pots, as well as milk foamers, ceramics and giftwear, or order a gift basket of all-Italian products in all price ranges, packed on attractive ceramic plates.

For tomorrow's supper, choose from pasta, immaculate sausages, meats and cold cuts, antipasti and oils and 25-year-old balsamic vinegars, costly enough to warrant using an eyedropper. Browse several varieties and brands of rice for risotto.

The produce is impeccable: fulsome fennel bulbs, healthy herbs and greens of many descriptions, blood oranges, berries, tomatoes, peppers and asparagus in season, and many mushrooms—portobellos, oyster, shiitake and field fungi, with dried packets positioned immediately above the fresh. At the cheese case, blue cheese hounds will find more than a dozen good blue cheeses to experiment with, along with domestic and Italian Asiago, and as many other varieties of Italian cheese as you might like to try.

Pecks of pickles and preserves predominate: La Conserva della Nonna's Italian *cotognata* spread, Croatian rose hip jam, Stonewall Kitchen's spicy pepper relish or red pepper jelly, Zinter Brown's peach pepper pot, an unexpected jar of sweet mango chutney by Patak's of India. Good flavours cross all borders, and Lina has taken a global tack.

If lunch or dinner to go is the goal, call in advance—for pizza or sandwiches, panzerotti or croquettes, lasagna or lamb. Take it home, reheat, then eat. Exemplary in-house products include bruschetta, black and green olive spreads, roasted vegetable dip, fresh sauces and pastas, crispy pizzas, exemplary frozen raw pizza dough, lasagna and lumaci, and grilled and roasted vegetables, *arancini* and *panzerotti*, all worth the hubbub of a busy lunch lineup.

• *House Specialties*: HMRs, house-made baked goods, deli, produce, kitchenware, dry goods and cheeses.

SOUTHEAST

Bite Groceteria

Established: 2007 • Owners: Doug Taub & Julie Denhamer
1212A–9 Avenue SE
Phone: 263•3966
Monday noon–3:00 pm, 4:00 pm–6:00 pm
Tuesday–Friday 10:00 am–3:00 pm, 4:00 pm–8:00 pm
Saturday 10:00 am–6:00 pm, Sunday 12 noon–6:00 pm
V, MC, Debit, $

THE motto here could be "Go big or go home." After a year of importing and selling wholesale to high-end restaurants around town—under their i3 label—has made a home in Inglewood. Co-owners are Doug Taub, a big-picture advertising guy and longtime food lover and Julie Denhamer, who has the born retailer's detail-driven mind and eye for quality. This new specialty food shop is a funky melding of styles too—shop under a crystal chandelier that dangles from a conduit-lined ceiling—the modern rococo-meets-industry look. Inglewood deserves this great idea. Buy large Rougié ducks, a cross-bred Mulard with dense and meaty legs, breasts and foie gras lobes. Oy, so good. Bite into local products here, including **Fairwinds Farm** and **Vital Green Farms** dairy products, **Driview Farms** lamb, **tnik teas** and *tisanes*, and seasonally available produce from **Broxburn Vegetables & Café**. Local knife meister Kevin Kent of **Knifeworks** has his edged tools and knowledge available at Bite Groceteria. Choose from deluxe European imports, ingredients that many of the city's finest chefs swear by—great Italian cherry tomatoes, squid ink pasta, or omega-3 egg pasta, white anchovies, fig roll made in heaven, Evian's exclusive distributorship, classic Italian rices for risotto, Laguiole cutlery and tableware from El Bulli in Spain.

- *House Specialties*: Rougié duck, high-end local and European ingredients.
- *Also Available*: 13 wholesales to restaurants in Calgary and the Bow Valley, including Rouge and Crazyweed Kitchen in Canmore.

DinoRosa's Italian Market

Established: 2002 • Owners: Dean & Rose Petrillo
9136 Macleod Trail South
Phone: 255•6011
Monday–Friday 9:30 am–5:30 pm, Saturday 9:00 am–5:00 pm
V, MC, AE, Debit, $

DEAN and Rose Petrillo, born in Canada to Italian-born parents, bought this long-standing Italian market, updated it, and pride themselves on their customer service. The licensed, casual seating area accommodates 35–40, and lunch is busy—veal scaloppini, thin crust pizza, house-made *focaccia*, great cappuccino and *gelato* bar featuring *cannoli*, cream horns, cakes, tiramisu.

It smells good in this shop. Be prepared to drool and to want lunch NOW! The biggest news here is the HMR area. In-a-hurry Italophiles can gather up ready to heat in-house specialties: two styles of lasagna, cannelloni with veal, or spinach and cheese, fresh sauces and pastas to cook, pizza dough, sauce and toppings, or "half-cooked" pizza for finishing at home. Try the bruschetta or the Sicilian olives—stuffed in-house with roasted pepper and feta, or artichoke and asiago.

Butcher and deli counters offer veal shank, Montreal veal scaloppini, house-made sweet and hot sausage, and an array of Italian and Canadian cheeses. Shelves carry sun-dried tomato and feta stuffed olives and a wide choice of oils—olive, grapeseed, walnut, hazelnut, flaxseed and pumpkin seed—and balsamic vinegars, young and old—aged from six months to 25 years. Look for luscious Callipo tuna packed in olive oil, vermouth-infused olives, grape leaves stuffed with rice, bruschetta, and equally lush grilled eggplant stuffed with provolone and sun-dried tomatoes. Rice, too, for risotto.

At coffee time, look for Illy or Lavazza espresso beans, and instant espresso for home tiramisu makers. Yum! Italian-style cooks with time to browse can shop for Italian ceramic tableware and tools—espresso makers, manual pasta makers and ravioli cutters.

- *House Specialties*: HMRs, pasta dishes, antipasti, staples, meats, deli, lunch.

Dutch Cash & Carry

Established: Late 1950's • Owner: Hessel Kielstra (since 1987)
3815–16 Street SE
Phone: 298•5899
Monday–Friday 8:00 am–4:30 pm, Saturday 9:00 am–3:00 pm
V, MC, Debit, Cheque, $

HIDDEN away on the Eastside, in Bonnybrook, this unprepossessing retail business is also an importer. The store is full of things Dutch, with a selection of cheeses leading the sales. Close behind are cookies and sweets, especially black licorice.

Diehard Dutch fans can find more than cheese and cookies: canned fish are to be expected—herring, mackerel, sardines, and cod liver, a phalanx of gingerbread, several sizes and shapes of *speculaas*, sturdy FinnCrisp and Wasa crackers. Sweets take up space too, from Dr. Oetker mixes and Hero jams, honey, fruit syrups, and hazelnut chocolate spread. The Dutch taste for eating chocolate is evident in choices from Droste, DeBron, and Verkade.

The Dutch sphere of influence in colonial Indonesia is visible, in jars of *ketjap manis*, *sambal oelek*, *sambal manis*, satay sticks, prawn crackers and an array of noodles. The familiar blue and white of Dutch dishes—in teapots, decorative plates, and tiles—fills one wall, with Dutch cleaning products tucked away into one corner. All in all, a worthwhile trip for all things Dutch!

- *House Specialties*: Dutch cookies, cheeses, black licorice, fish, Indonesian ingredients and Dutch tableware.

www.vyfieldenterprises.ca

SOUTHWEST

Francesco's Italian Food Store & Deli

Established: 2000 • Owners: Don & Agnes Hagel
3413–26 Avenue SW
Phone: 249•1151
Tuesday–Friday 10:00–5:30 pm, Saturday 10:00 am–5:00 pm
V, MC, Debit, $

IN the heart of Killarney, owners Don and Agnes Hagel have lots of parking and little local competition. White truffle oil is a good deal here; so is Alberta-made frozen ravioli—choose from gorgonzola and pear, prosciutto, or fig and mascarpone. A small selection of olive oils is offset by a wide range of Italian and Canadian cold cuts and cheeses—try *Gorgonzola dolce* or locally-made *bocconcini* and ricotta. Italian tomato products—canned tomatoes, paste in tubes, robust house-made tomato sauce—and Calgary-made pesto are ideal toppers for good Italian brands of pasta. The shop produces good calzone and pizza dough, and has branched into meals-to-go.

- *House Specialties*: House-made tomato sauce, calzone, takeout dinners, pizza dough, dry goods and pasta.
- *Also Available*: **Calgary Farmers' Market.**

Mercato

Established: 1974 • Owner: Dominic Caracciolo
2224–4 Street SW
Phone: 263•5535
Monday–Friday 9:30 am–7:00 pm, Saturday 9:00 am–7:00 pm
Sunday 1:00 pm–6:30 pm
V, MC, AE, Debit, $

DOMINIC Caracciolo has retooled and relocated his family's landmark, the long-standing Italian Centre and Meat Market that was a Bridgeland fixture for decades. Now in Mission, it has morphed into a contemporary, cutting-edge market with a dining counter surrounding a glittering open kitchen. Eat in at the bar, or take dinner home from the retail area that leads off to the left, with in-house pasta and sauces formerly made at Italian Gourmet Foods. Expect high prices: Dominic has figured out that food has a story to be told, and a price tag. You get both here.

Caracciolo is aggressively targeting high-end dishes to go, one-stop shopping for the busy crowd who need home meal replacements (HMRs) and pre-made pastas. Choose from lasagna, lumaconi, veal cannelloni, 15 sauces and at least 20 fresh pastas. His pasta-making team makes concessions to the Atkins diet with a new whole wheat line of pasta in various shapes. Besides quick-cooking fresh pasta and house-made sauces, look for yummy veal cannelloni, lumaconi, and lasagna, and pasta dinners.

At the meat counter, Uncle Dom's famous fennel-laced sausages are being made by Mama Cathy. The shop stocks lamb and veal, tidily trimmed, as well as marinated free-range chicken, *braciole* and stuffed veal breast. Mama Cathy's famous stuffed vegetables are also a good bet.

Check out the hard-to-find Italian cheeses in the cheese display, most emphatically Italian: *Formaggi di Tartufo*, Crotinese sheep's milk cheese, *Mozzarella di Bufala*, Reggiano wheels, wine-soaked *Umbriaco*.

Find a wide assortment of Italian specialties, from rice to Uncle Luigi's Calabrian olive oil. The old location held a 45-gallon drum and customers brought their own bottles to fill. Here, modern glass bottles are filled and waiting.

Almost all the produce is imported from Holland in wintertime, although in summer, British Columbia-grown produce arrives. Big bags of herbs ("Don't break off the basil stems!' admonishes a sign) are in a cooler to one side, but are often waning and dried. A clutch of costly fresh mushrooms—hedgehog, chanterelles, shiitake, portobello, oyster, porcini—crowd the herbs for company. Beyond the Italian asparagus and pepper pickles, there are jars of French and Canadian preserves and jellies—white cherries, ginger jelly, late-vintage wine jelly—all the things you didn't quite have time to put up yourself! When all else fails, just book a seat at the counter and sit down while the staff feed you some very good food.

- *House Specialties*: HMRs, meats, deli, cheeses, Italian dry goods.
- *Also Available*: **Mountain Mercato Specialty Food Market.**

www.mercatogourmet.com

Mueller's Delicatessen Bakery & Imports Ltd.

Established: 1987 • Owner: Eva & Harry Mueller
8409 Elbow Drive SW (Haysboro Centre)
Phone: 244•0570
Monday–Friday 9:00 am–6:00 pm, Saturday 8:30 am–5:30 pm
V, MC, AE, Debit, $

EVA Mueller makes the finest Florentine cookies in the city, with caramelized almond edges that contrast with their dark chocolate coating. Her sweets are all house-made classics from another continent: apple, plum or sweet cheese *kuchen* or cake, streusel-topped strawberry and rhubarb *kuchen*, strudel of fresh apple, poppyseed, walnut, or hazelnut. Her weekends-only veal loaf in a kaiser bun from **Günther's Fine Baking Ltd.** is substantial and yummy. Eva's sausages and cold cuts are made elsewhere, but everything else in the refrigerated case is made by her hands: *roschti,* fat and perfectly accented with onion; immaculate quiches; crumb-coated schnitzel.

Shelves hold Eva's own jams, spicy German ketchup, sauerkraut, pickles, egg noodles, cookies, chocolate, and crackers, and a wide assortment of mackerel, herring, kippers, and sardines. On a busy Saturday, a long-time fan brought Eva a clutch of flowers from his garden. That is customer loyalty.

• *House Specialties*: Veal loaf, florentines, strudel, schnitzel, *kuchen, roschti.*

NORTHWEST

British Pantry

Established: 1997 • Owner: Hamida Rashid
125–4820 Northland Drive NW (Northland Plaza)
Phone: 220•1406
Monday–Wednesday 10:00 am–6:00 pm, Thursday 10:00 am–8:00 pm
Friday & Saturday 10:00 am–6:00 pm, Sunday noon–5:00 pm
V, MC, Debit, $

THIS bastion of Empire has been a steadfast outpost for over a decade. Owner Hamida Rashid arrived in Calgary from the UK in 1992; when she missed her homeland's foodstuffs too intolerably, she decided to do something about it, and founded the company. Look for packaged goods, especially very good loose tea from Taylors of Harrogate. Sweet teeth will recognize British-made candies and chocolates, plus biscuits and seasonings. Shelves are rounded out with giftware and magazines. In the fridges, Calgary-made meatpies from **MacEwan's Meats** have the sensibility and stamp of the British Isles.

• *House Specialties*: Loose Taylors of Harrogate teas, British-made candies and chocolates, meatpies, biscuits.

www.britishpantrycanada.com

Farmers' Markets

SOME ENVIRONMENTS ARE MORE LIKELY than others to promote growth. For a small food business, the best glasshouse is often the farmers' market. At the market, a small business has willing and interested customers walking within metres of the stall, with mouths, curiosity, and wallets wide open. A 2004 study co-authored by the Alberta government's Ag-Entrepreneurship division showed that 59 percent of Albertans make at least one annual purchase at a farmers' market, to an annual (2004) value of $232 million. With 24 percent growth projected, that means many dollars, carrots, beets, sausages, and cheeses will change hands. Everyone wins: shoppers depart with full baskets and hands, vendors head home with empty baskets and full wallets. It is an ideal synergy. Farmers' markets are clearly incubators for positive growth!

But markets are not just about business. Farmers' markets feed us in more ways than one. They are social hubs and meeting places, filling souls, plates, menus and hours with love and connection along with the beets and cheeses. We have our best conversations over food. Stroll a market for audible, tangible evidence.

The market scene in and around Calgary is diverse and well established. Each market has its own personality, and its own cast of vendors, although many vendors appear at more than one market over the course of each week, and some are seasonal, appearing only as their produce and the weather dictate.

Support the local cash economy. Visit several markets to find the mix of close-to-home goods and growers that meets your needs.

Note: An asterisk (*) denotes Alberta government approved farmers' markets that comply with the 80:20 percent requirement of "make it, bake it, or grow it." Watch for the "Sunnygirl" logo that marks more than 100 Alberta approved markets in the province. Consult the Bow Valley and Beyond, Points North, East, South, and West for additional listings of Farmers' Markets.

www.albertamarkets.com • www.agric.gov.ab.ca

SOUTHEAST

Blackfoot Farmers' Market

Established: 1976 • Contact: Maxine Pelrine
5600–11 Street SE
Phone: 243•0065
July–October: Friday & Saturday 10:00 am–5:00 pm, Sunday 10:00 am–4:00 pm
$ only

BLACKFOOT Farmers' Market, which began in 1976, is now under the management of Maxine Pelrine, a former vendor. Longstanding regular vendors include SK Gardens from Vauxhall and a pair of Hutterite colonies.

Newcomers are Benchland Orchards' Okanagan-grown, certified-organic fruit and vegetables. The second row of this outdoor market's booths now houses swap meet vendors, and the petting zoo welcomes children of all ages.
www.blackfootfarmersmarket.com

Crossroads Market

Established: 2000 • Market Manager: Matthew McDonald
1235–26 Avenue SE (Blackfoot Trail and Ogden Road SE)
Phone: 291•5208
Outdoor Fresh Food Vendors
July–September: Friday–Sunday 9:00 am–5:00 pm
Indoor Flea Market & Farmers' Market
Year Round: Friday–Sunday 9:00 am–5:00 pm
$ only

ESTABLISHED in 1987 in Fire Park at the intersection of 16 Avenue and Barlow Trail NE, Crossroads Market moved to its present Ogden location in 2000. Shoppers have a wealth of choices—seasonal sales from farmers alongside other facilities, including an art gallery, indoor retail shops that are open year-round, and a flea market. Rows of Ray Henry's honeys from around the world line the entrance to the market proper. **Chongo's Produce Market** sells truckloads of prime British Columbia fruit in the summer and diverse international produce all year, from pomegranates to passionfruit. Bill and Joan Tough of **Say Cheese Fromagerie** are knowledgeable and approachable, their bustling central kiosk spills across the aisle, where Bill's bargains are stacked beside a diverse collection of oils and condiments. Down the hall is **Regina's Fine Meats**, where Regina Marr-Fortier sells fine German-style smoked meats. This busy year-round market sees 10,000 visitors per day at the peak of the summer season, when outdoor vendors offer seasonal fruit and vegetables in a labyrinth of canopied stalls. An increasing number of vendors take payments by debit and credit card.
www.crossroadsmarket.ca

Green Market*

Established: 2006 • Manager: Bridget Lacey
228–8 Avenue SE (Olympic Plaza)
Phone: 618•7591
June–September: Thursday 11:00 am–7:00 pm
$ only

GREEN Market 17 began as a grassroots initiative, and has now relocated twice—from its inaugural spot in Connaught Park and more recently from Tompkins Park—to settle in the Olympic Plaza for the coming summer of 2008. Market manager Bridget Lacey and grower Kristian Vester of **Blue Mountain Biodynamic Farms** hope to see it grow from its current 20 vendors to a maximum of 40. Criteria for vendors include local and bio-regional production including the British Columbia "food shed," sustainable practices, and fair trade for imports. Look for produce, but food is outnumbered by clothing and crafts—including biodegradable bird houses made from paper.

South Fish Creek Recreation Association Farmers' Market
Established: 2003 • Contact: Variable
South Arena Lot, 333 Shawville Boulevard SE (South Fish Creek Complex)
Phone: 201•8652
June–September: Friday 3:00 pm–7:00 pm
$ only

ON the Southside, this fledgling market is small, with about 16 vendors, offering a viable alternative to urban residents who are unable to drive all the way to Millarville. An increasing number of vendors take payment by debit and credit card.

www.sfcra.ca

SOUTHWEST

Calgary Farmers' Market*
Established: 2004 • Market Manager: Darrell Komick
H6, 4421 Quesnay Wood Drive SW (former CFB Currie Barracks)
Phone: 244•4548
Friday & Saturday 9:00 am–5:00 pm, Sunday 9:00 am–4:00 pm
Debit, $ (ATM on site)

THE Calgary Farmers' Market is open year-round, and has become the city's most visible market. It is housed in an old hangar on the former CFB Currie Barracks in the heart of Garrison Woods. Manager Darrell Komick oversees close to 100 vendors in this thriving year-round market. "Organic Row" is home to organic goods—**Lund's Organic Produce** has great carrots, beets and lettuces, **Sunworks** organic meat, poultry and eggs, **Blush Lane**, features their own orchard fruits and the goods of other local growers like **Hotchkiss Herbs & Produce**, there's organic milk, yoghurt, butter and heavy cream from Alberta's first organic dairy **Vital Green Farms**, and **Hoven Farms'** beef. **The Cookbook Company Cooks** has a small kiosk here too.

On the building's other side, find Jackson's Deli, **Old Country Sausage Shop**, Stock & Sauce Co., **Daily Bagel**, **Grazin' Acres**, **Francesco's Italian Food Store & Deli**, **Simple Simon's Pies** and **Pearson's Berry Farm & Gordo's Foods**.

There are stellar bakers to visit as well—Debbie Mandelbaum at **Tutti Frutti**, **Rustic Sourdough Bakery**, and the wizards at **A Ladybug Belgian Pâtisserie**.

Produce from British Columbia and Alberta is available at *The Cherry Pit*, in season at *Habina's Harvest*, and *Innisfail Growers* (**Edgar Farms** and **The Jungle**) vegetables and meats, and **Walker's Own**, which also grows fruit at their Okanagan orchard. Sip stellar coffee from **Phil & Sebastian**, buy award-winning Gouda from **Sylvan Star Cheese Farm**, nurture Terra Farms' beautiful potted herbs, or try **Valta Bison's** Peace Country meats.

Bagels for breakfast, sausage and cheese for supper—it takes more than one visit to graze your way from one end of the hangar to the other, and then you can buy plants, books, jewellery, garden furniture, and lunch to take home. An increasing number of vendors take payment by debit as well as credit card, and there are several ATMs onsite.

www.calgaryfarmersmarket.ca

NORTHWEST

Bearspaw Farmers' Market*

Established: 1991 • Manager: Gerry Kerran
Nagway Road off Highway 1A, (Bearspaw Lions Grounds)
Phone: 239•0201
June–September: Sunday 11:00 am–3:00 pm
$ only

AT the northwest corner of town, not quite in the city but close enough to spit, Bearspaw Farmers' Market offers a pancake breakfast on Sunday mornings at Lions Hall, with 100 vendors to visit afterwards. Three Sisters Pies is here, with handcrafted certified-organic fresh fruit pies. Produce from *Innisfail Growers* is regularly reliable, and Oliver-based orchardist Alvin Souto returns annually, like taxes, but his British Columbia fruits are sweeter than the federal government's tax collectors.

www.bearspawlions.com

Tips for Farmers' Market Shopping

- Take a cooler and ice packs.
- Take the kids. Many markets have kid-friendly activities, and this is an ideal environment, second only to visiting farms, for kids to learn about the origins of their breakfast milk and cereal.
- Take shopping bags.
- Take cash; many markets are $ only!
- Take your time. Choose a time of day that suits you.
- Take an open mind: buy what is in season, buy heirloom varieties you are unfamiliar with, buy a new ingredient, buy local.
- Take your conversational skills and curiosity. Ask vendors for details and provenance; they very likely made, baked, or grew it.

Grassroots Northland Farmers' Market*

Established: 1992 • Manager: Val Laferrière
Southeast Lot, 5111 Northland Drive NW (Northland Village Mall)
Phone: 289•7629
June–September: Tuesday 3:30 pm–7:00 pm
$ only

ON the Northside, Grassroots Northland Farmers' Market has moved to the southeast parking lot of the Northland Village mall. Grassroots began in 1992 when Grassroots Northwest, a community-minded organization that initiated recycling in the Northwest, observed the absence of a grocery store in the mall. "Near, nude, and natural" is the market's slogan. In 2007, the market's parent organization was awarded the Alberta Emerald Foundation award in the community category. Hard to miss at Grassroots is the big reefer truck parked against the east fence. The table in front is piled high with dark burgundy Van cherries from the Okanagan, trucked in by grower Gary Koenig, of Penticton's Garden of Eatin' Produce, a stalwart vendor since the market's beginnings. Buy bison from the hills west of Olds, sold by Peter and Judy Haase of **Buffalo Horn Ranch**, who also make an appearance at several other local markets. Sandi Pinto, formerly a hat maker, observed the absence of freshly baked breads several years ago, stepped into the oven trade, and now produces baked goods under her own My Bread label, at a handful of markets across the city.

Hillhurst–Sunnyside Farmers' Market*

Established: pre-1992 • Coordinator: Paula Barrington
North Lot, 1320–5 Avenue NW
Phone: 283•0554, ext. 247
June–October: Wednesday 3:30 pm–8:00 pm
$ only

IN the inner city on the Northside, the north parking lot of the Hillhurst-Sunnyside Community Association hosts a midweek market with up to 30 vendors. Look for Alberta-grown organic strawberries at the **Blush Lane** organics booth. Tim Petros, son of restaurateur Nick Petros, has a solid following for his yummy "From the Heart" frozen pizza, available here, and at other markets. It cooks as well on the backyard grill as in the oven, and is available in multi-grain, whole wheat or white crust. A new vendor in the city is Peak Perfection, an English-built ice cream truck. What is summer without soft ice cream cones and a chocolate wafer stick?

Farmgate Sales

EACH YEAR, I sift through maps, lists, and websites, drive dusty back roads and ride rock-hard highways, visiting good local producers and growers who offer farmgate sales. Each year, the magic vine that connects good eaters to good growers adds another tendril or two, via phone calls and enthusiastic e-mails, telling me about this or that little farm, about this beef or bison rancher or honey harvester. The thrill in finding great growers, especially sustainability-minded food producers, is almost as great as walking the fields and crouching over berry patches in the high prairie sunlight. We all benefit from supporting local food producers, and a trip to the farm gives urban residents an opportunity to experience the very literal grounding nature of walking a farm.

Please remember that these are family businesses and call ahead to confirm both produce and humans are available. Like most urban families, farm families seek a balance between family life and business commitments, while visibly supporting top-quality food, small-scale agriculture, and a thriving sense of community.

When you visit, take a cooler, and take cash: many of these farms are not equipped for credit or debit cards. Take the kids, but leave the family pets at home.

In addition to these farmgate family businesses located very close to Calgary, many more are presented in our section called The Bow Valley and Beyond, Points North, East, South and West. Check the listings for a full complement of businesses offering farmgate sales.

In addition, check the list of Local Producers, of which Farmgate Sales are a de-facto sub-set. That is, farmgate vendors are also local producers. The local producers listed as such do not receive visitors at the farmgate, choosing instead to make their produce and goods available at local farmers' markets and other retail outlets. Please respect their privacy in this case.

The other large detail that requires observance is that of biosecurity. At its simplest, this means closing gates to keep animals from straying, but it can also refer to what my Yorkshire-born business partner, Jeremy, calls "wellie-washing." If a farm host asks you to dip your boots—or the tires on your vehicle—in a disinfectant cleaning solution, it is to prevent the transmission of disease from one farm to the next. Some farmers suggest visiting only one farm per day. Others suggest not visiting multiple poultry or pig farms within three days of each other. They all agree that working farms are not petting zoos. Unless you have permission to do otherwise, it is better to play safe and keep your children's hands off the livestock.

13 Reasons to Buy Direct from the Farmer

- Local, fresh food tastes best.
- Buying locally keeps local farmers on the farm. Dollars spent locally stay in the neighbourhood, going straight into the grower's jeans, without a cut to middlemen, distributors, brokers, warehousers or truckers.
- Local food doesn't collect Air Miles.
- Local food has visible provenance. Consumers are more concerned than ever before about where, and how, their food is raised.
- Local food reflects its place, or *terroir*. Heart, soul, food, place—it is all entwined. Eat your view.
- Local foods are often heritage varieties of plants and animals. Heritage species preserve genetic diversity even if they need to be picked ripe, are too fragile to ship long distances, or don't keep more than a few days at their peak. They taste real because they are often original varieties.
- Local farmers are likely to plant cover crops, so soil erosion and global warming can be held at bay. Many small farms also support wetlands, or bird sanctuaries, harbouring indigenous species of wildlife, insects, and birds.
- Buying locally preserves farmland in an era when our cities are annexing our agricultural land.
- Local food in season is freshly harvested, so it is more nutritious, and it saves on our medical bills by nourishing us.
- Farmland is taxed at a lower rate than urban land, so supporting local growers helps keep our taxes down.
- Buying locally gives us the opportunity to practice expressing our gratitude. Each time I look into the eyes of the people who grew our food and say "Thank you," I remember that it was not my labour that planted, or nurtured, or harvested what I am putting into my shopping bag, or my child's mouth. I am grateful to be nourished.
- Buying locally allows us to educate our children about where their sustenance truly originates.
- Buying locally restores the face to food and food production, and removes the "commodity" aspect that has poisoned the well.

SOUTHEAST

Bee Prepared Honey Farms

Established: 1972 • Owners: Peter & Louise Beermann
Mailing Address: 233244 Range Road 282, Rocky View, Alberta T1X 0H2
Phone: 279•9283
Hours by Appointment
Cheque, $

PETER Beermann came to Canada in 1957 to dodge the bullets of the
Hungarian revolution. Now retired, he has been tending bees for over
40 years, with 250 hives, each occupied by 65,000 hard-working bees.
Beermann is concerned about the "endangered species" classification that
hangs over bees and their keepers. Bees, hugely important for crop pollination,
are at risk from crop spraying that doesn't differentiate between "good" and
"bad" insects.

- *Directions*: Drive east on Glenmore Trail SE. East of the city limits at 84
  Street SE (or Shepard Road), Glenmore Trail becomes Highway 560.
  Continue east for 6.4 kilometres.
- *House Specialties*: Honey and all things to do with bees and their output—
  clover-alfalfa honey, honey-sweetened sour cherry, Nanking cherry, plum,
  and berry jams, beeswax candles, honey soaps, pollen.
- *Also Available*: **Northlands Grassroots Farmers' Market** and **Strathmore
  Farmers' Market.**

Premium Organic Farms Inc.

Established 1998 • Owners: Paul Schneider & Sheila Buckley
Mailing Address: 230183 Range Road 284, Rocky View, Alberta T1X 0G9
Phone: 235•6000
Hours by Appointment
$ only

PAUL Schneider and Sheila Buckley's farm is located southeast of Calgary.
They sell free-range vacuum-packed and frozen chickens, and organically
certified beef by the side, available frozen and ordered in advance for custom
cutting. They also grow potatoes in several varieties, and a variety of
strawberries, raspberries, carrots, and mixed vegetables, as Mother Nature
allows. They have been certified organic for more than 5 years.

- *Directions*: Drive east of the city limits on Highway 22X for 3.2 kilometres
  past 88 Street SE. North 1.6 kilometres on Range Road 285. West 0.2
  kilometres on Township Road 230. North 1 kilometres on Range Road
  284. The driveway is on the west side.
- *House Specialties*: Certified organic beef, chicken, vegetables, berries.

Other Sources of Farmgate Information

- Alberta Farm Fresh Producers Association is a valuable source of information for farms and market gardens, complete with driving directions. Go to <www. albertafarmfresh.com>, or telephone, toll-free (800) 661•2642.
- Travel Alberta and Agriculture Tourism's new website <www. chomparoundalberta.com>, is a culinary guide for travellers.
- Dine Alberta's website <www.dinealberta.ca>, provides a listing of Alberta growers and restaurants which use Alberta-raised ingredients as part of their menus on a monthly, seasonal, or continuous basis, and who participates in the annual Dine Alberta local food program.
- The Fruit Growers Society of Alberta maintains an up-to-date website of its members at <www.albertafruit.com>.
- *Sylvan Lake Farmgate Guide* at <www.sylvanlakefarmgateguide. com>, includes 31 farm-related locations and events.
- Regional exploration of agriculture, from accommodations to growers and lifestyle, is possible via self-guided tours based on Country Treasures located "off the corridor" between Calgary and Red Deer. Look online at <www.sunmaze.ca/countrytreasures. htm> for a list of participants.
- Award-winning writer Jennifer Cockrall-King is co-publisher of *The Edible Prairie Journal*, available by subscription, quarterly on paper or online. For further details, check out her websites at <www.food girl.ca> and <www.edibleprairie.ca>.

Fishmongers

NOT MANY FOODS ARE CONVERSATIONAL DYNAMITE. Fish is! Shopping for fish can stimulate a variety of discussions—at the family table or while shopping—as consumers seek answers to questions, and wrestle with complex issues—both of an ethical and philosophical nature—never mind the actual expense. It is a both a broad and deep sea swimming with complicated issues, and no easy answers to hook. Wild? Farmed? Neither? Within any family, opinions and political beliefs about fish and shellfish vary, from the picky (fish is hard to cook, cooking fish indoors smells up the house, fish has bones) to the practical (fish is costly), and the political (some wild fish stocks are threatened by over-fishing, some farmed fish and environs are polluted). Many consumers have simply given up eating fish altogether, and food professionals—fish retailers and chefs alike—struggle with the issues of supply, demand, and making a living from the living seas.

When you go shopping for fish, ask questions beyond "What's freshest today?" There are myriad issues consumers can consider, beginning with the pros and cons of wild versus farmed: over-fishing, *by-catch*, habitat damage, *aquaculture*, mercury and PCB contamination, the escape of farmed fish into the wild—with associated risks of disease transference or genetic weakening of wild stocks, and methods of fishing—bottom-dragging versus line-catching, just for starters.

Provenance is as important for fish as it is for any other food. Canada's Seafood Guide, *SeaChoice*, produces a list, available in wallet-size and online, of what is safe to eat and what is not: peruse the "Don't Eat" red list, and the green "Guilt-free" category for guidance on which species are at risk and which are secure at present. The listings change as stocks become endangered or as numbers recover. Ask for local, sustainably-raised alternatives instead of at-risk species of fish. For more information on fishy issues, look online at:

- <www.seachoice.org> is where you will find Canada's seafood guide *SeaChoice* from the Sustainable Seafood Canada coalition.
- <www.oceansalive.org> is one of several initiatives of the US-based Environmental Defense Network.
- <www.seafoodchoices.com> is the website for the international (USA, UK, and France) Seafood Choices Alliance.
- <http://seafood.audubon.org/> is where you will find the National Audubon Society's *Seafood Lover's Guide* in pdf format.
- <www.montereybayaquarium.org/cr/seafoodwatch.asp> is where you will find details of the Seafood Watch program of the California-based Monterey Bay Aquarium Foundation.

Shopping Tips for Fish

BUY fish where it is not wrapped in plastic and placed on Styrofoam trays. Buy from a fish specialist, one who can answer your questions, and preferably someone with whom you can cultivate a long-term relationship.

The fresher the better. Live tanks rule! However, fish that is quick-frozen at sea soon after it was caught is far better than "fresh" fish that is heading towards putrefaction after too many miles in transit. The reality is that we live inland, not on a coastline.

A good fishmonger will dispatch and clean your living fish—from tilapia to lobster or crab. If you order a whole fish, your supplier will scale it for you, or cut it into steaks or fillets, and give you sound ideas on how to cook the goods. The good ones might pull the pin bones too. Ask! Most fish is now sold as portions instead of whole, so ask if you need fish *frames* for stock-making. Following are some of the finer fish markets in the city. While they may not necessarily be able to help you determine your own "fish-based" position, when you have made up your mind, they can surely help you get the goods.

SOUTHEAST

Atlantic Pacific Fish Market & Bakery

Established: 1990 • Owners: Manuel & Palmina Albano
201, 4909–17 Avenue SE (Little Saigon Town Square)
Phone: 235•5313
Monday–Friday 9:00 am–6:00 pm, Saturday 9:00 am–5:00 pm
Debit, Cheque, $

MANUEL and Palmina Albano bring in Portuguese specialties, including dried salt cod. The fish is all frozen: tuna, whiting, crab legs, sardines, snapper, halibut, horse mackerel, and bream.

Both are bakers, and produce good workman-like versions of Portuguese breads. Look for sweet bread on Tuesdays, and cornbread on Fridays and Saturdays.

Chorizo sausages, St. George cheeses and Catholic statues share shelf space, although, as Manuel jokes, you don't buy statues every day like you do food. Shop like the regulars from Angola—a former Portuguese colony—and the Portuguese ex-pats. Buy tuna fish—packed in olive oil—from the Azores, frozen salt cod, ceramic Portuguese *assadeiras* for oven-cooking, and ceramic chestnut roasters for fire-roasting chestnuts.

- *House Specialties*: Portuguese fish, especially salt cod, house-made cornbread, *chorizo* and cheeses.

Eastern Lake

Established: 2003 • Manager: Ricky Chung
Basement, 114–3 Avenue SE
Phone: 263•6663
Monday–Sunday 10:30 am–7:00 pm
Debit, $

L IVE action is the only game in town in this lower-level shop. Tanks are filled with local tilapia, buffalo fish, crabs, lobsters, clams, mussels, and oysters. The other option is the freezer, filled with exotic fish from far-away seas. Vietnamese leather jackets, China yellow croakers, Australian *burramundi*, golden threadfin bream, *dace* fish, and grey mullet are filleted and frozen, along with fish heads and New Zealand green-shell mussels.
• *House Specialties*: Tanks of live lobster, crab, tilapia, clams, and mussels.

North Sea Fish Market

Established: 2002 • Manager: Mark Pulfer
10816 Macleod Trail South (Willow Park Village)
Phone: 225•3460
Monday–Wednesday, Friday & Saturday 10:00 am–6:00 pm
Thursday 10:00 am–8:00 pm, Sunday noon–4:00 pm
V, MC, Debit, $

N ORTH Sea wholesale fish co-owners, Brent Muir, Doug Sutherland and Ron Faithful, opened this Southside retail shop. Much of the business is high-end home meal replacements (HMRs) in two styles. Shoppers on the rapid current can choose from rarely seen classics like lobster thermidor, coquilles St. Jacques, bisque, seafood lasagna in tomato and cream sauce. Or they can opt for simpler, ready-when-you-are meals and everyday dishes like seafood quiche, Boston and Manhattan chowder, crab cakes, and macaroni with lobster and cheddar cheese.

The store stocks frozen wild sockeye salmon, shucked oysters—from Fanny Bay, Quebec, or PEI—and live lobster, clams, and mussels. Fresh fish include ahi tuna, sea bass, snapper, cod, sole, haddock, pickerel, blue marlin or swordfish on weekends, skate wing on occasion, halibut and wild salmon in season, and Atlantic farmed salmon year-round.

Shelves hold oils and vinegars, and **Brassica Mustards**. Fresh meats are in the fridge: AAA Black Angus steaks, striploin and rib-eye, pork chops, free-range whole chicken and chicken breasts, **Valbella Meats/Valbella Deli & Café** bacons, sausages, and *pâtés*.
• *House Specialties*: Special-event and homestyle HMRs, fresh and frozen fish, fresh meats and charcuterie, condiments.
• *Also Available*: **Calgary Farmers' Market**.

SOUTHWEST

Boyd's Lobster Shop

Established: 1983 • Owners: Paul & Gerard Cormier
1515D–14 Street SW
Phone: 245•6300
Monday–Saturday 9:00 am–7:00 pm, Sunday 11:00 am–6:00 pm
V, MC, Debit, $

BROTHERS Paul and Gerard Cormier bought Boyd's from Nova Scotian native and founder Blaise Boyd in December 2001. This well-regarded shop brings in fish five or six times per week, selling fresh fish and shellfish. Look for halibut, scallops, clams, shrimp and prawns, mussels, oysters, snapper, cod, swordfish and tuna along with salmon: both farmed Atlantic and wild sockeye in season (June to August), as well as spring salmon (from March through June.) Tanks hold lobsters, Dungeness crabs, clams and mussels. Freezers contain squid tubes (cleaned), scallops, roughy, haddock, cod loins, Cuban lobster tails, scampi and langoustines, king and snow crab legs, crab meat, and smoked salmon. Several kinds of fish roe—salmon, Spanish mullet, and herring—are on hand, and high-end caviar—beluga, sevruga, or osetra—can be ordered on request.
• *House Specialties*: Salmon, halibut, shrimp, scallops—fresh and frozen.

NORTHWEST

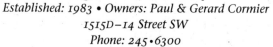

Billingsgate Fresh Fish Specialists

Established: 1907 • Manager: Brian Falwell
2B, 1941 Uxbridge Drive NW (Stadium Shopping Plaza)
Phone: 269•3474
Monday–Wednesday 9:00 am–6:00 pm, Thursday & Friday 9:00 am–8:00 pm
Saturday 9:00 am–6:00 pm, Sunday 11:00 am–5:00 pm
V, MC, Debit, Cheque, $

BILLINGSGATE was founded in 1907. Manager Brian Falwell is the fourth generation to be involved in the family business. In its Northside location, the business has narrowed its focus to retail and a café. This is well down from what Falwell describes as the "overstretched" phase, when more than 125 employees and a runaway wholesale side nearly ate him. His shop specializes in fresh and the hard-to-find, stocking alligator, *burramundi*, striped and European bass, *lutefisk*, as well as standards like tuna and swordfish. Wild sockeye salmon is fresh in season, from June to August. Spring salmon is fresh from March to June, and frozen the rest of the year. Farmed Atlantic salmon can be purchased year-round. Look for clams and mussels from both coasts, scallops in the shell, and a changing array of East Coast oysters (often PEI Malpeque or Village Bay from New Brunswick). There is a lobster and Dungeness crab tank, and Alaskan crab legs in the freezer, along with scampi

Tips for Fresh Fish Success

When buying whole fish:

- Assess the look of the eyes; they should be bright and smooth, not dull, faded, or sunken.
- Scales should be firmly attached, and the fish's surface should be shiny, not slimy.
- Gills should be bright pink or red.
- Fish flesh should be firm.
- Fresh fish should smell sweetly and vaguely of the sea, not fishy or ammoniated; if it stinks, return it promptly and express your grave disappointment!
- Cut fish should be the same colour as whole fish, not faded or dull.
- Textures should be firm, without dry patches.
- *Mollusks* should be tightly closed. *Crustaceans* should be moving.

Ask for an ice pack when transporting fish home, especially on warm days, and refrigerate the fish immediately when you get home. Store mollusks in a colander over a bowl, covering the shellfish with a damp cloth and ice on top. Only cook the ones that are tightly closed. Cook fish the same day you buy it.

and Cuban lobster. An in-house smoker does hot-smoking, cold-smoking, and custom smoking. Soup cooks can acquire frozen fish stock, or heads and *frames* to make their own *fumet*. Lunchtime fish and chips are cooked fresh to order.
- *House Specialties*: Fresh fish, café.
- *Also Available*: 7331-104 Street, Edmonton.
www.billingsgate.com

King's Seafood Distributors (inside Lambda Market)
Established: 1977 • Contact: Francis Wan
1423 Centre A Street NW
Phone: 277•0889
Sunday–Thursday 10:00 am–6:00 pm, Friday & Saturday 10:00 am–7:00 pm
$ only

THE tanks here hold fish, finned (rock cod, buffalo, tilapia) and in shells. I shop here for Dungeness crab and immaculately fresh *mollusks*.
- *House Specialties*: Live fish—rock cod, buffalo fish, tilapia, clams and oysters in the shell, Dungeness crab and lobster—all in the tanks.

Gems

SOME BUSINESSES ARE CLEAR STANDOUTS, occupying unique niches and growing into the role of community leader. Such businesses may be multi-faceted and impossible to classify, so that even multiple cross-referencing complicates things, with its implications of primary and secondary strengths. Alternatively, a business could be so single-mindedly focused that it blows all others in the field out of the water. Either way, leaders deserve recognition and acknowledgement as such.

In this and all successive editions of *Shop talk*, an extended profile of one or more outstanding, food-industry-related retail businesses or producers will be features in Gems.

In this inaugural edition: **The Cookbook Company Cooks!**

SOUTHWEST

The Cookbook Company Cooks
Established 1983 • Owner: Gail Norton
722–11 Avenue SW (Main Store)
Phone: 265•6066 (Store) or 265•8192 (Catering & Private Classes)
Monday–Friday 10:00 am–8:00 pm, Saturday 10:00 am–5:30 pm
Sunday noon–5:00 pm
V, MC, Debit, $

GAIL Norton's The Cookbook Company Cooks shares walls, bricks and mortar with **Brûlée Pâtisserie**, a restaurant, an art gallery, and **Metrovino** in a synergistic food emporium.

The Cookbook Company Cooks began with 350 book titles. More than two decades later, it stocks in excess of 2,000 titles, and has grown into its current stature as the heartbeat of Calgary's culinary community. Not just a bookstore anymore, The Cookbook Company Cooks houses specialty pantry items, a cheese counter, hand tools, ceramics, kitchenwares, knives, a cooking school, a catering company, and a travelling school that offers classes in Europe. Norton is also the founder of Calgary's *City Palate*, the bimonthly all-food-and-only-food publication. She has created a hub for food professionals and home cooks alike, through her tireless and genuinely modest "big picture" vision of contemporary cuisine in Calgary.

This cooking school is the most extensive in the city, offering two terms of scheduled cooking classes each year and personalized corporate and private classes in a panoramic range—from knife skills to Thai and Vietnamese specialties, and hands-on workshops. Dinners and classes are led by Calgary's leading chefs and educators, with frequent appearances by visiting chefs, authors, television celebrities, and food gurus from across North America.

Kids learn too, in hands-on classes held each term, and at summer camps. The school has two kitchens: a spacious and bright main floor kitchen opened in January 2007, and a basement kitchen which has its fans in those who appreciate its intimate European subterranean style. Hands-on classes in Europe are offered twice-yearly in Languedoc, France and in Tuscany, Italy.

The cheese counter stocks a varying collection, but tilts to St. Agur and Papillon Roquefort, *lait cru* Morbier, a flexible supply of Spanish *quesos*, outstanding Quèbecois goat's milk cheddar, **Sylvan Star Cheese Farm's** top-line Gouda and **Fairwinds Farm** *chèvre* from Fort Macleod. Some great crackers are cheesemates, including Lesley Stowe's Raincoast Crisps and Prince Phillips' Duchy collection.

This store has a mind-boggling collection of condiments to choose from. Spanish, French, Californian, and Italian olive oils, a wealth of salts, herbs and spices, vinegars and *verjus*, preserves and condiments, and more mustards than any cook ever needs. Some are local lines, including **Highwood Crossing Farm's** cold-pressed canola oil and **Brassica Mustards**. Italian, Middle Eastern, pan-Asian and Spanish ingredients, including awesome Marcona almonds and smoked paprika, are shelved geographically. Choose handmade artisanal pasta, *bomba* rice, or *vialone nano, carnaroli* or *arborio* for risotto, a treasury of heirloom pulses, and good coffee from **Big Mountain Coffee Roasters**.

Indulge in a staggering selection of expensive chocolate, some so good we want to weep: Cluisel, Schokinag—family-made artisan chocolate with a 80-year history in southern Germany, Scharffen Berger—made in the USA, a wonderful array of Valrhona, infused Dolfin from Belgium, or Coppeneur—a standout German brand.

In the freezer: ducks—leg, breast, confit and foie gras lobes. Find local specialties too: **Cunningham's Scotch Cold Smoking** smoked fish, a changing array of locally made sausages and cured **Valbella Meats/Valbella Deli & Café's** duck breasts, sausages, and pâtés, house-made confit, stocks and soups. Fine fresh herbs are the prime reason this shop has a produce cooler, stocked with seasonal local goods like **Gull Valley Greenhouse** tomatoes.

Find a wealth of silicone tools—spatulas, pastry brushes, whisks, rolling pins, paper and baking sheet covers. The battery of hand tools that makes a kitchen efficient are here too. Look at rasps, graters, whisks in a gazillion shapes and sizes, plus nesting cookie cutters. Baskets and crocks hold beechwood French pins, large and little offset spatulas. Sturdy Le Creuset cast iron enameled pots, nesting mixing bowls and cute individual-portion ceramic casseroles are stacked by boxes of AllClad pots and pans. French cotton table linens are draped across from cutting-edge knives and sharpeners made by MAC, Chroma, Global and Kasumi.

Slow Food Calgary events and the annual *City Palate "Foodie Tootle"* are booked through The Cookbook Company Cooks. A decade old in 2008, the *Foodie Tootle* is a popular annual late-summer bus tour that takes urbanites to a changing roster of farms and local producers. Participants bring cash and a cooler, shopping at each farmgate, enjoying lunch en route. The day culminates with dinner at the final stop. It is all about local.

- *Also Available*: A smaller satellite version of the shop is tucked into the **Calgary Farmers' Market.**

www.cookbookcooks.com

Greengrocers

BUYING FRUIT AND VEGETABLES in Calgary during February and March can be a grim task. Produce on the shelf can be tired, too travelled, too limited, and far too expensive. While we love supporting local growers and their crunchy Alberta-grown carrots and rich beets, sometimes we need a bit of variety. That is when we compensate by shopping from the global village, eating food that is in season in another country or on another continent—arugula from California, peppers from Texas, or mangoes from Mexico. But we pay dearly for that privilege.

Yes, we can have salad and mangoes year-round. But they come at a steep price, with much of the real costs—to the planet, growers, and consumers—concealed. Travelling produce has no shelf life, having spent its youth on the road, and its nutritional value declines with each mile travelled. Those miles travelled cost us too—even if we do not recognise the dollars are coming directly out of our wallets—in infrastructure and fuel.

Support local markets and stores where there are people to help us find things, answer questions, address provenance, and keep the produce bins looking clean and uncluttered. Choose vegetables with verve, and fruits that don't flop. If produce is wilted and tired, it won't last long once you get it home, so always buy the best. My personal benchmark of a produce team's skill is to see how they treat fresh herbs: if herbs are wilted or worse, move on.

SOUTHEAST

Chongo's Produce Market

Established: 1987 • Owner: Jason Wiebe
1235–26 Avenue SE (Crossroads Market)
Phone: 921•4554
Thursday 1:00 pm–5:00 pm, Friday 8:00 am–6:00 pm
Saturday & Sunday 8:00 am–5:00 pm
V, MC, Debit, $

THE best way to sell food is by word of mouth—literally! Samples! Every variety of this popular spot's produce has a freshly sliced tub of samples waiting for appraisal. Taste the difference between Fuji, Gala, and Jonagold apples, then buy a 10-pound bag or go by the pound. Founders Rick Chong and Kim Hoang merged her fruit stand with his dad's produce store, the original Chongo's. New owner Jason Wiebe acquired Chongo's in 2007. The new business occupies 4,000 square feet, sells 40,000 pounds of cherries—my favourite food of all time—per week during the brief cherry season. Beyond cherries, look for a world of produce, from apples to *dragonfruit* and *lychees*.
• *House Specialties*: Fruit and vegetables.

Choosing Cherries

"Ask the birds, and children, how cherries and strawberries taste."
JOHANN VON GOETHE

THIS harbinger of summer—my favourite fruit—has a brief, glorious season. Look for the largest, but be ready to pay a premium for size. Some growers ship their prime cherries to Taiwan, where prestige-conscious consumers pay the equivalent of $12.50/pound for Grade A cherries the size of Ping-Pong balls.

Cherry stems should be attached, and should be green, not brown. The skins of fresh cherries should have a noticeable sheen. In white cherries like Rainiers (which are really yellow and light red), red skin flecks indicate high sugar content. Textures range from soft to ultra-firm, depending on the variety.

Supplies of sour, or pie cherries, such as Montmorencys and Morellos, are dwindling; they are fragile and need to be babied during picking, packing and shipping. Growers become impatient with the lower price they command too, and rip out their orchards to plant tougher new sweet cherry varieties of high-yield "spindle" styles of trees, as illustrated by newer plantings of cherry varieties from the Summerland Research Station, easily identified by names beginning with "S." The spindles grow a single upright bough, with little spreading, making it easier to plant more trees in a smaller space, and simplifying the picking process too. Sonata, Sweetheart, Sunburst and Staccata are all black or red cherries. Red Sonnets have a red exterior and white inner flesh. Sultan, is still in the experimental stage and some other experimental varieties, like Number 770, are not named until the testing phase is completed.

Popular and costly, Rainiers are white cherries, as are old-time Queen Annes. Other varieties worth looking for are Lapin, a new and highly popular black cherry, and Van, an older variety with a firm, crunchy texture, distinguishable by a flattened bottom and short stem.

Market Produce

Established 1982 • Owner: Bob Holladay (since 2007)
5315–17 Avenue SE
Phone: 273•6669
Monday–Wednesday 10:00 am–6:00 pm, Thursday–Saturday 9:30 am–6:00 pm
Sunday 9:30 am–5:30 pm
Debit, $

THIS market is a pleasant surprise, busy on a midweek midday, with faces of every possible colour perusing the produce. The shop is clean, and staff is constantly tidying all displays. Discretion is necessary: not all produce is prime, some pieces are definitely candidates for the bargain bin, so have a good boo before you buy. But there are great things to be found: a wide array of "hot stuff" includes *Scotch bonnets, jalapeños,* and Thai bird chilies. In the Caribbean vein, find *boniato,* yams, *cassava, jicama,* and okra. Look for fat satsumas, astounding deals on sweet bell peppers, Alberta tomatoes, beautiful mangoes and perfectly ripe fragrant Hami melons. Gorgeous little striped eggplant—perfect to paint as well as cook, date palms, *rapini* and *karela,* plus *methi* make this cook happy. Then peruse the Pink Lady apples, pomegranates, *plantains,* pomelos, papayas, Asian pears and persimmons—maybe the produce purveyor has a propensity for P's, perchance? No Q's (quinces) in evidence on any of my visits, but query, quickly.

A *Halal* meat counter—pay at the greengrocer's—is just through the curved arches. Goat, lamb, and chicken are offset by a few shelves filled with dry goods of Middle Eastern provenance—*tahini, baklava,* nuts. All are somehow balanced in my ever hungry belly by the Indian sweets in the freezer.

• *House Specialties*: Fresh produce.

www.marketproduce.ca

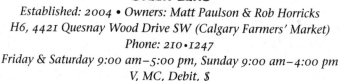

SOUTHWEST

Blush Lane

Established: 2004 • Owners: Matt Paulson & Rob Horricks
H6, 4421 Quesnay Wood Drive SW (Calgary Farmers' Market)
Phone: 210•1247
Friday & Saturday 9:00 am–5:00 pm, Sunday 9:00 am–4:00 pm
V, MC, Debit, $

THIS young produce business began as a strawberry project for Erin Hamilton and her husband Matt Paulson, daughter and son-in-law of organic veterans Ron and Sheila Hamilton of **Sunworks Farm**. But it quickly grew. The pair added a partner, Rob Horricks, with a background in organics and retail, then grew a garden...well, an orchard. Now the business has a stall at the **Calgary Farmers' Market**, selling organic produce, its own, and from other sources, local-first, including **Hotchkiss Herbs & Produce**. Not all is local, but when in season, it is, and can you ever taste it. In August 2007, I wept in the orchard as I ate Blush Lane's organic peaches, standing under the trees in the desert-like Similkameen Valley of southern British Columbia. This shop is owned by young people who know we make decisions with our taste buds, so they have samples to taste. Wrap your lips around plums, peaches, pears, or apples, then buy the variety you like best.

• *House Specialties*: Organic produce in season, house-grown as available, then sourced from local growers, then regional, and beyond.

• *Also Available*: **Grassroots Northland Farmers' Market, Bison Mountain Bistro & General Store**. In conjunction with **Sunworks Farm** and **A Ladybug Belgian Pâtisserie**, a new location will open at 10 Aspen Stone Boulevard SW in May 2008.

www.blushlane.com

Nutraceuticals or Functional Foods

FRESH food has always been intimately connected with wellness. Science's study of nutraceuticals, or functional foods (those foods containing phytonutrients, compounds from edible plants that are health-supportive), now supports what our grandmothers have told us for centuries: eat your fruit and vegetables, they are good for you! Known phytonutrients include beta carotene, anthocyanine, and antioxidants. Research is ongoing: studies in epidemiology have proven a correlation between antioxidants and a reduction in cancer.

Walker's Own

Established: 1981 • Owners: Gordon & Suzanne Nakonechny
H6, 4421 Quesnay Wood Drive SW (Calgary Farmers' Market)
Phone: 605•8555
Friday & Saturday 9:00 am–5:00 pm, Sunday 9:00 am–4:00 pm
V, MC, Debit, Cheque, $

THE Nakonechny family co-ops with Okanagan Harvest, an orchard owned by Greg and Chris Norton in Oliver, BC. A co-op is an old idea made new. Participating families share the risk, effort, cost, and profit, and each family can focus on its strengths. The grower can devote time and attention to the crop, and the retailer markets the goods. The south Okanagan farm is changing, to fit what the market is asking for in Calgary, but philosophically, it tilts towards integrated pest management (IPM). Gordon trucks all the fruits to Calgary—cherries, peaches, plums, apples in several types, including early Jersey Macs, Galas, and late-season Jonagolds. He also brings in vegetables from other growers, supplementing Norton's fruit as needed too.

- *House Specialties*: House apple juice, partly filtered, from about ten varieties of Okanagan apples, fruit from the co-op-owned orchards in the Okanagan, and vegetables.
- *Also Available*: **Grassroots Northland Farmers' Market, Bearspaw Farmers' Market** and several Edmonton markets.

Home Delivery

IN NOT SO LONG-AGO DECADES, milk and other foodstuffs were delivered door to door. Some businesses have returned to the old ways, bringing food directly to our homes, although they mostly use modern methods of online or telephone ordering. Online ordering can be an advantage, allowing customers to place orders at un-business-like hours, although it is an inflexible medium of communication. Delivery inevitably brings a human face to the transaction. Remember food is perishable, and needs a human being to handle it at some point. Be prepared for computer and human glitches, pay promptly, tip the delivery service—especially on cold or wet days—and make arrangements to keep things chilled and protected if it is too hot or cold for it to safely await your return home.

CITY WIDE

Farm Fresh Organics Home Delivery Ltd.
Established: 2000 • Owner: Darrel Graham
PO Box 40504, Highfield RPO, Calgary, Alberta T2G 5G8
Phone: 210•3700 • E-mail: service@freshorganics.ca
Deliveries: Northside–Wednesday, Southside–Thursday, Downtown–Friday
6:00 am–9:00 am, 3:00 pm–6:00 pm each day but subject to change
V, MC

HARMONY with nature is part of this business's mission statement, achieved by supporting local organic growers. I like this business's underlying philosophy because it allows growers to do what they do best, without disruption. With Farm Fresh Organics Home Delivery Ltd. doing the deliveries, farmers needn't acquire a marketing degree nor additional hours in their workday to compensate for time-intensive deliveries. The method is a weekly or bi-weekly delivery system. Clients choose from several options: the Family Fare Bin, (a changing selection of 14 to 16 fruits and vegetables, ideal for a family of four); the Bachelor Box (scaled down to fit a single appetite); Salad Bowl (vegetables only); and Fruit Basket (fruit only). Occasional deliveries of food baskets, bulk fruits, or organic groceries can be arranged for a modest delivery charge. Calgary is covered on three days depending on neighbourhood: Northside on Wednesday; Southside on Thursday; Downtown on Friday. Canmore (on Wednesday) and Edmonton (Thursday and Friday) are also served. Find order forms online, along with reasonable cancellation and substitution policies, with "anytime" cancellation.
- *House Specialties*: Home delivery of certified-organic local produce, groceries and dairy products.

www.freshorganics.ca

Small Potatoes Urban Delivery (SPUD)

Established: 2005 • General Manager: Kevin Burbank
Warehouse & Office: 3, 4709–14 Street NE
Phone: 615•3663
Calgary: Wednesday, Thursday & Friday noon–9:00 pm
V, MC, Debit (pre-authorized)

THIS British Columbia-born ethics-based delivery business merged in 2005 with Calgary-based Organic Express, which was founded by Rob Horricks, now a partner in **Blush Lane**. It has close ties with local organic growers, flagging locally raised products and posting kilometres travelled by each food from source to SPUD warehouse. SPUD provides organic produce and a range of groceries, but the service does not come cheaply. Choices include a weekly "Harvest Box," "Fruit Lovers Box," standing orders, and case lots. Minimum order is $35, and there are no delivery charges. Order online 1 to 2 days in advance. Deliveries to Banff are made on Friday, between 1:00–2:00 pm with pick-up at Weeds & Seeds, 211 Bear Street (Bison Courtyard). The future promises expanded service with deliveries to Okotoks, Bragg Creek, Drumheller, and Edmonton.

• *House Specialties*: Organic groceries.

www.spud.ca

SOUTH WEST

Spoon Fed Soup

Established: 2005 • Owner: Carmie Nearing
Studio 2, 5524–1A Street SW
Phone: 452•3977
Residential Deliveries: Sunday 9:00 am–4:00 pm
Downtown Deliveries: Monday 9:00 am–4:00 pm
Pick-up at the kitchen: Tuesday–Thursday 9:00 am–3:00 pm
V, MC, Cheque, $

CAPE Breton-born soup queen Carmie Nearing grew up on her family's chowders and stews, so it is hardly surprising she advocates better living through soup. She makes adventurous, tummy-warming, robust potfuls as a conscious way to slow down. She keeps it local, servicing a small corner of the world with doorstep delivery, keeping her footprint small by travelling only to inner-city neighbourhoods. Three weekly selections, mostly named for Carmie's family members (hint: Daisy and Jack are her kids), always include one vegetarian (the soup, not the relatives!) as well as carnivore and vegan options. Carmie says, "Global domination is not our objective," so she only makes 300 litres of soup each week. It sells out quickly, so order yours early, online. Sunday is delivery day, with a fallback of Monday, for delivery to offices. Be home or leave a cooler out, and pay by credit card. Add a deposit for the glass jars.

• *House Specialties*: Hearty house-made soups delivered weekly or picked up at the kitchen.

www.spoonfedsoup.com

Kitchenware

L IKE ANY HANDMADE SPECIALTY, cooking—the crafting of perfect Béarnaise, baking cookies, or slowly braising short ribs—is better accomplished with the right equipment. But finding job-specific tools can be a challenge. Some kitchenware stores specialize in electronics or tableware. Others carry mostly smallwares—the small, hand-held detailing tools that make the most of digital dexterity—and still others sell big appliances. Specialization is the name of the game, as exemplified by the number of stores that only carry knives and sharp-edged implements.

When looking for large appliances, remember that home kitchens are not the same as restaurants, despite the sleek restaurant kitchen look that many of us love. Professional stoves run at higher heat output, or British Thermal Units (BTU) than home insulation can withstand, and are built for "zero clearance," snugged up to stainless steel walls without any gaps. Most civic residential permit-granting departments, including Calgary's Building Regulations Division, will not allow them in home kitchens, so most professional range manufacturers have a home line to simulate the look of restaurant stoves. If the pro look is for you, examine the options closely, and ask for details about the ramifications of installing big-draw cubic-feet-per-minute (CFM) ventilation systems above your new range.

Not all restaurant supply businesses welcome individuals as customers. Those that do, included below, may employ variations of "cash and carry," with or without discounts that may or may not be negated by any requirement for home delivery. Ask!

Do not overlook garage sales or artistic relatives in your hunt for equipment. My favourite basket-style pot rack was located by my sharp-eyed son at a garage sale. Its replacement for the next house was re-created by a buddy who happens to be a mechanical engineer as well as an all-hands-handy farmer. (He likely learned how to weld in order to fix his cultivator. My gain!) Consider artists as potential creators of backsplashes—my metal-sculptor brother built and embossed my stainless steel backsplash. Alternatively, decorative ceramic tile backsplashes are not beyond the skill of a moderately handy man or woman. Some things cannot be purchased at a store.

NORTHEAST

A Touch of Italy (ATOI)
Established: 1984 • Owner: Lorenzo Lecce
8, 606 Meredith Road NE (DeWaal Block)
Phone: 229•1066
Tuesday–Friday 10:00 am–6:00 pm, Saturday 10:00 am–5:00 pm
V, Debit, Cheque, $

LORENZO Lecce's father and mother founded this import and distribution business in 1983, now with two locations—in Bridgeland's elegant 1912 DeWaal Block that also houses Il Sogno Ristorante, and in Okotoks. Expect effortlessly stylish Italian design: from Brasilia's Mini Classic espresso machine featuring professional-calibre fittings, to hand-pounded pyramid stovetop pots and Ancap's ceramic-stainless stovetop Moka, both stylish enough to come to the table. Alternatively, buy a Bugatti coffee machine, made in Birmingham, England. Its lines betray its provenance, but it is a reliable workhorse. For ranges in small spaces, look at CE's component kitchen in 24" segments: a gas four-burner, a bar grill powered by electricity, an electric two-burner. Add elegant and functional three-ply ICM pots and pans (also available in Harrod's) in the Cose Casa homestyle line, or purchase elegant Mauviel copper pots, Italian platters and serving items, and stainless triple-ply pots big enough to boil the biggest pud. Then buy the makings: Callipo olive oil-packed tuna is hard to beat, and Misura whole wheat pastas, also *kamut* or *spelt* pasta for reduced-gluten pasta fans. Then cast your vote for Italian-style dining.
- *House Specialties*: Coffee machines, Italian pots and dishes, specialty foods.
- *Also Available*: 94 Elma Street, Okotoks. Some imported ingredients at specialty food stores, including **Bon Ton Meat Market, DinoRosa's Italian Market, Italian Store, Sobey's/IGA, Sunterra Quality Food Market,** and **Mountain Mercato Specialty Food Market** in Canmore.
www.atouchofitaly.ca

Dragons Den Knives
Established: 2004 • Manager: Vanessa Fauth
Street Address: 901–64 Avenue NE (Deerfoot Outlet Mall)
Phone: 731•9100
Monday–Friday 10:00 am–9:00 pm, Saturday 9:30 am–7:00 pm
Sunday 11:00 am–5:00 pm
V, MC, Debit, $

THIS shop in the Northeast carries a narrow selection of kitchen knives, focusing on Victorinox and Henckels. Look too for utilitarian steels, whetstones, and wheeled draw-through knife sharpeners.
- *House Specialties*: Hunting and pocket knives, Victorinox, Henckels knives, whetstones and sharpeners.
www.dragonsdenknives.com

Geanel Restaurant Supplies Ltd.

Established: 1976 • Manager: Carolyn Fry
1, 1231–36 Avenue NE
Phone: 291•9800
Monday–Friday 7:30 am–4:30 pm
Cheque, $

THIS established business offers design services as well as a complete range of tablewares, large pieces of industrial equipment and kitchen tools. When it is time to set the table, Steelite bowls and plates are tough. In fact, I still have half a dozen—the final remnant of my restaurant, sold in 1994! So choose carefully. They won't wear out. Buy Riedel or Spiegelau stemware to make the most of your wines, and anything from forks to flatware, but only in case lots—so set the table for a dozen.

• *House Specialties*: Steelite plates, Riedel glasses, Garland ranges, Vollrath equipment.

www.geanel.com

Handles & More

Established: 1991 • Owner: John Peters, Manager: Evelyn Thompson
103, 3928 Edmonton Trail NE
Phone: 230•4098
Monday–Friday 8:00 am–5:30 pm, Saturday 9:00 am–5:00 pm
V, MC, Debit, $

POT racks are the smartest way to store pots, suspended from ceiling or wall. Floor stands have a place in the right kitchen too. Look up in this surprising shop, one of my favourite spots when I am in home reno mode. They carry Kootenay Forge's hammered iron rustic racks, ideal in a farmstyle room, and Enclume's glowing copper racks, perfect to showcase your Mauviel copper pots' clean lines and gleaming light. Or maybe you need an entertainment cart or island, with a hardwood top, with wine storage and hooks for hand tools, or perhaps an under-counter swing-out storage unit. Oasis Concepts' smartly designed folding carts can be put to work in a kitchen, dining room, or patio. Herbeau's handsome farmhouse kitchen sinks are elegant in an uncluttered way. When it is "Open Sesame" time, door and drawer pulls, knobs and towel racks or hooks are *de rigueur* in every kitchen. Handles & More made their name on handles. Literally!

• *House Specialties*: Pot racks, door and drawer pulls, hardware, storage units.

www.handlesandmore.ca

Trail Appliances

Established: 1974 • General Manager: Jason Frohlick
2745–29 Street NE
Phone: 250•2818
Monday–Wednesday & Friday 9:00 am–6:00 pm, Thursday 9:00 am–8:00 pm
Saturday 9:00 am–5:00 pm, Sunday noon–5:00 pm
V, MC, AE, Debit, Cheque, $

MY contacts at Trail suggest that shoppers do their due diligence before they sign on the dotted line for large appliances. Google the maker, check features, read reviews, consult an interior designer if you plan to spend serious money, get references on designer and cabinet maker, and view a wide array of display kitchens. Form your own opinion based on how you live and cook, then arrive at the store, armed with information. Once through the door, examine the many choices closely: Viking—one of the most recognized brand names in home ranges, ovens and fridges, Dacor—trend-setter and elegant, MOV130's—European-style convection oven, Thermador fridges—designed to go head to head with SubZero. If you are buying stainless steel appliances, expect to pay a premium for top-drawer materials.

Personal experience has taught me that Miele's dishwashers really are quieter than Bosch's, but that new does not always mean improved. My new KitchenAid range's computerized front panel includes unacceptably slow temperature recovery time after the oven door is opened—bad news for an oven queen. I want my reliable old KitchenAid back. *Caveat emptor.*

• *House Specialties*: Kitchen appliances.
• *Also Available*: 6880–11 Street SE and ten other locations across western Canada.

www.trailappliances.com

SOUTHEAST

Brown's Food Service Equipment Sales

Established: 1945 • Owner: Brian Tychonick
403 Riverfront Avenue SE
Phone: 262•6009
Monday–Friday 8:30 am–5:00 pm
Debit, Cheque, $

THIS family-run Calgary business opened in 1945, beside the river on the Eastside of downtown. Walk-in shoppers can pay by cash or cheque, for knives, pots, cutlery, tableware, and heavy equipment—anything from the front door of a restaurant to its inner workings, including True restaurant coolers, although they are loud to listen to. For your outdoor kitchen, examine BBQs fired by propane or natural gas, and Imperial domestic ranges for inside the heart of the home. Fill the range's top surface with Thermalloy pots, made of stainless steel with a heat-conductive 3-ply bottom, in sizes from 12 to 40 quarts, or choose lovely copper Strauss pots. For the counter, examine the biggest KitchenAid mixer, in "pro-size" 6-quart capacity, or top-line stainless steel Waring blenders with a "big bang" motor and cloverleaf design that moves food effectively into the bottom blades. VitaMix blenders are available on request. Choose glassware from a wide range, including Arcoroc's high-end Durand French line, available in tempered glass or crystal, to Libbey's daily use glassware.

- *House Specialties*: Restaurant smallwares, large equipment, tableware, electricals.

The Compleat Cook

Established: 1987 • Owner: Tawni Van Grieken
232, 10816 Macleod Trail South (Willow Park Village)
Phone: 278•1220
Monday–Wednesday & Friday 10:00 am–6:00 pm, Thursday 10:00 am–8:00 pm
Saturday 10:00 am–5:00 pm
Sunday 12:00–4:00 pm from early November through Christmas
V, MC, AE, Debit, $

THIS trio of very good stores has just about everything a cook could need, beginning with bowls, bowls, bowls—made of glass, ceramic, melamine, stainless—in all sizes. A baker can never have too many bowls, especially bowls with pour spouts, and Molto Mario's melamine measurables. The shelves are crammed with clear squeeze bottles for sauces, pudding moulds with lids, *madeleine* moulds, collapsible measuring cups, and a full range of baking tins and pans, as well as hand tools and silicon oven mitts or pot holders. The knife selection is quite cutting edge: Global, Wüstof Trident, Henckels, Kasumi's elegant Damascus blades, and colourful ceramic blades from Kuhn Rikon. There are several options for knife-edge maintenance, led by diamond sharpeners, my favourite draw-through made by Mino, and classic whetstones needing oil.

Stovetop stuff includes great reliables from Le Creuset, All Clad, WMF Gourmet, the ultra-sexy copper pots made by Mauviel, and Chicago Metallic bakeware. The range of electricals include Cuisinart, Viking, Vitamix, and Krupps coffee grinders for that first perfect cuppa to go with your waffles or smoothie. Caffeine hounds can vacillate between Gaggia, Vitro, or Bialetti— plug it in or sling it on the stove. For teatime, nothing says steeped quite as beautifully as Alessi teakettles—some whistling. The Velvet Rabbit screwpull for wine service is an ergonomically elegant bunny, even if only for its whimsical name. Look up for pot racks to store pots, then around the corner on shelves for Peugeot peppermills, and handtools by Oxo Good Grips and Kuhn Rikon, both intelligently designed brands. After all that, a cook needs plates. Here be Denby, Wedgewood, Rosenthal. Serve it forth in style.

- *House Specialties*: Pots and pans, silicon stuff, electricals, dishes, good gadgets.
- *Also Available*: 221, 315–8 Avenue SW (Bankers Hall) and 131, 5005 Dalhousie Drive NW (Dalhousie Station).

Crown Restaurant Equipment

Established: 1984 • Contact: Nick Poulos
5307–4 Street SE
Phone: 253•4888
Monday–Friday 8:30 am–5:00 pm, Saturday 10:00 am–2:00 pm
Debit, Cheque, $

NICK Poulos began selling used equipment in 1984, and sold a four-burner Wolf range to me for my small restaurant in an earlier stage of my life. Crown now mostly sells new kitchen equipment. The small front of the store is crowded with catalogues, display cases, smallwares and dishes, but the heart of the business is the back warehouse. If it isn't in sight, ask: Poulos is in the process of expanding both departments—retail and to the trade.
• *House Specialties*: Restaurant equipment, smallwares, tableware.
• *Also Available*: Lethbridge.
www.crownfoodequipment.com

Hendrix Foodservice Equipment & Supply Professionals

Established: 2006 • Manager: Gill Maurice
457–42 Avenue SE
Phone: 243•5539
Monday–Friday 9:00 am–5:00 pm, Saturday 10:00 am–4:00 pm
V, MC, Debit, $

THIS Ontario-based business, established in Brockville in 1981, arrived in Alberta in September 2006. Geared primarily to the commercial food trade, it has expanded into retail. Look here for KitchenAid mixers, Paderno baking pans, and handfuls of hand tools. Cake fans can collect Nordic Ware's heavy non-stick cast aluminum specialty cakes moulds in seasonal shapes. Finicky fingers with a flair for detail can finesse a fine herd of miniatures: tartlets—in fluted, round, rectangles and hearts, mini kugel, bundt and loaf pans, mini springforms. Pastry queens can add adventurous rolling pins— marble or water-filled—then use them to roll out dough for clutches of cookie cutters in inventive shapes.

For caffeine fixes, there are many options: burr coffee grinders by KitchenAid or Cuisinart, Saeco coffeemakers, Krupps coffee grinders and makers, Bodum tea and coffee equipment. For stovetop and oven use, select Le Creuset enameled cast iron, ideal for braising, or *peut-être* Le Cuistot is more to your taste. If knives are the need, examine and hold Wüstof Trident, MAC, Global or Victorinox. But knives need an edge, so consider sharpeners—and ways to store them—wooden blocks, knife cases, and rolls to transport edges safely.

For pureed soups to frapped drinks, Waring blenders and immersion wands make the job simple. On the counter and under, examine Waring's Pro Line homestyle deep fryers and wine coolers. Want to cool off with house-made ice cream? Cuisinart ice cream makers make good *gelato* and sorbet.
• *House Specialties*: Le Creuset, KitchenAid, and Cuisinart, smallwares, electricals, baking equipment and tools, knives.
www.hendrixequip.com

88888888888888888

House of Knives

Established: 1978 (2000 in Calgary) • Manager: Sharon Rosinke
320, 100 Anderson Road SE (Southcentre Mall)
Phone: 278•0326
Monday–Friday 9:30 am–9:00 pm, Saturday 9:30 am–8:00 pm
Sunday 11:00 am–5:00 pm
V, MC, AE, Debit, $
[see NW Kitcheware for main entry on p. 136]

Ikea

Established: 1943 • Contact: Any Staffperson
8000–11 Street SE (Deerfoot Meadows)
Phone: 273•4338
Monday–Saturday 10:00 am–9:00 pm, Sunday 10:00 am–6:00 pm
V, MC, Debit, $

ASIDE from the stacks of racks, whisks, strainers, colanders, pots, stacks of bowls, platters, and cutlery, look here for cupboards, butcher blocks and heavy kitchen equipment, from stoves to fridges. Fill your cupboards after you design the space: choose the cupboards, the countertop surface, the storage racks. It is all here. Ikea published its first catalogue in 1951 and opened its first store, in Sweden, in 1953. The first Canadian store opened in 1976, in Burlington, Ontario. Ikea arrived in Calgary in 1979.
• *House Specialties*: cupboards, counters, sinks and ranges, pots and pans, smallwares, butcher blocks, cutting boards, dishes and glassware.
www.ikea.com

Knifewear

Established: 2007 • Owner: Kevin Kent
1212A–9 Avenue SE (within Bite Grocteria)
Phone: 514•0577 • E-mail: kevin@knifewear.com
Wednesday: Hours by Appointment, Thursday & Friday 10:00 am–8:00 pm
Saturday 10:00 am–6:00 pm, Sunday noon–6:00 pm
V, MC, AE, Cheque, $

KEVIN Kent has left his cheffing day job to pursue his knife fetishist's dream fulltime. (About time, we all knew, Kevin!) He has opened a shop-within-a-shop, a knifery, called a Hamono-ya in Japanese, at **Bite Groceteria**. He stocks several lines of handmade Japanese knives, including a trio made by Takeo Murata-san. A living legend in Japan, Murata makes some of the most exquisite knives in the world, and has unparalleled skill at forging Yasuki-Aogani Number One blue steel. Murata's knives are in high demand among aficionados, and are preferred for ease of re-sharpening, superior edge retention, and razor's edge sharpness. Other labels Kent brings in include Artisan, Best Clad, New Tradition, Tamahagane, Sirou Kamo and JKC 63 layer blades, (chrome-vanadium high carbon core, laminated with 62 layers of nickel stainless). The collection is rounded out with a variety of traditional sushi blades, Damascus blades, King silicone carbide waterstones in graduating grits for sharpening knives and Spanish cleavers from Arcos. These are well-weighted, indestructible blades, made for butchery, not finely mincing vegetables. Kent has turned to Jay Patel of the British-based Japanese Knife Co. as his sensei, or mentor, and offers knife repairs and sharpening instruction accrued from that relationship. Give a person a fishing pole... Look too at the funky foodie shirts. Shop in person, online, or by phone.

• *House Specialties*: Handmade Japanese knives, Spanish cleavers, sharpening stones, sharpening/repair service, and knife fetishist shirts and cookin' street wear.

www.knifewear.com

Lee Valley Tools Ltd.

Established: 1978 • Founder: Leonard Lee
7261–11 Street SE
Phone: 253•2066
Monday–Wednesday 9:00 am–6:00 pm, Thursday & Friday 9:00 am–9:00 pm
Saturday 9:00 am–6:00 pm
V, MC, AE, Debit, $

WHEN I took the pink silicone Food Loops off the shelf, I worried that maybe this was the final set available. It took a tour of the rest of the store to realize that catalogue shopping is alive and well: that single specimen was exactly that—a specimen. Get an order sheet and pencil, peruse the store's catalogues or the computer screen (at home or in-store), then stand in line at the rear of the shop to place your order with the stock keepers. There are high-calibre gadgets here to interest cooks. Lee Valley's metal rasp is the gold standard, and pink silicone Food Loops are terrific for tying things up before they go into the oven. A silicone strainer is a collapsible space-saver, and the knives in the display case were either the old elephant of the ancient Sabatier line, or a Japanese chop-style signature. The available Japanese knives are the smartly sandwiched ones, made of high carbon and stainless steel. All knives need a sharpener: good water stones, worth their weight in sharp edges, are on view just a few cabinets over from the knives. A micro torch will burn brulée crusts without risk, and an apple peeler of the crank variety is ideal to keep *tarte Tatin* on any menu. Cooks without a fear of sharp edges find French stainless *mandolins* irresistible. All the rest is hardware: door pulls, and cleverly designed storage shelves and racks for pantries, awkward corners, below-sink spots, pull-down shelves for inaccessible high spots. It is simplest to order online, for doorstep delivery. Classes are offered on many crafty subjects, including knife sharpening.

• *House Specialties*: Tools for kitchens and gardens, knives and knife sharpeners, drawer and door pulls, and storage gadgets.

• *Also Available*: 12 other locations across Canada. Consult their website.

www.leevalley.com

Mr. Cappuccino

Established: 1979 • Owner: Yvonne Cattoni
BI, 416 Meridian Road SE
Phone: 230•8636
Monday–Friday 9:00 am–5:00 pm, Saturday 10:00 am–4:00 pm
V, MC, Debit, $

IT is easy to cook with good tools, and the stuff here is good. Find electric extruder-style pasta machines, plus Avancini dough mixers that hold up to 5 kilograms of dough. If you have space, make room for a wood-burning *forno* by Ambrogi, in a design dating back to 1948, sold assembled and needing only a chimney. If you have a hankering for a fine Italian example of grilled cheese and pancetta or proscuitto, maybe a *panini* grill is in store for you. That old "I need ice cream" fix can get taken care of in the Italian style, with a Corema *gelato* machine, made to commercial quality with a 2-litre capacity container—a quantity worth sharing.
- *House Specialties*: All things coffee: Rancilio, Ascaso, Magister, Mazzer, *panini* grills, ice cream makers, wood-burning ovens.

www.mrcappuccino.com

Russell Food Equipment

Established: 1944 • General Manager: Brent Baker
5707–4 Street SE
Phone: 253•1383
Monday–Friday 8:00 am–5:00 pm
V, MC, Debit, Cheque, $

RUSSELL Food Equipment began in Vancouver in 1944, selling equipment to the restaurant chain White Spot. It now covers Canada with 14 locations. Individuals shopping here are eligible for a 5 percent cash-and-carry discount, but if you require delivery, the discount is negated. Spacious home kitchens may benefit from back bars and under-counter coolers that tidily fit under 36" standard-height counters, in runs up to 9' in length. Look at stainless steel heavy gauge and induction-capable sandwiched-steel pots, or a raft of smallwares that includes wire whisks and industrial-calibre tongs and serving spoons. If you need to stock up for a wedding or party, buy wine glasses by the dozen or case—Libbey, Riedel, and Oneida Arcococ. Free parking and a large showroom make life easier.
- *House Specialties*: Induction cookware, under-counter coolers, glassware, smallwares.

www.russellfood.ca

Trail Appliances

Established: 1974 • General Manager: Rick Owen
6880–11 Street SE
Phone: 253•5442
Monday–Wednesday & Friday 9:00 am–6:00 pm, Thursday 9:00 am–9:00 pm
Saturday 9:00 am–5:00 pm, Sunday noon–5:00 pm
V, MC, AE, Debit, Cheque, $
[see NE Kitcheware for main entry on p. 126]

SOUTHWEST

Art of Hardware (ah!)

Established: 2000 • Owner: Jeanne Milne
730–10 Avenue SW
Phone: 244•4960
Monday–Wednesday & Friday 8:00 am–6:00 pm, Thursday 8:00 am–8:00 pm
Saturday 10:00 am–4:00 pm
V, MC, AE, Debit, Cheque, $

Yᴏᴜ'ᴠᴇ gotta be able to open the doors and drawers. This artsy "form follows function" shop moved recently from its back alley destination to a front door in the Beltline's Design District. Even the drawer pulls are artistic, from copper-tone twigs to pounded silver towel racks. If you need a state of the art sink, towel rack or hook, look and say, "*ah!*" Then open wide the wallet. Costly but drop-dead gorgeous art, oh, such lovely things: hand-pounded metal sinks, glass sinks beautiful enough to frame. Oh my! Things and designs and suppliers change as artists and trends evolve. Go look!

• *House Specialties*: Artful hardware.
• *Also Available*: Studio B, 11807–105 Avenue, Edmonton.
www.artofhardware.com

The Compleat Cook

221, 315–8 Avenue SW (Bankers Hall)
Phone: 264•0449
Monday–Wednesday 10:00 am–6:00 pm, Thursday & Friday 10:00 am–8:00 pm
Saturday 10:00 am–5:30 pm
Sunday noon–5 pm for 2 weeks prior to Christmas
V, MC, AE, Debit, $
[see Kitchenware SE for main entry on p. 127]

Happy Cooker

Established: 1985 • Owners: Marguerite McVicar & Kanan Patel

132, 555 Strathcona Boulevard SW
(Strathcona Square Shopping Centre)
Phone: 242•6788

1600–90 Avenue SW
(Glenmore Landing)
Phone: 258•3230

Monday–Saturday 10:00 am–6:00 pm, Sunday noon–5:00 pm
V, MC, AE, Debit, $

THIS well-established cookware store, founded in 1985 by Marguerite McVicar and Kanan Patel, offers bi-weekly classes specializing in East Indian, Thai, and BBQ. The owners say that their clientele of dedicated eaters have always loved ethnic fare. "Thai and East Indian food are our most popular classes, and have been from the beginning," says McVicar. She serves signature non-alcoholic beverages at classes, which are casual two-hour events that feature accessible recipes for home cooks, and not elaborate restaurant constructs.

The store carries practical kitchen equipment that will make the home cooking experience easier to execute. Nesting Mason Cash bowls from England will keep a baker's hands and heart happy. A cool collection of copper cookie cutters—highlighted by an elaborate cutout baker—and bunches of hand tools almost obscure a stack of French poplar baking baskets lined with parchment. Busy bakers will appreciate the rolling pins, Silpat mats, French tart pans, ceramic shortbread moulds, and cookie sprinkles and "shimmer dust" for glitzy cookies. Bosch machines lessen labour, and Krups burr grinders make mincemeat out of coffee beans.

- *House Specialties*: Kitchen tools, baking equipment, Bosch machines, bowls, smallwares, classes.
- *Also Available*: 3625 Shaganappi Trail NW (Market Mall).

www.happycooker.ca

The Knifery

Established: 1978 • Owner: Daniel Goldstein, Manager: Robert McKnight
163, 6455 Macleod Trail South (Chinook Centre)
Phone: 259•5397
Monday–Saturday 9:30 am–9:00 pm, Sunday 11:00 am–6:00 pm
V, MC, AE, Debit, $

THIS shop is a knife hound's heaven. Find many makes and models here, including Cermax, made of Japanese M66 steel with a high Rockwell rating—that indicates metal's degree of hardness compared to diamond—the hardest naturally occuring substance on the planet with a Rockwell rating of 100. Like classic Japanese knives, it sandwiches high carbon steel, a hard centre and softer outer edges, to increase flex and durability.

There are many other choices: Wüstof Trident, a German brand whose pedigree dates back to 1814, a new forged Victorinox made in Germany with riveted handle and full bolster to protect the cook's knife hand, Canadian Grohman knives made in Pictou, Nova Scotia, for kitchen and outdoors, Japanese Global, MAC and Haiku Damascus, similar to Shun. Custom fans may prefer William Henry's semi-custom knives, set with semi-precious stones, made of 32 folded layers of Damascus steel with a semi-bolster, and a 67 Rockwell rating. Custom costs cash!

Knives need an edge. Ask about the Tru Hone grinder, and entrust your Japanese blades to in-store sharpening on water and ceramic whetstones. Take-home sharpeners are the standard whetstone in oil or water, ceramic and diamond. Alternatives include several Global pull-throughs, and the Lansky system, similar to Spyderco's set-angle V for outdoor knives or small knives: clamp and jig, then go back to the carrots and onions with edge restored.

Keep blades and fingers safe in a comprehensive collection of storage systems, including wall magnets, wood blocks made of oak and birch, metal blocks, rollups for transport, and sheaths called "blade savers" that eliminate risk during travel.

• *House Specialties*: Victorinox, MAC, Henckels, Grohmann.

www.theknifery.ca

Target Knives & Survival

Established: 1975 • *Owner: Rowland Gibbs*
5005 Macleod Trail South
Phone: 243•6996
Monday–Friday 9:00 am–6:00 pm, Saturday 9:00 am–5:00 pm
Sunday noon–4:00 pm
V, MC, Debit, $

THE owner says that he sees each knife as a work of art. As with anything edged and sharp, safety counts, so the staff teaches product information and responsibility in the handling of knives. A good range of blades includes Laguiole, William Henry, Shun, Kershaw, Victorinox, and custom blades made in Calgary by Brian Lyttle upon request. For hunters, find field knives for those messy jobs, both custom-made and stock.

• *House Specialties*: Wüstof Trident, Asian makes, custom-made Brian Lyttle knives.

www.targetknives.com

Williams-Sonoma Canada Inc.

Established: 1956 • *General Manager: Debora Horton*
123A, 6455 Macleod Trail South (Chinook Mall)
Phone: 410•9191
Monday–Saturday 9:30 am–9:00 pm, Sunday 11:00 am–6:00 pm
V, MC, AE, Debit, $

THIS is the motherlode for high-calibre pans and tools, and charges accordingly. Admire the KitchenAid 600-series electric mixer, a 6-quart behemoth powered by 575 watts. Other electricals include Breville from Australia, Capresso, Cuisinart food processors and ice cream makers, and more varieties of coffee makers than even a dedicated caffeine hound needs.

Shelves are stacked with French bakeware, in two finishes—traditional tinned steel and nonstick, from 35-centimeter oblongs perfect for a frangipane tart to 10-centimeter minis that serve one or two. The French family is gathered here: *madeleine* plaques, *charlotte* moulds, *baba* and *brioche* tins too, along with *mandolins* of stainless steel and a comprehensive collection of rolling pins of wood, silicone, or marble. Examine a wide range of knives, all locked in wall display cabinets, so ask to hold the ones you are considering. Hand-held is the only way to assess and buy a knife. For flibberty-gibbet hand tools, there is a wide collection to choose from: collapsible brightly-coloured silicone measuring cups are cool, as are expanding latex sponges for quick clean-up, and sexy citrus, cassis, or chestnut hand lotion will soothe your bakers' hands. A select collection of cookbooks will guide your trend-tracking, television cooking, and taste-making tours.

I was skeptical about Williams-Sonoma's exclusive Goldtouch nonstick finish, a ceramic-reinforced finish available on heavy-gauge aluminized steel baking sheets, springforms, cake pans, and muffin tins, so I bought a muffin pan, for a lot of jingle, but it performs exactly as advertised—baked muffins drop out intact and unsullied *sans* messy paper liners, and washing up is just as easy.

You do not need every gadget going, but do choose the goods that will make cooking easier and better.

• *House Specialties*: Pots and pans, especially AllClad, Le Creuset, and Mauviel, smallwares, bakeware, linens and lotions, knives and sharpeners, electricals and books.

www.williamssonoma.com

NORTHWEST

B & J Restaurant Supply Ltd.
Established: 1995 • Owner: Feng Cheung
1101 Centre Street North
Phone: 230•0039
Monday–Sunday 10:00 am–6:00 pm
V, MC, Debit, $

CITY chefs congregate in this small Northside shop for all things Asian: woks and cleavers, rice steamers and platters, chopsticks, bowls and teapots. I have never before seen woks as big as those found here!
• *House Specialties*: Asian dishes, stovetop equipment.

The Compleat Cook
131, 5005 Dalhousie Drive NW (Dalhousie Station)
Phone: 286•5220
Monday–Friday 10:00 am–6:00 pm, Saturday 10:00 am–5:00 pm
Sunday 12:00 am–5:00 pm for 2 Sundays prior to Christmas
V, MC, AE, Debit, $
[see Kitchenware SE for main entry on p. 127]

Cutting Edge Cutlery

Established: 1997 • Manager: Carey Daoust
1632–14 Avenue NW (North Hill Shopping Centre)
Phone: 276•3340
Monday–Friday 10:00 am–9:00 pm, Saturday 9:30 am–6:00 pm
Sunday 11:00 am–5:00 pm
V, MC, Debit, $

FROM wall decorations of ornate if somewhat barbaric splendour, to practical tools for the field or kitchen, this shop has some elaborately lovely knives. I love the folded Damascus steel of Shun in particular, from a 6" Nakiri blunt-nosed chopper to an elegant santoku—they all have exquisite balance. Look too at an abbreviated Henckels collection; savour some well-balanced Spyderco edges, including a few ceramic knives, and a few Wasabi and Wüstof Trident blades. Sharpeners are led by Spyderco's removable arm V-shaped ceramic rods, with a few diamond steels, whetstones, and draw-through sharpeners.
• *House Specialties*: Kershaw, Shun, and hunting knives by Cold Steel and Puma.
www.cuttingedgecutleryco.ca

Happy Cooker

Established: 1985 • Owners: Marguerite McVicar & Kanan Patel
3625 Shaganappi Trail NW (Market Mall)
Phone: 288•6220
Monday–Friday 10:00 am–9:00 pm, Saturday 9:30 am–8:00 pm
Sunday 11:00 am–6:00 pm
V, MC, AE, Debit, $
[see SW Kitcheware for main entry on p. 132]

House of Knives

Established: 1978 (2000 in Calgary) • Manager: Michelle Prior
3625 Shaganappi Trail NW (Market Mall)
Phone: 288•3361
Monday–Friday 10:00 am–9:00 pm, Saturday 9:30 am–8:00 pm
Sunday 11:00 am–6:00 pm
V, MC, AE, Debit, $

THIS small store carries knives and sharpening devices, but is light on information, so know what you want. Look at the mainline brands: Global, Shun, Wüstof Trident, Henckels, and Victorinox. Look too at the famous Laguiole pocket knives from France. For knife storage, the choices are magnets, drawer slots, and blocks. A few smallwares and Peugeot peppermills are tucked amongst the blades. For custom orders look in the books and ask. Ignore the fantasy and display daggers in favour of the real McCoy.
• *House Specialties*: Kitchen and sporting knives.
• *Also Available*: 320, 100 Anderson Road SE (Southcentre Mall); a Canada-wide company based in Ontario.
www.houseofknives.ca

Latin, Caribbean & African

THE MOST RECENT DETAILED Canadian census figures (2001) indicate that immigrants from Africa, the Caribbean, Central and South America residing in Calgary totaled over 25,000, well behind arrivals from the leading immigrant nations of China, India and the Philippines. With over 9,000 new arrivals from Latin, Caribbean and African countries arriving in Calgary since 2000, the shape and nature of the city is changing. In reflection of those changes, the shops providing services and goods have changed too. This section is one of the youngest, with most of the businesses being newly established, and non dating back father than 2000.

Food from "home" helps immigrants feel more at home in a new country. Beyond that, immigrant organizations have sprung up to support and assist newcomers to the community: the African Sudanese Association of Calgary (ASAC), the Calgary Immigrant Womans' Association, Lost Boys and Girls of Sudan, the Centre for Newcomers. These groups, among others offer services in integration, settlement, language training, employment skills and family support.

NORTHEAST

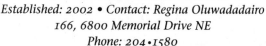

De Chosen African Market
Established: 2002 • Contact: Regina Oluwadadairo
166, 6800 Memorial Drive NE
Phone: 204•1580
Monday–Thursday 11:00 am–7:00 pm, Friday & Saturday 11:00 am–8:00 pm
V, MC, Debit, $

REGINA Oluwadadairo is the owner of De Chosen. "We are all sisters and brothers," says Regina, explaining how her family has adapted to life in this cold city. At work, on the phone in her busy store, she repeats and echoes the sentiment, addressing her caller as "my sister." "They are all my family, I know them all," she says candidly. The aisles of De Chosen are lined with sacks of beans and rice, and tidy shelves are stacked with dried versions of foods familiar to transplanted Nigerians—yam flour, *cassava* flour, ground melon seed, dried herbs and vegetables, dried shrimp, cod, and herring. In the freezers, rows of red snapper lie jowl by jowl with oxtail and shank, cows' feet and tripe, goat, and bright green vegetable purees. Drums, clothing, and cosmetics crowd the upper shelves above the freezers.

• *House Specialties*: African starches, fish and dry goods.

www.de-chosen.com

Joycee's Caribbean Foods

Established: 2007 • Contact: Lorna Murray
5, 630–1 Avenue NE
Phone: 234•9940
Tuesday–Saturday 10:00 am–6:00 pm
V. MC, Debit, $

LORNA Murray's mom is the Joycee of the shop's title. Lorna does a booming takeout lunch business in curried and jerk dishes, with or without rice and peas. Cooks can take home the makings if they want to do the deed themselves—here is where to buy jerk seasonings, salt cod and mackerel. Lorna's ginger beer is in the freezer. It is intensely gingery, with a fine afterburn. For afterburn off the scale, buy a few *Scotch bonnet* peppers, or dial it back with banana, *yucca*, *plantains* or sweet potatoes from produce baskets in the store's centre. Dried pulses, rice, frozen fish and oxtail, and dried hibiscus flowers all come together in this community-minded and convivial space.

• *House Specialties*: Ginger beer (non-alcoholic), jerk and curried dishes, Caribbean ingredients.

joyceescaribbeanfoods@shaw.ca

TK's African Products Inc.

Established: 2007 • Owner: Teresa Yankson
128, 3132–26 Street NE (Interpacific Business Park)
Phone: 590•0726
Tuesday–Sunday 11:30 am–8:00 pm
Debit, $

TERESA Yankson moved from Ghana to Canada in 1977. For 13 years, she supplied friends and family with the ingredients they missed before opening her shop in 2007. Her shelves are filled with starches and grains, dried pulses, canned fish, a few fresh vegetables and an array of dried herbs. Look for yams, *cassava* and *plantains*—fresh, dried, and pounded into flour for *fufu*. Black-eyed peas and barley, bitter leaf for greens and fish, palm oil for frying, dried shrimp, and aromatic freshly baked banana bread fill other shelves. Freezers are stocked with smoked fish—Nile perch (tilapia) and herring—as well as frozen snapper, *kingfish*, and unsmoked versions of tilapia and herring.

• *House Specialties*: *Plantain* and yam flour, smoked fish, dried pulses, and palm oil.

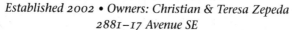

SOUTHEAST

El Bombazo Latino Market

Established 2002 • Owners: Christian & Teresa Zepeda
2881–17 Avenue SE
Phone: 204•3757
Sunday & Monday 11:00 am–7:00 pm, Wednesday–Saturday 10:30 am–8:00 pm
V, MC, AE, Debit, $

THIS tiny Latin shop stands adjacent to an equally small café boasting half a dozen tables. Tidy shelves and cooler hold a few carefully chosen staples—black beans, rice, fresh corn *tortillas, masa harina* and *hominy, queso fresco*. Boldo herb tea, a favourite of many Latins, also *yerba maté*, Mexican chocolate for hot chocolate and cooking, and *tamarind* paste are neatly displayed.
• *House Specialties*: Latin staples—corn *tortillas*, rice, black beans, and salsas.

Jubba-Nile Supermarket

Established: 2007 • Owners: Zulecha Noor & Mudhir Mohamed
4908–17 Avenue SE
Phone: 244•1909
Monday–Wednesday 11:00 am–9:00 pm, Thursday 11:00 am–6:00 pm
Friday–Sunday 11:00 am–9:00 pm
V, MC, Debit, $

THE family came from Mogadishu, Somalia and missed barley flour, sesame oil, and *sorghum* when they settled in Calgary, so they started this small Latin, Caribbean & African store to ease the homesickness. As we speak, an Ethiopian enters, asking for Calgary-made Queen of Sheba *injera*, but this flatbread won't come in for a few more days. He will be back for it, and may also collect *hawaji*, fava or *azuki* beans, palm or coconut oil. Other notables include frozen *molochia* and okra, *basmati* rice, *couscous*, red lentils, crunchy whole wheat berries, and fragrant Lebanese olive oil (a country that sounds more romantic *en français*, as *Terre du Cèdre*). A small meat counter in the rear retails freshly cut *Halal* meats.
• *House Specialties*: African ingredients including *injera*, barley flour, *couscous*, lentils and beans, *basmati* rice, and *Halal* meats.

La Tiendona

Established: 1993 • Owners: Luis & Nereida Villatoro
1836–36 Street SE
Phone: 272•4054
Tuesday–Friday 10:00 am–7:00 pm, Saturday 10:00 am–4:00 pm
V, MC, Debit, $

THIS Latin store wins top marks for genuine service and a wide array of traditional ingredients. It's like the Buena Vista Social Club, hanging out with chatty and cheerful Honduran owner Luis, leaning on the counter and learning about Latin American dishes. When a Spanish-language student comes looking for props to jack up his class mark, he leaves outfitted with candied *guava* paste and *queso fresco*, along with newly found self-confidence and a page of scribbled notes.

Shelves of canned goods flank the entry. Collect tinned *hominy, tomatillo salsa verde, chipotles in adobo sauce,* Mexican-made Valentina hot sauce (buy the big bottle), and a wide array of Mexican and Central American sweets, from *cajeta* to chocolate. Ibarra and Abuelita are Mexican dark chocolate discs, gritty with sugar. Colombian chocolate is even "rougher" than the Mexican choices, says Villatoro. He demonstrates how to use the wooden *molinillo*, and we debate the merits of goats' milk versus cows' milk *cajeta*, the burnt sugar caramel that is a dessert on its own.

Along one wall, a cooler holds stacks of fresh corn *tortillas* and *queso fresco.* Around the corner, the freezer is stacked with tidy packets of Andean blackberry pulp, frozen *tamales, cassava,* passionfruit pulp. Spice shelves hold the expected—*annatto,* cumin, *epazote, guajillo chilies, tamarind* paste, and hibiscus flowers for tea—as well as the unexpected, like Villatoro's preferred spice blend—a saffron substitute based on *annatto,* cumin, and corn flour. At the back, bigger-than-big bags of *masa harina,* rice, and black beans are the staples that support an uncomplicated cuisine. Hand tools are lined up on one shelf—*tortilla* presses and a heavy mortar and pestle. Behind the counter, videos of dance lessons teach beginners how simple it is to merengue and salsa. Somehow, it doesn't seem surprising.

• *House Specialties*: Corn *tortillas*, hot sauces, dry goods, ingredients and drinks from South and Central America.

Lloyd's Patty Plus

Established: 1984 • Owner: Lloyd Reid
202, 255–28 Street NE (Short Pants Plaza)
Phone: 207•4455
Monday–Saturday 10:00 am–6:30 pm
Debit, Cheque, $

THE patties stop here, in Short Pants Plaza! (Go ahead and laugh. Life is short. The short pants are worn by the plaza's owner...) You can find them (patties, not short pants) around town, stuffed with vegetables, chicken or beef, but here is ground zero, where Lloyd hangs his apron and offers a discount by the dozen. He might even pull up a stool and chat with you. Lloyd, who arrived in Canada from Jamaica more than three decades ago, is now in his early 60s. He says God gave him hands to work, so he is working still, after re-starting his business following a financial flounder. He makes chicken (hot and not), beef (hot and not), and vegetable patties in egg yolk-yellow pastry.

• *House Specialties*: Jamaican patties.
• *Also Available*: **Calgary Co-op, Canada Safeway, Sobey's/IGA** and City Hall cafeteria.

Mayfair Foods

Established: 1967 • Owner: Bob Faleh (since 1987)
4019D–17 Avenue SE
Phone: 272•2969
Monday–Saturday 10:00 am–8:00 pm, Sunday 10:00 am–6:00 pm
V, MC, Debit, $

IT is a wild and wonderful cross-cultural adventure at Mayfair Foods. Latin American, African, and Caribbean staples including dried beans, flours and cumin are shelved beside east coast Newfoundland classics like Mt. Scio savoury, fabric pudding bags and Purity dry goods and cookies. Latin food lovers can round up frozen turnip greens, big bags of rice, dried corn silk, fresh *Scotch bonnet* peppers, *banana leaves*, and frozen whole fish, salt cod and salt beef. Add a few yams, *plantains* and *cassava*, and the mélange is truly wonderful. Only in Canada.... But don't come too early.
• *House Specialties*: Latin American, Caribbean, and Newfoundland food.

SOUTHWEST

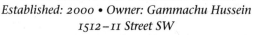

Boca Loca Fine Mexican Foods

Established: 2000 • Owner: Gammachu Hussein
1512–11 Street SW
Phone: 802•4600
Sunday–Tuesday 10:00 am–6:00 pm, Wednesday–Saturday 10 am–8:00 pm
V, MC, Debit, $

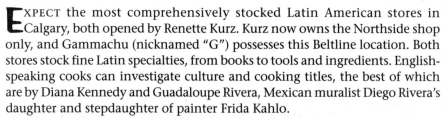

EXPECT the most comprehensively stocked Latin American stores in Calgary, both opened by Renette Kurz. Kurz now owns the Northside shop only, and Gammachu (nicknamed "G") possesses this Beltline location. Both stores stock fine Latin specialties, from books to tools and ingredients. English-speaking cooks can investigate culture and cooking titles, the best of which are by Diana Kennedy and Guadaloupe Rivera, Mexican muralist Diego Rivera's daughter and stepdaughter of painter Frida Kahlo.

Examine the wonderful tools and cookware available: presses, for *tortillas* and for citrus, mortar and pestle of cast iron, with and without a spout—in several sizes, a large *molcajete y tejolete*, traditional Yucatan-made wicker *tortilla* warmers or an ingenious American terra cotta version. Or maybe you need an electric *quesadilla* maker, like a wok with feet, it is a very cool way to make Latin-style grilled cheese sandwiches, or *panini*, if you feel Italian today. Other tools: *comal* and *paella* pans and *tamaleras* for making *tamales*.

Local **Missing Link Extraordinary Sausage** chicken sausages—Yucatan, *molé* and *chorizo* sausages—are big favourites. Add *tomatillos, jicama, tamarind* —whole, paste, and pods, *serrano chilies*, tiny but robustly flavoured Key limes, fresh cilantro and *epazote*, avocados, *banana leaves*, tomatoes from Mexico, *poblanos* and *plantains*, all *muy Latino*. Cheese fans may want to try Mexican-style *queso fresco*, a wonderful partner to *guava* paste, much like the classic Spanish pairing of quince paste with fresh cheese. If Latin-style cheeses are needed, reach for Spanish *Manchego* or American-made *Monterey Jack*. Packaged and processed supplies range from the benign fungus *cuitlacoche* to fiery and smoky *chipotles in adobo sauce*, and makings for *tamales*—corn husks and *hominy* corn. Indulge your sweet tooth with *cajeta* and Mexican *cajeta* candies. For drinking and cooking, buy Ibarra and Abuelita sweet-but-grainy Mexican chocolate discs containing *piloncillo*.

For dishes to go: enchilada casseroles filled with chicken rice and red or green sauce, *tamales*, classic *pico de gallo* or refreshing mango *jicama* salsa. Select shrimp ceviche or key lime pie with roasted pecan crust, impeccably fresh corn *tortillas*, *molé poblano*, *salsa verde*, roasted *guajillo* sauce—which smells like sun-dried tomatoes and could be disguised as an Italian sauce in a culinary pinch.

To learn about cooking in the traditions and techniques of the Mexican kitchen, hands-on, inquire about classes taught by Marta Hernandez at the north store.

• *House Specialties*: Mexican ingredients, fresh corn *tortillas* and *queso fresco*, tostadas, ready-made dishes, books, tools, kitchenware.

• *Also Available*: 777 Northmount Drive NW.

www.bocalocacalgary.com

NORTHWEST

Boca Loca Fine Mexican Foods
Established: 2000 • Owner: Renette Kurz
777 Northmount Drive NW (Cambrian Village)
Phone: 289•2202
Monday–Friday 10:00 am–6:00 pm, Saturday 10:00 am–5:00 pm
V, MC, Debit, $
[see SW Latin, Caribbean & African for main entry on p. 141]

Local Producers

WHERE OUR FOOD IS GROWN is not an esoteric debate. It has real implications for all of us—rural dwellers, city folk, and everyone in-between. Most of us do not grow our own food. We do not keep urban gardens, nor do we have many community gardens or community-supported agriculture (CSA), where a number of families buy shares in a farmer's yield.

Even though we don't grow it ourselves, it is surprisingly easy to ignore the question of where our food comes from. It is easy, in the face of our global market—pineapples from Brazil, soybeans from China, salad from California, cherries from Chile. But what will happen when that global garden's gate swings shut, by any of a number of man-made or natural disasters? War. The end of cheap oil. Earthquake. Pandemic. Floods or famine.

Data released in the May 2006 Canadian census shows that nearly 2.5 million Albertans—73 percent of the province's population—live in the "Calgary–Edmonton Corridor," the 400-kilometer band of land that connects the two cities, including the cities of Airdrie, Wetaskiwin, Red Deer, and Leduc, and the small towns along the way. Eighty-one percent of Albertans are urban residents; 71,660 of the province's population are farmers.

In the ten-year span from 1996 to 2006, the number of Albertan farms decreased by 9,576. We are surrounded by lost farmland.

Calgary housing development has swallowed much of the rich agricultural land around the city. Drive west and observe Springbank's remaining farms stitched to suburban sprawl. Bearspaw's high-bluff view of the big bend in the river is hemmed in by houses. Cochrane and Okotoks are now minutes from Calgary city limits. A recently approved racetrack and mall development in Balzac have buckled up the narrowing agricultural belt between Calgary and Airdrie. Farther north, farmland has been annexed by the town of Innisfail for residential development immediately north of the town's existing border. Add it up, and it's not hard to envision the corridor along the Queen Elizabeth II Highway as home to a mass of residents, with accompanying high-speed rail and electrical transmission lines. The drive north may eventually become one without views of open farmland under cultivation. It doesn't bode well for locally produced food.

The Alberta-made and Alberta-grown products of Local Producers listed here are worth looking for on retail shelves. Take them home, cook them, stir them into your dinner, add them to your kids' lunches. Locally raised meat, dairy products and produce have not travelled long miles from gate to plate, and are often heirloom varieties, flavourful and hardy; specialty products all—processed beyond their raw state and reflective of our prairie *terroir*.

Local Producers have been organized according to our major categories and currently include entries for: Booze, Cheese & Dairy, Chocolates & Sweets, Fishmongers, Greengrocers, Meat & Game, and a few listed under Others—

those not easily classified by any of our major categories. Unlike other *de facto* local producers—those which entertain visits to the farmgate (thus found in the Farmgate Sales sections of Calgary, and Bow Valley and Beyond: Points North, East, South, and West), some of these producers have their own retail shops; others do not currently entertain visits to their places of work or business. This could change in the future; expect that some businesses classified as Local Producers in this inaugural edition of *Shop talk* may be relocated to Farmgate Sales in subsequent editions. Until then, please honour these families' privacy and do not visit their homes without an invitation or permission to do so.

CHEESE & DAIRY

Vital Green Farms
Established: 1993 • Owner: Joe Mans
Mailing Address: Box 936, Picture Butte, Alberta TOK 1V0
Phone: 824•3072

JOE Mans and his Dutch-bred family, residents of Canada for a quarter-century, keep Holstein cows and are Alberta's first certified-organic dairy farmers. The cream of the crop of this farm's lush dairy products is a knockout 52 percent whipping cream, but they also produce milk and chocolate milk, yoghurt, a yoghurt-buttermilk drink and *crème fraîche*. Vital Green Farms milk is pasteurized, but not homogenized. The family has begun to make cheese, and its first batch of Gouda is now available.
- *House Specialties*: Organic milk, cream, yoghurt, *crème fraîche*, cheese and buttermilk.
- *Available*: **Amaranth Whole Foods Market**, the Sunworks Farm shop at **Calgary Farmers' Market**, **Community Natural Foods**, **Janice Beaton Fine Cheese**, **Planet Organic Market**, **Sunnyside Market** and catering/restaurant menus, including the Calgary Petroleum Club, **Infuse Catering/Forage Foods**, **Red Tree**, River Café and Rouge.

CHOCOLATE & SWEETS

Biscotti By Susan D
Established: 1990 • Owner: Susan M. Denike
Mailing Address: 2969 Oakmoor Crescent SW, Calgary, Alberta T2V 3Z8
Phone: 281•8479 • E-mail: susand1@shaw.ca

THIS baker makes eight flavours of biscotti, in a range from chocolate, lemon or gingerbread-spiced, to double ginger. Each flavour is available in one of three styles—organic, traditional, and wheat- and gluten-free made with rice flour. All of Susan's biscotti contain ground almonds, but can be made nut-free by special request. No butter or oil means the cookies are not only non-dairy, but good "keepers."

- *House Specialties*: Almond biscotti in mix 'n' match flavours and several styles for special diets: traditional, organic, gluten- and wheat-free.
- *Available*: Higher Ground, **Italian Supermarket**, Boardwalk Café in Bragg Creek and **Cochrane Coffee Traders** in Cochrane. The specialized organic, and wheat- and gluten-free varieties are available at **Planet Organic Market**; the wheat and gluten-free range at **Lakeview Bakery**. Direct orders can also be made by phone or e-mail.

FISHMONGERS

Cunningham's Scotch Smoked Fish
Established: 2002 • Owner: Joe Cunningham
Mailing Address: Box 3187, Pincher Creek, Alberta T0K 1W0
Phone: 627•6594 • E-mail: cunninghams@cunninghamscoldsmoking.com

JOE Cunningham is a bit of a loner, and would rather spend his time fishing the Oldman River or solving fish smoking problems than talking to people. He is a fussy perfectionist, by his own account, consumed with making the best, without necessarily considering the bottom line, and his line of work suits him to a tee. Cunningham cold-smokes rainbow trout and Arctic char, and makes candied trout plus *pâtés* of char, trout and sometimes salmon. He and his partner Janice, the practical and organizing force in his life, moved to Pincher Creek. The pace of life there suits him fine, along with the superlative fly-fishing. Standing waist deep in the river, he is completely absorbed in life. Hanging on a wall in his house, Cunningham has a pair of contrasting photos—the Oldman River, and the chaotic floor of the New York stock exchange. He prefers the river, and all it represents.

- *House Specialties*: cold-smoked rainbow trout and Arctic char; candied trout; trout, char and salmon *pâtés*.
- *Available*: **The Cookbook Company Cooks, Janice Beaton Fine Cheese, Second to None Meats, Sunnyside Market**. On the menu at Big Fish, **Infuse Catering/Forage Foods**, La Chaumière, **A Ladybug Belgian Pâtisserie**, River Café and **Route 40 Soup Company** in Turner Valley.
www.cunninghamscoldsmoking.com

GREENGROCERS

Alexandra's Butterfly Garden
Established: 1998 • Contact: Alexandra Luppold
Mailing Address: Box 1115, Black Diamond, Alberta T0L 0H0
Phone: 933•0004 • E-mail: alex@butterflygarden.ca

ALEXANDRA Luppold is a mystic, in the same way that Rudolph Steiner was a mystic. Like Steiner, she looks to the natural world to harmonize her spiritual questing with her place in the physical realm. "The big things,

Biodynamics

RUDOLPH Steiner, an Austrian philosopher born in 1861, founded the Waldorf school movement, now a global independent school movement with over 600 schools around the world. He gardened too, and devised *"biodynamics,"* believed to be the world's oldest non-chemical agricultural movement. One of the main principles of biodynamic farming is that the farm, like a human, is viewed and treated as a whole, a self-sustaining organism. Steiner advocated companion planting and crop rotation, but also more common practices like sowing and harvesting according to the lunar calendar, and esoterica such as the use of minute applications of homoeopathic-style infusions of mineral, plant, or manure extracts to heal and revitalize the soil. *Biodynamics* has a global following, with participating groups and members mostly concentrated in Europe, although several Alberta farms have adopted some or all of Steiner's methods. A trademark, Demeter™, named for the ancient goddess of the earth, is used to indicate certified farms where biodynamic principles are followed.

the sun, and the little things, the ants, are all part of the world. No one thing is more important than the other." Luppold, born in East Germany, arrived in Canada in 1998, hoping to realize her dream of an organic garden. She grows "cosmic" salad greens that chefs love in Black Diamond, staring down the physical demands of gardening and the struggles of high altitude growing. But she doesn't take things too seriously: ask her about slugs, and after she laughs, she will tell you how she keeps them out of her garden. Her garden is not certified-organic, but she follows organic and *biodynamic* principles.

- *House Specialties*: "Cosmic" salad greens.
- *Available*: In season, on the menu at Wild Horse Bistro in Black Diamond, River Café in Calgary and the **Route 40 Soup Company** in Turner Valley.
www.butterflygarden.ca

Gull Valley Greenhouse
Established: 1990 • Owner: Phil Tiemstra, Contact: Scott Epple
Mailing Address: RR#1, Blackfalds, Alberta TOM 0J0
Phone: 969•1670 • E-mail: sjnsons@telus.net

ACCORDING to owner and grower Phil Tiemstra, pesticide-free growing means using biological controls. They offer simple solutions to most tomato-growing challenges: tomato-loving aphids can be controlled with ladybugs; white flies require pro-active treatment with soap or wasps (the wasps lay their own eggs inside the eggs of the white fly, hatching out erstwhile "cuckoos" in the nest); bumblebees are necessary for pollination.

What began in 1990 as a deliberate crop diversification ploy has blossomed into three acres of hydroponic greenhouses, home to nearly a dozen tomato varieties, as well as the rampant pole beans that Tiemstra laughingly says are close to taking over. The eggplant and peppers grow in another 6 acres of greenhouses at nearby Doef's Greenhouse just north. At the markets, Scott Epple, Tiemstra's son-in-law, gently hands customers aromatic clusters of Cocktail and Clarence red tomatoes, glowing yellow and orange hybrids still attached to fuzzy green stalks, handfuls of sweet, tiny cherry and grape tomatoes, Romas in full and miniature sizes, his favourite beefsteaks, and a few bruise-like purple Chocolate Ugly heirlooms. His young kids like the pop-in pleasure of cherry tomatoes best, he says, and eat them like candy.

- *House Specialties*: Greenhouse tomatoes, peppers and cucumbers.
- *Available*: Available as Pic 'n' Pac at **Calgary Co-op** and **Sunnyside Market**, under their Gull Lake banner at **Calgary Farmers' Market, Grassroots Northlands Farmers' Market**, as well as Farmers' Markets in St. Albert and Old Strathcona, Edmonton. They supply about 30 restaurants in Calgary including the Calgary Petroleum Club and River Café.

Hotchkiss Herbs & Produce
Established: 1998 • Contact: Paul & Tracy Hotchkiss
Mailing Address: 283235 Township Road 224, Rocky View, Alberta T1X 0J6
Phone: 236•2963 • E-mail: info@hotchkissproduce.com

IT began in the late 1990s when Paul Hotchkiss could not find a delicious tomato for his favourite sandwich, a BLT. Now, a decade later, Paul and Tracy Hotchkiss supply home cooks, chefs, and retailers with some of Alberta's finest produce. And they deliver. They deliver their certified organic produce from the middle of May through until the end of October. This Calgary-area farm sells only what it grows in over half an acre of greenhouses, all colourful heirloom varieties that have become their trademark. Hotchkiss is noted for its tomatoes, which are now a new generation of Paul Hotchkiss's in-house cross-breeding program, undertaken at no small effort and cost to overcome tobacco mosaic virus. Look for varieties that resemble Green Zebras, Tigrella, Black Krim, and Brandywines in multiple colours. In addition, the greenhouses yield spinach, red romaine lettuce, arugula, rainbow Swiss chard, carrots, beans, striped calliope eggplant, Mediterranean cucumbers, Nor'easter pole beans, yellow cauliflower and multiple hues of beets. No delivery charges and a minimum $15 order are made possible by the existing restaurant and wholesale delivery schedule that Tracy Hotchkiss has implemented. Look online to see if you reside within the delivery regions, and enlist neighbours if you want to stretch the boundaries. Pay by cash and cheque for home delivery.

- *House Specialties*: Certified-organic heirloom-type tomatoes, vegetables and greens.
- *Available*: **Amaranth Whole Foods Market, Blush Lane, Community Natural Foods, Janice Beaton Fine Cheeses, Lina's Italian Market & Cappuccino Bar, Planet Organic Market, Second to None Meats** and **Sunnyside Market**.

www.hotchkissproduce.com

Lund's Organic Produce
Established: 1984 • Contact: Gert Lund
Mailing Address: Box 7, Site 18, RR#3, Innisfail, Alberta T4G 1T8
Phone: 227•2693 • E-mail: gertlund@lundsorganic.com

GERT and Betty Lund are pioneer organic growers in Alberta. They have been farming according to organic principles since 1984, and in 1988 were Alberta's first "certified organic" farm, under the auspices of the Sustainable Agriculture Association. Carrots love Albertan weather—our cool nights are perfect to convert their starches into sweet sugars—and Gert sells the province's most fabulous carrots, potatoes, onions, cabbage, broccoli, beets, brussel sprouts and lettuce.

Lund's carrots are a mainstay in my home, as in many other Albertan homes. My dog loves those crunchy sweet carrots, and so do my sons and I. The Lund's farm is just north of Innisfail's town border—their first farm was in the Kneehill Valley, 20 kilometres east of Innisfail, and they moved to their current 60-acre farm in 1992.

- *House Specialties*: Certified-organic vegetables—carrots, potatoes, onions, cabbage, broccoli, beets, brussel sprouts and lettuce.
- *Available*: **Calgary Farmers' Market.**

www.lundsorganic.com

Poplar Bluff Organic Farm
Established: 1986 • Contact: Rosemary Wotske & Robert Boschman
Mailing Address: Box 13, Site 5, RR#1, Strathmore, Alberta T1P 1J6
Phone: 934•5400

THE farm, certified organic since 1998, raises heritage-variety root vegetables that are seriously adored by chefs and home cooks. Rose Finn potatoes, oh my, are the finest this chef has ever cooked and eaten. Agria potatoes are this farm's bread and butter, so to speak, but they grow other heirloom root vegetables too. Beets come in many colours. Poplar Bluff Farm grows white, purple cylindrical, bulls' blood, golden, and striped pink *chioggia*. When you eat your carrots, you might like the round Thumbelina-like style, or a rainbow of red dragon, purple haze, white, yellow...even orange. As Wotske says, all crops depend on Mother Nature and the soil.

- *House Specialties*: organic heirloom beets, carrots, and potatoes.
- *Available*: **Amaranth Whole Foods Market, Community Natural Foods, Planet Organic Market, Sunnyside Market** and **Red Tree**, and on the menu at fine restaurants including Il Sogno, Rouge, Saint Germain, Wildwood and many more.

Carrots vs. Concrete

THE Lunds' farm is part of ten quarter-sections of land (1,600 acres, or 648 hectares) north and west of Innisfail which has recently been annexed by the town of Innisfail for future development.

Lund's farm taxes will hold steady for five years after annexation, then they will increase by 30 percent. Any increase in services will follow development. The Lunds have not decided on a course of action but, at age 55, Lund says he is too old to start again, and he doesn't know of any certified-organic land available in the vicinity. "Stand in the way of progress? You'll get run over. But if I was 20 years younger, I'd get a shark lawyer with big teeth. At this stage in my life, is it worth it?" he says. "All the little towns in central Alberta are expanding," he observes, adding that it takes at least three years to transition conventional land to organic production, plus another five years to realistically learn a patch's proclivities and nudge it into optimal production.

Dale Mather, Innisfail's chief administrative officer since 1986, says that farmers like Lund are free to sell or continue farming their land until development begins, which may be in five years or forty. He says, "Innisfail allows farmers to remain on a rural tax scheme until their land is developed or a subdivision is put in place."

The town of Innisfail has a current population of 7,700, including town councillor Jason Heistad, his wife and their three young daughters. "We don't want to be like the lower mainland of British Columbia," he says. "I am sure they didn't think that all that farmland in the Fraser Valley would be eaten up by paving, it is some of the best farmland in the country."

Innisfail Mayor Ken Graham does not understand why a Calgary food writer would be interested in land annexation in Innisfail. I try to explain the bigger issues for us all. Heistad expects growth—for Innisfail and along the entire corridor. The town is aware of the concerns of farmers, and sitting down and working with them is the best answer, he says, but adds that growth is a no-brainer. Perhaps it is. Except for the small wrinkle in seeing prime farmland converted from carrot production to concrete.

MEAT & GAME

Canadian Rocky Mountain Ranch

Established: 1997 • Contact: Terry Church & Brad O'Connor
Mailing Address: RR#8, Site 5, Box 54, Calgary, Alberta T2J 2T9
Phone: 410•7417 or (866) 563•2242 • E-mail: order@crmranch.com

THIS ranch is owned by Pat and Connie O'Connor of Canadian Rocky Mountain Resorts, which includes Buffalo Mountain Lodge, Deer Lodge,

Emerald Lake Lodge, Cilantro, The Ranche, Velvet at the Grand and Divino. The ranch is in DeWinton, southwest of Calgary, off Highway 22X near Priddis, and is home to elk, bison, and reindeer. Call first to see the herds. The Home Direct program sells their farm-raised game meat and sausages as well as tubs of game stock in a bid to encourage cooks to reproduce "Rocky Mountain" restaurant cuisine at home. Order online or by phone.

- *House Specialties*: Ranched game—elk, bison, reindeer, value-added meats.
- *Available*: Arrange pickup at Cilantro, The Ranche restaurant, or at the ranch itself. The meat is on the menu at all of the company's restaurants and resorts.

www.crmranch.com

Carmen Creek Gourmet Meats
Established: 2002 • Contact: Kelly Long
Mailing Address: 1919B, 4 Street SW Calgary, Alberta T2S 1W4
Phone: 233•9393 or (866) 945•3767 • E-mail: kelly.long@carmencreek.com

THIS business raises grass-fed bison that is naturally raised without additives or hormones, and *grain-finished*. Without doubt, this is some of the best bison I have eaten. Wild Rose Meats in the Peace Country is the parent company, with over 100 bison producers supplying the company. Bison is exceptionally lean, with significantly less fat than beef or pork, and is high in iron and zinc. Stellar cuts include double-cut rib-eye steaks found at some restaurants, rib-eye roasts, ground, tenderloin, and strip loin.

- *House Specialties*: Double-cut rib-eye, strip loin, tenderloin, ground.
- *Available*: **Canada Safeway**, **Master Meats**, Save-On Foods (Edmonton). On the menu at Blink, the Calgary Petroleum Club, Rouge, Tribune, and Wildwood.

www.carmencreek.com

Country Lane Farms Ltd.
Established: 1984 • Contact: Jerry & Nancy Kamphuis
Mailing Adddress: RR#1, Site 3, Box 14, Strathmore, Alberta T1P 1J6
Phone: 934•2755
V, MC, Debit, cheque, $

JERRY and Nancy Kamphuis have raised birds since 1984 on their farm east of Calgary near Strathmore. They come to Calgary bi-weekly on regularly scheduled trips, with a refrigerated truck, park in quiet corners of some of the city's hotel parking lots, and open the doors to their patiently waiting customers. They are committed to producing clean, healthy, unstressed food, and the large birds are antibiotic-free, hormone-free, and live in a large barn that is computer-monitored. They sell whole and cut-up chicken, hormone-and-antibiotic free beef aged 21 days, in "packs" of assorted cuts as well as ground, and salmon—in several forms, from filets to candied— from Cloyoquot Sound off Vancouver Island. Eggs and honey are available on a "first-come, first served" basis. Kamphuis suggests ordering ahead online

or by phone, as they do run out. Jerry and his refrigerated truck arrive in one-hour time windows at specified times at 11 locations (mostly hotel parking lots) in Northside and Southside Calgary, Canmore, and Red Deer. Check online when ordering, as details and schedules are updated regularly.
- *House Specialties*: Antibiotic-free and hormone-free chickens and beef; salmon from Cloyoquot Sound.
- *Available*: **Master Meats** and 11 hotel parking lots in Calgary, Canmore, and Red Deer.
www.great-chicken.com • www.countrylanefarms.com

Diamond Willow Organics Ltd.
Established: 1996 • Contact: Keith Everts
Mailing Address: Box 1718, Pincher Creek, Alberta TOK 1W0
Phone: 627•4983 or Cell: 627•6442 • E-mail: info@diamondwillow.ca

THIS seven-family ranching corporation raises certified-organic *grain-finished* beef in the Foothills south of Calgary on a total of 63,000 acres of land. Francis and Bonnie Gardner live and ranch on Mount Sentinel Ranch, Cass and Jamie Freeman own Freeman Ranch, Larry and Jan Frith work Frith Ranch, Keith and Bev Everts own Stillridge Ranch, Janet Main, Charlie Straessle, Mac Main and their families run MX Ranch, Salix Enterprises is the home of Bill and Carol Elton, and Ketaorati Ranch is run by Norman and Hilah Simmons. Some of the families involved have been ranching for generations, on land that has been in their families for more than a century, and their children are making plans to be involved on the ranches. Keith Everts says that the word "organic" was a hard sell to his fellow ranchers in the mid-1990s, when the families joined forces, but the management practices underlying organic ranching were a match for those men and women with an intimate knowledge of their land and ecosystem. Many of the ranchers in the Diamond Willow organization are also involved in the Southern Alberta Land Trust.
- *House Specialties*: Certified-organic grass-fed, *grain-finished* beef.
- *Available*: **Community Natural Foods**, and Save-On Foods. On the menu at the Banff Springs Hotel, Belgo, River Café, and Saint Germain.
www.diamondwillow.ca

Elbow Falls Wapiti
Established: 1990 • Owner: Win Niebler
Mailing Address: RR#1, Priddis, Alberta TOL 1W0
Phone: 931•2427 • E-mail: win.niebler@3web.net

WIN Niebler of Elbow Falls Wapiti pastures 100 head of elk near Priddis, and has a long-standing history of involvement with local food and drink as a co-founder of *Brew Brothers Brew Pub* in Canmore. "I like to have a beer with my elk," he says, not really joking at all. The herd and its care keep him balanced, he maintains. He is a staunch advocate of local. "Why cross borders into exotic food when we have the freshest air and cleanest water right here? And the elk, they were here long before we arrived." Niebler describes elk meat as lean, with finely textured muscle tissue, ideal for slow braised osso buco. "That slow simmer at 70 degrees is what converts elk shank from Michelin-tire-tough into fall-apart tender." Specialties are elk sausages in the Swiss style, with neither fat nor sodium nitrate.

• *House Specialties*: Elk meat and Swiss-style elk sausages.
• *Available*: frozen at **Amaranth Whole Foods Market, Community Natural Foods**, and on the menu at **Big Rock Brewery**, the Bavarian Inn, La Chaumière, Rouge, and Wildwood.

Grazin' Acres
Established: 2004 • Contacts: Jan & Wil De Boer
Mailing Address: Box 56, Two Hills, Alberta T0B 4K0
Phone: (780) 657•2001 or (888) 657•2001
Friday & Saturday 9:00 am–5:00 pm, Sunday 9:00 am–4:00 pm (at CFM)
V, MC, Debit, $

Parents Jan and Wil (Wilhelmina) De Boer are the faces at the market. Offspring John and wife Helene are the hardworking animal tenders living near Two Hills. Their poultry (ducks, geese, chickens and turkey, plus eggs) are certified organic and the lamb is naturally raised. The pork comes from a neighbouring farm. If you wish to sample it, there is horse tenderloin in the freezer, along with Lethbridge-raised rabbit. Sausages are made to specification by the De Boers' butcher, and freezer fans can purchase a whole lamb or a whole carcass or side of pork, so long as they order ahead.

• *House Specialties*: Organically-raised poultry, and naturally-raised lamb.
• *Available*: **Calgary Farmers' Market.**
www.grazinacres.ca

Hoven Farms
Established: 1909 • Owners: Tim & Lori Hoven
Mailing Address: RR#3, Eckville, Alberta T0M 0X0
Phone: 217•2343
Friday & Saturday 9:00 am–5:00 pm, Sunday 9:00 am–4:00 pm (at CFM)
V, MC, Debit, $

This century-old family ranch business likes to say that the great outdoors is its cooler. Translation: it gets no fresher than this, and no cleaner. Tim Hoven is a fourth generation rancher. He and his wife Lori, their six kids, and Tim's folks, Cecil and Carol, run the ranch near Olds. Their meats are available as freezer packages, from whole animals to sides to personalized packs. Otherwise, choose from prime cuts, sausages and jerky, and cooks can buy bones for soup or stock-making. There's fare for Fido too.

• *House Specialties*: Certified-organic beef, available as individual cuts, sides, freezer packs; beef bones, sausages and jerky.
• *Available*: **Amaranth Whole Foods Market, Calgary Farmers' Market, Community Natural Foods, Planet Organic Market, SPUD, Sunnyside Market**, and **Nutter's Bulk & Natural Foods** in Canmore.
www.hovenfarms.com

Old Country Sausage Shop

Established: 2000 • Contact: Klaus & Mary Lee Schurmann
Mailing Address: Box 775, Raymond, Alberta TOK 2SO
Phone: 752•3006
Friday & Saturday 9:00 am–5:00 pm, Sunday 9:00 am–4:00 pm (at CFM)
V, MC, Debit, $

THIS award-winning family business, owned by Klaus and Mary Lee Schurmann, has a presence at the **Calgary Farmers' Market**. Klaus makes more than 50 varieties of sausages, without fillers, MSG, sugar, dairy, flour, nitrites, artificial colour or binders. Taste standouts are *andouille* or *kielbasa*. Cured, smoked, and air dried choices include pork or bison pepperoni. Fresh sausages worth noting are *merguez*, maple breakfast, and *chorizo*. Cooked varieties include mild *weisswurst* and bratwurst. Of the several types of bacon available, dry-cured is saltier than you may be accustomed to, but the flavour is outstanding. Newest sausages include turkey and mango, and leek and cabbage sausage. Fresh meats—beef, lamb and bison—are free-range but the poultry is not.

- *House Specialties*: Sizzlers, dry-cured bacon, cured, smoked and dried sausages without fillers, MSG, sugar, dairy, flour, nitrites, artificial colour or binders.
- *Available*: **Calgary Farmers' Market**, **High River Farmers' Market** and Lethbridge Farmers' Market in season, a shop in Lethbridge, and on Golf Course Road, Raymond.

www.oldcountrysausages.com

Sunworks Farm

Established: 1998 • Owners: Ron & Sheila Hamilton
Mailing Address: Box 55, Armena, Alberta TOB 0G0
Phone: (780) 672•9799 or Toll Free: (877) 393•3133
Friday & Saturday 9:00 am–5:00 pm, Sunday 9:00 am–4:00 pm (at CFM)
V, MC, Debit, $

THE Hamilton family's foray into organic foods began with illness, but has blossomed into a success story—and health—of several generations and several branches of an extended family. The farm was certified organic in 1997. The farm's pork, beef, chickens and turkeys are certified organic, grass-fed and free-ranging. They raise grass-fed Muscovy ducks and geese, and the Hamiltons' extended family farm near Armena raises lamb. At the shop, look at the selection of celiac-safe sausages, wieners, hams and bacon, all free of nitrates and gluten, eggs, dairy, MSG, and sulphates. In the case, find eggs, and **Vital Green Farms** dairy products. The family's second generation, daughter Erin and her partner, Matt Paulson, operates **Blush Lane** in the adjacent stall with organics guy Rob Horricks.

- *House Specialties*: Certified organic free-range chicken, pork, duck, lamb, turkey, sausages, and eggs.

- *Available*: **Calgary Farmers' Market**. In conjunction with **Blush Lane** and **A Ladybug Belgian Pâtisserie**, a new location will open at 10 Aspen Stone Boulevard SW in May 2008.

www.sunworksfarm.com

Valta Bison

Established: 2004 • Contact: Darlene & Gil Hegel
Mailing Address: PO Box 22, Valhalla Centre, Alberta TOH 0M0
Phone: (780) 356•3627

703–23 Avenue SE	*H6, 4421 Quesnay Wood Drive SW*
(Ramsay Shop)	*(Calgary Farmers' Market)*
Phone: 237•9667	*Cell: 650•2425*
Monday–Friday 9:00 am–7:00 pm	*Friday & Saturday 9:00 am–5:00 pm*
Saturday 9:00 am–5:00 pm	*Sunday 9:00 am–4:00 pm*

V, MC, Debit, $

BOTH Gil and Darlene were raised in the Peace Country, and are proud of their region, and their family history. Darlene loves to recount her Norwegian family's settling of the home farm, and the family's connection to the Valhalla Centre Mercantile. Their bison is mouth-filling, delicious, available in cuts and value-added forms like sausage and child-friendly pepperoni sticks.

As we stand talking at the market, a small child comes by and buys his first-ever "I bought it alone" bison pepperoni stick. Darlene gives him two to mark the occasion. These Peace Country ranchers have made a warm name for themselves, based on their successful and low-key marketing of bison as an un-intimidating meat, one stick of pepperoni at a time.

The recently opened store in Ramsay has a sense of history. Gil laughs and says, "It has a 1911 front with a 1945 house on back, and I am sure it was up to code in 1945." Natural and smoked sausages are the core of their business, including Mennonite, smokies, sun-dried tomato, garlic coil, and those pepperoni sticks in four flavours. The cozy shop stocks some Alberta vegetables, and the house line of meat, and may soon embark on expansion into more prepared dishes. Darlene makes a mean bison chili. They also sell bacon, Montreal smoked bison, roast, and ground bison, in burgers and not. Don't forget to buy a tub of chili.

- *House Specialties*: Bison, value-added cuts, sausages, pepperoni and dishes, local foods.
- *Also Available*: Farmgate sales at the ranch in Valhalla Centre, in Northwest Alberta's Peace Country, and at Sweetgrass Market, 873–85 Street SW (West Springs Village).

www.valtabison.com

Wapiti Ways

Established: 2001 • Owner: Craig Armstrong
Mailing Address: 107, 1726–14 Avenue NW, Calgary, Alberta T2N 4Y8
Phone: (888) 927•4849 (WAPITIW) • E-mail: craigarm1967@telus.net

CRAIG Armstrong raises farmed elk on a ranch near Wetaskiwin, is a member of **Slow Food Calgary**, and attended Slow Food's "United Nations" of food, Terra Madre, in Turin, Italy, in 2006. The meat is available both fresh and frozen, as steaks, roasts, and ground, as well as by sides or whole carcass. If you prefer value-added, try elk jerky, lasagna, pizza, calzone, sausage rolls, and gumbo. For Fido, take home big bones. The dog may not notice, but your body will: elk is a healthy source of protein, significantly higher in protein and iron, and lower in cholesterol and fat than most other meats. This ranch is fast becoming a "zero-carbon-footprint" location, using wind turbines, solar panels, and a bio-diesel generator to power the 320 acres the family has occupied since 2001.

• *Available*: **Calgary Farmers' Market, Infuse Catering/Forage Foods**, and on the menu at Juniper Resort and River Café.

www.wapitiways.com

OTHERS

Brassica Mustard

Established: 1995 • Owners: Desmond Johnston & Karen Davis
Mailing Address: 608–23 Avenue NE, Calgary, Alberta T2E 1W4
Phone: 277•3301 • E-mail: desmond@brassicamustard.com

MUSTARD seed is a prairie staple. Its yellow flag waves along our highways and byways, but for years, the seeds were shipped to France, India or Bangladesh, returning as costly value-added French Dijon, or pungent mustard oil. Finally, it is staying home on the range. Calgary chef Desmond Johnston and his wife Karen Davis are mustard makers, in a solid bid to create a sustainable business based on Albertan ingredients, and a lifestyle that is more family-friendly than restaurant life. Their mustard evolved out of their gift-giving habit and their desire to get chef and dad Desmond out of restaurant kitchens and into the fabric of self-employed family life. It worked, but although the deed was done in the kitchen, don't call him Colonel Mustard! This prairie classic is reborn in a jazzy blend of flavours: cranberry and honey—sharp and sweet, like Billie Holliday on her best day, roasted garlic mustard—robust and roundly-flavoured, horseradish—as pungent a breath as Satchmo's cornet, or dill—a sleek sidle of herbs. Try the gift pack and get them all. Music not included.

• *House Specialties*: Mustards.
• *Available*: **Bon Ton Meat Market, Community Natural Foods, The Cookbook Company Cooks, Janice Beaton Fine Cheese, North Sea Fine Fish, Red Tree**, and **Sunterra Quality Food Markets**.

www.brassicamustard.com

Grainworks Inc.

Established: 1986 • Owners: Dwayne & Doreen Smith
Mailing Address: Box 30, Vulcan, Alberta TOL 2B0
Phone: 485•2808 or Toll Free: (800) 563•3756 • E-mail:smith@grainworks.com

THE farm was homesteaded in 1912 near Vulcan by Dwayne's family. Now, Dwayne and Doreen raise triticale, barley, flax, several strains of wheat, dry edible beans, and lentils too. Milling and packaging is all done on location, producing grains, flours, cracked grains, multi-grain mix and seven-grain cereal. The farm has been certified organic since 1986.

• *House Specialties*: Certified-organic grains, pulses, flours, cereals.
• *Available*: **Amaranth Whole Foods Market**, **Community Natural Foods**, **Sunnyside Market**, and **Nutter's Bulk & Natural Foods** in Canmore, as well as many local area bakeries and restaurants.

www.grainworks.com

Hamilton's Barley Flour

Established: 1990 • Contact: Donna & Alex Hamilton
Mailing Address: RR#2, Olds, Alberta T4H 1P3
Phone: 556•8493 • E-mail: info@hamiltonsbarley.com

LIKE wheat, barley is a star of Herculean proportions, in far-off times and far-off lands. Big in ancient and modern beer making, where it is the primary agent for malting, barley was also a dietary staple in northern Europe centuries after it fed the gladiators of ancient Rome. But in present times, barley has been relegated to second-drawer status, and is used in the main as animal fodder, and of course in beer making.

Barley flour—in a brown paper bag—has been on the grocery shelves in Alberta for decades.

Donna Hamilton is the matriarch of the Hamilton family, owners of Hamilton's Barley Flour. Theirs is a success story of crop diversification and value-added smarts. Their barley flour has been on the mark from the beginning, packed in an earth-friendly brown paper bag that first attracted the attention of health food stores and people struggling with wheat-free diets. Barley belies its simple packaging. Not only does barley have a lower gluten content than wheat and great absorption capability, but it also bakes up in a range of tones—dark to pale. Bakers need to thoughtfully reconstruct recipes that enhance the pluses—notably barley's great nutty taste, its wholesome high-fibre profile and an ability to keep baked goods moist.

• *House Specialties*: Barley flour.
• *Available*: **Calgary Co-op** and **Canada Safeway**.

www.hamiltonsbarley.com

Highwood Crossing Farm Ltd.

Established: 1989 • Contact: Tony & Penny Marshall
Mailing Address: Box 25, Aldersyde, Alberta TOL OAO
Phone: 652•1910 • E-mail: tony@highwoodcrossing.com

TONY and Penny Marshall reside on Highwood Crossing Farm south of Calgary. The farm has been in the family for more than a century. In this era, they produce and bottle cold-pressed certified-organic canola oil and flax seed oil, Alberta originals that are sought after by chefs, cooks and locavores. The oil press is closely monitored to eliminate light, heat, and oxidization during pressing. Dark glass bottles are filled, labeled and promptly refrigerated before their short trip to retail shelves. In an ingenious marketing move, the extruded solids are sold to Joe Mans at **Vital Green Farms**, as feed for organically raised poultry and livestock. A certified-organic processing facility on the Highwood Crossing Farm is where they produce and package organic granola, flax seed muffin and pancake mix, stone ground flours as well as whole grains and cereals and 'Power Grains' wheat-free hot cereal. The family are strong members of **Slow Food Calgary**, and have attended "the UN of food," Terra Madre, held biennially in Turin, Italy, as Alberta delegates.

- *House Specialties*: cold-pressed certified-organic canola and flax seed oils, grains, wheat-free 'Power Grains" cereal, muffin and pancake mixes.
- *Available*: **Amaranth Whole Foods Market, Calgary Co-op, Canada Safeway, Community Natural Foods, The Cookbook Company Cooks, Infuse Catering/Forage Foods, Lakeview Bakery, The Main Dish, Planet Organic Market, Sunterra Market, Bison Mountain Bistro & General Store** in Banff, **Griesser Spoon Custom Catering/Railway Deli** and **Nutter's Bulk & Natural Foods** in Canmore, and **Route 40 Soup Company** in Turner Valley.

www.highwoodcrossing.com

Soft Path Cuisine

Established: 1997 • Contact: Di Slater
Mailing Address: 2220–20 Avenue NW Calgary, Alberta T2M 1J2
Phone: 282•8080 or Cell: 850•6979 • E-mail: inquiries@softpathcuisine.com

DI Slater is the vivacious one-woman engine that has driven Soft Path Cuisine into backpacking and mountaineering stores across the country with her flavourful dried fare for hikers. Since 1997, a day spent in her kitchen is a withering experience for fruits and vegetables as they are transformed into dried goods suitable for hikers, campers, climbers and outdoor enthusiasts. Her organic dishes offer convenience, longevity, and lightweight portability, all key issues for backpackers, climbers, and hikers. Packets are healthy, nutritious and organic and are large, generous meals, even by hiking standards. Packaged for campers but ideal for those at-home mornings that just cry out for something warm and nourishing, one popular dish is Hot & Corny Cereal, a grain-based brekkie of cornmeal and *couscous* spiked with dried fruit and cinnamon. It is easy to tart up as an accompaniment for the evening's savoury seafood stew, saffron-scented vegetable and chickpea *tagine*, olive-rich braised lamb or grilled game. The label sums up the portion expectations: "Feeds 2 ravenous, 3 hungry or 4 small appetites." So share with someone you love. It'll sustain you both.

- *House Specialties*: Dried organic foods for outdoor enthusiasts.
- *Available*: **Amaranth Whole Foods Market, Community Natural Foods,** Mountain Equipment Co-op, **Planet Organic Market, Sunnyside Market,** and **Nutter's Bulk & Natural Foods** in Canmore.

www.softpathcuisine.com

Zora's Lemonade Ltd.

Established: 1996 • Contact: Liz Pedersen
Mailing Address: 2147 Vimy Way SW, Calgary, Alberta T2T 6C2
Phone: 246•2046 • E-mail:zoraslemonade@shaw.ca

Liz Pedersen acquired Zora's in 1999, from founder Julie Kerr, who has moved on to fame as a bluegrass singer and songwriter. Back porch swings and June Carter Cash make fine inspiration for cool summer beverages. Zora's is an organic lemonade concentrate that just requires water. Say aaah!

- *House Specialties*: Organic lemonade concentrate.
- *Available*: **The Cookbook Company Cooks, Francesco's Italian Food Store & Deli, Sunnyside Market, Sunterra Market, Mountain Mercato Specialty Food Market** in Canmore, and during the summer season, at the **Bearspaw Farmers' Market** and **Millarville Farmer's Market.**

Make 'n' Take Meals/HMRs

HOME COOKING IS ONE of the regrettable casualties of a rapidly spinning globe: as the pace of life picks up, many consumers have stopped putting three squares on the table. We may be too busy to cook, or we have decided that cooking is not pleasurable or important, or that we cannot spare the time. But we still need to eat every day.

Fortunately, growing cadres of practical cooks and chefs have whipped up a new food group to circumvent the unappetizing alternatives—the perils of processed fast food, the belly-aching pangs of diner's remorse incurred at costly restaurants, or the contents of a cardboard box.

The "make 'n' take" idea is simple: they are ready-to-cook or ready-to-reheat meals, assembled by the consumer in a professional's well-stocked kitchen. The concept appeals to the busy dining public—singles, single parents, double-income workaholics, families with conflicting schedules and obligations, or anyone else who has moaned the refrain, "I'm too busy to cook!" The corollary benefits are numerous: the financial and timely efficiency of assembly-line packaging and volume purchasing, access—in some instances—to top-quality ingredients, tapping into the bloodless time-saving knife skills, organizational abilities, and cooking talents of seasoned kitchen professionals.

Each of these businesses offers a subtle variant on meals to go, at differing price-points, with various degrees of effort required by the home non-cook. How each business functions is similar and straightforward: book time and selected dishes online or by phone, to be assembled by an individual or groups. Some main courses include side dishes or starches, some don't. Ask!

On-site, expect racks of aprons, banks of well-organized refrigerators and freezers, lines of counters and refrigerated salad bars stocked with tidy containers holding prepared ingredients—some raw, some cooked—for each dish. Don the apron and follow the explicit assembly instructions posted prominently at each station. Scoop, package and pay. Take home detailed finishing and serving instructions with your meals. Many food retailers have added HMRs (Home Meal Replacements) to their product lines. This means ready-to-cook or ready-to-reheat meals, already assembled, made in the professional's kitchen, for pickup and consumption at home. Consult the back-of-book lists for comprehensive lists of businesses offering these services.

CITY WIDE

Baby Gourmet

Established: 2005 • Owners: Jill Vos & Jennifer Broe
Mailing Address: 50 Elkton Way SW, Calgary T3H 4Y8
Phone: 614•9821 • E-mail: info@babygourmetfood.com

THE market for high-quality baby food is...um, booming. Some parents do not cook at all, others want better quality or wider choices than thatshelved at supermarkets, and some parents want a healthy alternative to mass-produced baby food. This business, built by two sisters, serves up 40+ types of food for baby. All dishes containing meats are made with organically sourced hormone- and steroid-free meats. Sister Jill saw few options when she had her baby, so she began to make her own baby food, then friends wanted some for their tiny tykes. In the classic pattern, things grew, as do babies. The sisters shop for farmers' market fresh produce. No additives or preservatives are used, and all meals are frozen, and require only thawing and heating.

First-stage foods—for babies up to 6 months of age—are purees of mostly single ingredients—including favourites like broccoli, beets, or sweet potatoes. There are a few interesting combinations as well, such as carrot-apple-ginger and a root vegetable medley. For Stage 2 diners of under one year, the combos have some texture: fruity chicken and rice, with mango and apricot. By Stage 3, all ingredients in dishes like chicken minestrone are whole but tender, and perfect for tiny teeth to tackle. Millet and *quinoa* recipes are under development, and gluten-free choices are being considered for future tweaking. The business is growing into a strictly wholesale operation.

• *House Specialties*: Three stages (birth–6 months, 6–12 months, and 12+ months) of baby foods, all available frozen.

www.babygourmetfoods.com

Dashing Dishes Inc.

Established: 2005 • Owners: Kim & Michael Grech
City wide
Phone: 471•1395
Office: Monday–Friday 10:00 am–6:00 pm
Prearranged assembly evenings at sites city wide from 5:30 pm–9:00 pm
V, MC, Cheque, $

DASHING Dishes was founded by Kim and Michael Grech in 2005, and in 2006, this moveable feast of a business won the Calgary Chamber of Commerce's prestigious Bennett-Jones Emerging Enterprise of the Year award. Their business style is geared to flex-minded foodies on a budget. Meal assembly is mobile, with no fixed address, occurring instead at a variety of specified venues, mostly community halls. Clients book online for a spot in their preferred locations and dates. On-site, clients move from station to station, assembling dishes, in packs of either 8 or 12 different meals, each feeding 4–6 persons. They take home raw ready-to-cook meals, mostly meat-based, and all are suitable for freezing. No side dishes are included. Register online.

• *House Specialties*: Family-friendly client-assembled meals with monthly menu changes, held at a changing list of venues.

www.dashingdishes.com

NORTHEAST

The Main Dish

Established: 2006 • Owner: Jason Zaran
903 General Avenue NE (The Piazza)
Phone: 265•3474 (DISH)
Monday–Thursday 7:00 am–10:00 pm, Friday 7:00 am–midnight
Saturday 9:00 am–midnight, Sunday 9:00 am–9:00 pm
V, MC, AE, Debit, Cheque, $

IT looks like a cafeteria or coffee bar, and offers limited seating, but the heart of the business is ready-made meals to-go, made under the observant eyes of executive chefs Kevin Outhet and Kevin Pelissier. "Walk in, point, carry it home, heat it up and eat," says the owner, Jason Zaran. Customers can choose from chilled "chef's fare" tucked inside a 30-foot deli case, or they can carry on around the stylish curve of the counter to the "hot cuisine" area to order hot dishes and side accompaniments. A rotating menu keeps appetites perked and attentive—ribs on Monday night to gnaw on during the football or hockey game, or an upscale dine-in experience on the weekend. In addition to dinner to go, Main Dish offers "dinner theatre," a four-course (small-portion) meal with wine tasting and closed-circuit screens showing the kitchen's live action. A dedicated cooler provides "healthy essentials" meal components, ready to reheat, stemming from Olympic athletic sponsorships that the business has undertaken.

A former food service sales guy, Zaran studied the trends, and realized that restaurants were doing 20 percent take-away business, often without even advertising or targeting that niche. "The world of food is changing. Gen X'ers are special-occasion cooks who are used to high quality. For us, the perfect-storm client understands good food and shuns fast food, but is busy," Zaran says. "We are in the time business, to buy back your time for you." A growing grocery-to-go department and catering arm has been added. Online ordering arrives in 2008.

www.tmdish.com

SOUTHWEST

Mise En Place

Established: 2006 • Owner: Kathleen Spelliscy
11, 6449 Crowchild Trail SW (Lakeview Plaza)
Phone: 262•6333
Monday & Tuesday 10:00 am–6:00 pm
Wednesday & Thursday 10:00 am–9:00 pm
Friday 10:00 am–6:00 pm, Saturday 10:00 am–5:00 pm
V, MC, Debit, $

IN the Southside community of Lakeview, Kathleen Spelliscy opened Mise En Place (a French culinary term that translates as "having all ingredients for a dish prepared and put in place before cooking") in 2006. Spelliscy—a busy lawyer and mother of three youngsters—saw the light when her son complained (loudly) about having to eat pizza (yet again). Her underlying motives are deeper than simply ducking dinnertime cooking chores. Spelliscy believes that studies by Harvard University in Cambridge, Massachussetts and Columbia University in New York City—tracking the correlation between drug use, lower school performance, obesity, and the decline in sitting down to family dinners—are an indictment of societal choices. She believes that eating dinner together is a step towards the solution. Thus Mise En Place, where cooks "sweat and sauté and make sauces so you don't have to!"

Executive chef Judy Wood has developed signature dishes, stylish but simple, in a broad spectrum of global influences and styles. Wood and her staff do the preparation. Some items are cooked, and most proteins are raw. There are 16 items to choose from, changing monthly, encompassing low-fat, vegetarian, or other dietary regimes. Upgrades to organic and specialized ingredients are available on request, with commensurate fee adjustments. Timeslots for individuals, or for a private group event may be booked in advance. The wood-trimmed elegant shop does not feel like a commercial kitchen, but if you prefer the ambiance of your own kitchen, Mise en Place's Kitchen Parties bring the kitchen to your home so you can host in-house meal assemblies. The business has branched into homestyle and gourmet HMRs, some dishes ready to reheat, others ready to cook. Some side dishes are add-ons. Delivery is available for a sliding fee that is based on distance driven.

- *House Specialties*: Meal assembly, kitchen parties and Home Meal Replacements (HMRs).
- *Also Available*: 511, 15566 McIvor Boulevard SE (Copperfield Corner) Opening mid-2008.

www.miseenplace.ca

Stock & Sauce Co.

Established: 2002 • Owners: Debbie Catling & Kari Faba
H6, 4421 Quesnay Wood Drive SW (Calgary Farmers' Market)
Phone: 619•0122 or 836•4020
Friday & Saturday 9:00 am–5:00 pm, Sunday 9:00 am–4:00 pm
Debit, $

THIS business does the slow simmer so you needn't. Their big pots simmer liquid gold for cooks: indispensable *glace de viande*, rich and gelatinous stocks based on chicken and veal, pasta sauces and dips, comforting, hearty soups with character. The stocks and soups are frozen. The pasta sauces, dips and pasta are fresh and refrigerated. Fourteen thaw-and-heat soups change seasonally, from beef and barley, vegan mulligatawny, cream of wild mushroom, or Boston clam chowder, to cauliflower and Stilton. The two busy mothers at the helm (with a total of 13 kids between them!) have plans to add stews and slow-simmered dishes to their repertoire.
• *House Specialties*: Stocks, soups and dips.
• *Also Available*: **Millarville Farmers' Market** (in season).
www.stockandsauce.ca

NORTHWEST

The Liberated Cook

Established: 2006 • Owner: Charles Lawton
16, 1941 Uxbridge Drive NW (Stadium Shopping Centre)
Phone: 233•2665
Monday–Friday 9:30 am–6:30 pm, Saturday 9:30 am–5:30 pm
Make 'n' Take – Hours by Appointment
V, MC, Debit, Cheque, $

ANDREW Hewson, late of Catch and currently a culinary instructor at SAIT, opened The Liberated Cook in June 2006, then sold the business to Charles Lawton when two jobs became one too many. The business offers several options for hungry non-cooks: spontaneously walk directly to the back fridges and select from a rotating collection of cooked dinner components. House specialties include succulent smoked pulled pork enchiladas or braised short ribs, with a changing selection of side dishes and starches. Plan and then order ahead of time a set number of meals, then come in and assemble them, or pay extra for The Liberated Cook staff to assemble and deliver your selections. Alternatively, those suffering acute kitchen avoidance can hire the Liberated Cook's catering arm. The goal is to provide everyday meals made to restaurant quality at affordable home-cooked prices.
• *House Specialties*: Soups, ready-made cooked frozen meats and refrigerated vegetables and side dishes, book-ahead make 'n' take sessions, catering.
www.theliberatedcook.com

Meat & Game

IT USED TO BE EASIER. Ask your hunter-gatherer for meat, and he'd lumber into the back cave, haul out some dry-aged mastodon meat or a rack of pterodactyl ribs and fling it on the coals. Nowadays, you need a meat market, a specialist, and a linguistics degree to decipher meaty terms. It is always best to know your producer, or at next best degree of separation, your butcher.

In 2003, BSE altered the business of beef in Canada. Many beef producers resorted to fire sale pricing and direct marketing to survive the crash. Some ranchers sold their herds, some butchered them all, unable to afford the grain or grass it cost to keep them. Some growers are still relying on direct sales. "Branding" emerged, more figuratively than in Western history, as many ranchers learned to market their meats under a distinctive label, often the name of their ranch, in an effort to differentiate and add value.

BSE has not been the only force changing the nature of butcher shops in Calgary. Immigration has altered meat shopping too. Calgary has welcomed thousands of Hindus who eat no pork or beef, and thousands of Muslims who eat only *Halal* meat. New shops have arisen to supply these specific needs.

According to Syed Sohowardy of the Islamic Supreme Council of Calgary, there are now 85,000 Muslims residing in the city, with an influx of 10,000 between the years of 2005–2007. Butcher shops offering *Halal* meats have increased to keep pace with the growing population.

Animals slaughtered according to *Halal* principles are blessed before they are humanely dispatched with a sharp knife. The animals must be in the most comfortable position possible and are usually not stunned beforehand.

Certifying meat as *"kosher"* or "proper" follows long-standing Jewish traditions under the supervision of a rabbi. Meats considered *kosher* are the front quarters of animals which chew their cud and are cloven-hoofed— such as cattle, bison, venison, goats and sheep, fish with fins and scales, and specific breeds of poultry—including ducks, chicken, geese, and turkey. The process begins with a meticulous and quick blade, then the meat is inspected. Any forbidden fats, nodes or nerves are excised, then the meat is soaked in cool water, and salted to remove any blood.

What makes a good butcher shop? Quality meats, of course, but I vote too for providing provenance, personalized service, custom cutting and applied knowledge. A good butcher will willingly take out unwanted bones for knife-challenged clients, then cheerfully apply strings, skewers, and stuffing on request. An outstanding butcher will also be a good cook, able to suggest appropriate cooking methods for specific cuts of meat.

It is worthwhile noting that standards of cleanliness vary with cultures. Walking into a meat shop where English is not the first language can be like stepping onto another continent where street markets are the norm. I hope that standards will climb in those locations that require better housekeeping practices. Many are not exclusively meat shops, but do have a meat counter or freezer in conjunction with other foods.

Meat Matters & Lingo

How does a cook assess raw meat? Poking packaged meat with an uninformed fingertip tells no useful tales. It is best to understand what the labels and terminology mean.

- *Grading*: refers to eating quality. Canada's top grades are Prime, AAA, AA and A, and are differentiated by their *marbling*, from Prime, containing the highest, to A, which is the leanest. Less than 10 percent of Canadian meat is Prime and it is mostly sold to restaurants or exported.
- *Marbling*: fine white streaks of fat running through lean beef which increases tenderness, juiciness, and flavour.
- *Maturity*: cattle 30 months and younger meet criteria for Canada's top grades. Age is important because of its relationship to tenderness, and older animals have been implicated in BSE.
- *Colour*: meat should be bright red. Fat must be firm and white.
- *Texture*: firm muscle texture is associated with optimal eating quality and cooking consistency. All Grade A and higher has firm, fine-grained muscle.
- *Grass-fed*: cattle or bison which are fed only grass.
- *Grain-finished*: cattle or bison which are fed grain for the final 3–5 months of life, for a higher *marbling* or fat content. (Usually the grain is barley in the west and corn in eastern Canada.)
- *Aging*: the length of time (usually 7–21 days) sides of beef are hung under specific conditions before being cut into retail sizes. Aging allows enzymes in the meat to break down connective tissue and tenderize it.
- *Wet aging*: cuts of meat that are Cryovac'd after cutting. They can be kept under refrigeration for up to 6 weeks, but there is no further enzyme action, nor loss of volume or weight.
- *Dry aging*: additional aging for sides or cuts of meat, left uncovered for an additional 21–28 days under refrigeration. Ongoing enzyme action breaks down muscle tissue further, and accounts for an additional 25 percent moisture loss by weight and volume. Further trimming removes dried and discoloured surfaces. The result is densely textured and much more expensive meat. Many butchers cannot afford dry aging's cooler space or time requirements.

NORTHEAST

APNA Desi Meat Masala

Established: 2005 • Contact: Balbeb Gill
734, 5075 Falconridge Boulevard NE (Castleridge Plaza)
Phone: 568•4455
Monday–Sunday 10:30 am–10:00 pm
V, MC, Debit, $

THIS tidy shop specializes in a variety of marinated raw meats with East Indian flavourings: chicken in yoghurt, chicken in spicy rubs of ginger, hot chilies, and mint—or lamb chops, goat, shish kebabs and salmon fillets, all seasoned and ready to cook.
• *House Specialties*: Marinated chicken, lamb, goat, and salmon.

Calgary Meats & Deli

Established: 1974 • Owner: Bob Scherle
1204 Edmonton Trail NE
Phone: 276•1423
Tuesday–Friday 9:00 am–6:00 pm, Saturday 9:00 am–5:00 pm
V, MC, Debit, $

THIS clean, bright, and well-maintained family business is soundly based on the skills of Swiss-born Bob Scherle, who has more than 34 years in the trade. His wife Eleanor does the books and ordering, and daughter Stefanie works in the shop. The on-site smokehouse and sausage production team produces a wide range of products—*chorizo*, smokies, *chimneysticks*, bratwurst, bison *landjaeger* and jerky. A healthy respect for another talent means the house stocks many **Valbella Meats/Valbella Deli & Café** products from Canmore's classic smokehouse, from a large array of sausages to cold cuts, bacon, *pâtés*, hams, *bündnerfleisch* and *tohess speck*. Soup and stock makers can buy beef bones and chicken backs and necks. Time savers can acquire house-made beef or chicken pies, *rouladen* and Swiss meatballs, with special requests accommodated. The butcher business does a healthy AAA fresh meat and freezer trade, and can accommodate hunters (provenance tags required) if their bounty is clean and ready. Ask for "wascally wabbit" (a.k.a. *lapin*), duck, and turkey in season, and add a few European products from the preserves and pickles on the shelves.
• *House Specialties*: Fresh meats and value-added meats, smokies, garlic sausages, chicken *cordon bleu*, jerky, rabbit, duck and turkey in season, wild game processing by appointment.
• *Also Available*: on the menu at Il Chianti, Mikonos, Sandro's Cucina.
www.calgarymeatsanddeli.com

Central Halal Meat

Established: 1999 • Owner: Nasim Ali
205, 4655–54 Avenue NE
Phone: 280•4959
Monday & Wednesday–Sunday 10:30 am–6:30 pm
V, MC, Debit, $

ON a Saturday morning, the lineup at this bustling and tidy meat counter is six deep. The band saws whine as meat is cut to order, and customers wind through the aisles, shopping for Pakistani dry goods as they wait for their turn to order chicken, lamb, goat, or beef. Sort through stocks of *basmati* rice, spice *masalas*, fig jams, Ceylon *black* teas, cardamom pods and other spices, mustard, and coconut oils, *hummus* and pulses. It is a good spot to fill the East Indian pantry shelf.

• *House Specialties*: *Halal* Alberta beef and East Indian dry goods.

Chinook Edge Lamb & Goat

Established: 1993 • Owners: Ravi Fanda & Jerry Sanghera
404, 4656 Westwinds Drive NE (Westwinds Business Park)
Phone: 250•2250 or 615•9196 or Cell: 630•9196
Monday–Sunday 10:00 am–8:30 pm
V, MC, AE, Debit, Cheque, $

IN 1992, when Ravi was 16, he emigrated to join his father in Canada. At that time, "there was no *Halal* meat to be found in Calgary," he says. The family had been butchers in India, so Ravi's dad, from Punjab, opened Chinook Edge. Looking for a whole animal to spit? Or for goat meat? You found it! You can also buy game of a more unusual sort—farmed venison and elk, ostrich, bison, llama, and alligator. Birds too, both out of the ordinary and mundane: free-range chicken and eggs, goose, quail, pheasant, guinea fowl and duck. *Halal* meat is available on request even though there is no sign. So ask! There is veal, but no pork, and Ravi will source organic meats upon request.

• *House Specialties*: Whole lamb and goat, rabbit, venison, alligator, and poultry.

• *Also Available*: 1235–26 Avenue SE (**Crossroads Market**).

Horizon Meats

Established: 1983 • Owners: Stu Symes & Todd McEwen
1, 3610–29 Street NE
Phone: 291•0595
Tuesday–Friday 9:00 am–6:00 pm, Saturday 8:00 am–4:00 pm
V, MC, Debit, $

THERE is always evidence of a lot going on at this airport location, from sawdust on the floor to the waft of smoke from the in-house smoker and the hanging sides of Black Angus *dry aging* in the walk-in. If that isn't enough to lure you to this Northside destination, ask about the free-range chickens and **Winter's Turkeys** free-range birds, or geese from Rosebud farmer John

Green, frozen year-round and fresh for the high holidays. In the freezer, find Brome Lake ducks—whole and breasts—as well as quail and pheasant. There are more than 50 value-added products—chicken in marinade, teriyaki Maui ribs (thinly-cut beef ribs that cook quickly), London broil, bison and elk marinated roasts, Cornish hens vacuum-packed and frozen. Sausage is the big thing with more than 100 selections, in a variety of meats, all unadulterated. Try yak, or beef bacon—a low-fat sub for pork-based bacon. The education component of this hidden gem is matched by its high humour quotient, but don't forget why you came through the door.

• *House Specialties*: Sausages, *dry aged* Black Angus beef, value-added meats, poultry.

www.horizonmeats.ca

Mann Brothers Meat Shop
Established: 2002 • Owners: Kuljit & Jasbir Mann
618, 5075 Falconridge Boulevard NE (Castleridge Plaza)
Phone: 568•6997
Monday–Sunday 10:30 am–8:00 pm
V, MC, AE, Debit, $

THIS Sikh team of brothers is crackerjack busy, but despite their location in this multi-ethnic plaza, they do not sell *Halal* meat. They do sell fresh goat and lamb—more than 40 head each week—in their gleamingly tidy shop, along with more than two tons of chicken, mostly in marinades made in-house. Look for chicken in yoghurt-based marinades—some spicy, some not—or in rubs of ginger, chilies and lemon. Yum!

• *House Specialties*: Marinated chicken, lamb, and goat.

Rocky's Meats & Delicatessen
Established: 2008 • Owner: Rocky Schermer
37–4 Street NE
Phone: 286•7060
Tuesday–Friday 9:00 pm–5:30 pm, Saturday 9:00 am–5:00 pm
Debit, $

ROCKY Schermer, a third-generation butcher, has taken over the Bridgeland space (effective June 2008) formerly occupied by Richard Paolini, who remains in operation farther south. Rocky cuts Alberta-raised Galloway beef to order, and brings in lovely **Ewe-Nique Farms** lamb, **Winter's Turkeys** free-range or organic birds, and Springdale Colony Hutterite birds, also free-range and antibiotic- and growth hormone-free. Rocky makes good sausages as well.

• *House Specialties*: Beef, local lamb, sausages.

SOUTHEAST

Better Butcher
Established: 1994 • Owner: Randy Hnatuk
377 Heritage Drive SE (Acadia Centre)
Phone: 252•7171
Tuesday–Friday 9:00 am–6:00 pm, Saturday 9:00 am–5:00 pm
V, MC, Debit, $

THIS shop sells huge, free-range Craigmyle Hutterite Colony chickens that are hormone-and antibiotic-free, incoming every six weeks. In the autumn, order free-run, grain-fed turkeys, geese and ducks, raised on Ewelme Colony. Francophiles will enjoy finding rabbit to braise, duck fat for confit, ox tails and short ribs, all of which are pretty wow. Look too for immaculately trimmed Alberta AA beef, **Ewe-Nique Farms'** lamb, Alberta bison and pork, and ten types of house-made sausages. I like Randy's bangers. Ground veal, ground beef, ground chicken, and bison too, it is all here, so adventurous cooks with a sausage-stuffing horn attachment for their meat grinders can make their own. Local stuff includes hams from **Valbella Meats/Valbella's Deli & Café**, and meat pies from **MacEwan's Meats** and some produce in season, particularly **Poplar Bluff Farm** potatoes, the best in the province, oh my. Special requests are welcomed. Non-red-meat types can peruse the freezer for some fish—halibut, salmon, shrimp and prawns. In the freezer too are nice pierogies made by Randy's aunt Thelma, nearly 80 years young.
• *House Specialties*: Immaculate AA Alberta beef, sausages, poultry, meat pies and some produce in season.

Heaslip Venture Meats Ltd.
Established: 1975 • Owner: Rick Heaslip
Bay 14, 7400 Macleod Trail SE
Phone: 252•9924
Tuesday–Saturday 10:00 am–6:00 pm
V, MC, Debit, $

THIS shop has been in the business more than three decades. Even the sausage-stuffing machine has a nam—"Trixie". Look for naturally raised, *dry aged* AA and AAA beef, and a gaggle of sausages, local lamb and pork. Rick Heaslip, the owner since 1999, will bring in frozen ducks on request. In addition to **Winter's Turkeys** in season, house-smoked turkey breast—mildly hot-smoked over hickory—is available upon request. Large Huttterite free-run birds—geese, ducks, roasting chickens—all free of antibiotics, are on offer as well. You want links? Smokies are all-beef, breakfast sausage is made of fresh pork, or try turkey and chicken sausage, to a count of about two dozen types. If you don't see what you want, ask. Beef is cut to order, and game is processed if provenance is supplied. Whole-carcasss and by-the-side freezer beef is available, and the freezer contains pierogies, ground veal, burgers, bison, plus pies from **Simple Simon Pies**, and **MacEwan's Meats**. Fresh produce is on one shelf, and local as available.
• *House Specialties*: *Dry aged* natural beef, sausages, local lamb and pork.

Hungarian Deli

Established: 1999 • Owners: Zvonko, Rose & Sacha Cahunek
4020–26 Street SE
Phone: 207•8505
Tuesday–Friday 9:00 am–5:00 pm, Saturday 9:00 am–3:00 pm
Debit, $

THIS immaculate shop hidden in Dover sets the gold standard. Maple is the smoking wood of choice, and it is put to great effect in the many Hungarian-style smoked pork and sausage products made by Zvonko Cahunek and sold by his wife Rose. Standouts: shaved smoky back bacon—the finest I have eaten, smoked and roasted pork loin on the bone with cracklings, astoundingly good sausages—smoked or fresh Hungarian, *letcho, kransjska* and *debrecini*, mild or spiced with paprika, *kilebasa*, and *hurka* (made with rice). Try white bacon, *kaiser bacon*, and "piggy pops" of jowl crisps. For Muslim clients, Zvonko makes *suduk*.

Rose brings in sweets that her Hungarian clients remember from the Old Country—chocolates and almonds at Christmas, and a proliferation of preserves, including chestnut puree, sour cherries, jams and stuffed plums. Tea grannies will find many herbal *tisanes*, and cookies to munch.

• *Also Available*: 1235–26 Avenue SE (**Crossroads Market**), July–October.

Illichmann's Sausage Shop

Established: 1967 • Owners: Dana & Ken Meissinger
1840–36 Street SE
Phone: 272•1673
Tuesday–Friday 9:00 am–6:00 pm, Saturday 8:00 am–5:00 pm
V, Debit, $

THIS sausage house dates back at least 40 years, with several branches of Dana and Ken Meissinger's family involved at one time or another. Look for Christmas goose, Hutterite Colony birds, and fresh beef, cut to order. Sausage hounds can try smoked Hungarian, *landjaeger*, garlic, and fresh sausages in a handful of styles. Dog owners can buy pig ears and smoked jowls. Centre-of-store shelves have a limited selection of sauerkraut, pickles, jars of white asparagus, red peppers and cheeses.

• *House Specialties*: Fresh beef cut to order, sausages, poultry.
www.illichmannsausage.com

New Sunrise Spices & Halal Meat

Established: 2005 • Contact: Ghulam & Tauqueer Hussain
3, 5320–8 Avenue SE (Penbrooke Plaza)
Phone: 248•3101
Sunday & Tuesday–Thursday 10:30 am–8:00 pm
Friday & Saturday 10:30 am–9:00 pm
V, MC, Debit, $

MOVING from Pakistan to Kuwait, this family arrived in Canada in 1993, and opened the shop 8 years later. This tidy shop unwinds and unfurls as you go deeper into it. Near the front, find a comprehensive cross-cultural blend of East Indian and Middle Eastern oils and spices, herbs and rices, *tahini* and *ghee*, pulses and grains, pomegranate juice, and a wide range of flours (*cassava, channa,* soybean, *urad, gram, dhokla,* corn, *atta*). A *Halal* meat counter is recessed at the rear, and locally-made Queen of Sheba *injera* is available on Fridays at the front counter, along with Afghani flatbread and pita. The back freezer contains huge *kingfish, rahu* fish, and *Halal* wieners and beef patties. Pakistani mangoes are highly regarded here, available in the spring. Rent a movie or music before you put away your wallet.

• *House Specialties*: Middle Eastern and East Indian spices, dry goods and *Halal* meats.

Old Fashioned Meat Products & Delicatessen

Established: 1993 • Owner: Greg Skalka
532 Cleveland Crescent SE
Phone: 287•1511
Tuesday–Thursday 10:00 am–6:00 pm, Friday 10:00 am–7:00 pm
Saturday 9:00 am–5:00 pm
Debit, $

STEP into Old Krakow when you enter this small store. Greg Skalka is the man behind the counter. He left Poland to run the business begun in 1993 by his parents, Janina & Mieczyslaw Skalka. This is not the place to say, "*Nie jem mesa,*" ("I don't eat meat," in Polish.) Greg makes a prolific variety of sausages—12 smoked styles and 7 fresh types. Samples line the counter, sliced off for tasting. Either help yourself, or point and ask. Hanging in the air with the heavy scent of hickory smoke are the guttural sounds of Polish. Don't worry about a translator, the many regulars in the line and some of the women behind the counter speak English as well. Air-dried sausages hang at the back, and the front case is full of fresh and smoked meats and sausages, including dense and meaty hunter sausage, *kabanosy,* and village sausage— the shop's most popular links. Take home smoked tongue, smoked turkey sausage, smoked chickens or smoked ribs. There is fresh meat too, including organ meats: liver, short ribs, pork loins, and chickens.

A comprehensively stocked European deli includes herbal *tisanes,* cosmetics, canned meats and fish, rows of preserves, pickles, fruits and fruit syrups (gooseberry, Morello cherry, plums...), and Viennese wafers for tortes.

In the fridges find Polish unsalted butter, cheese, *kefir* and dry-curd cottage cheeses, smoked trout, mackerel, and eel. The freezers are full with fruit or cheese pierogies, soups, *bigos*, and tripe, for tripe triflers. Buy Polish rye and mini baguettes, chocolate, and cheesecake. This store is a treasure.

- *House Specialties*: Hickory-smoked meats and sausages, European dry goods, dairy, and preserves.

Paolini's Sausage & Meats

Established: 1985 • Owners: Christina & Richard Paolini
5735–3 Street SE
Phone: 252•9000
Tuesday–Friday 9:00 am–5:30 pm, Saturday 9:00 am–4:30 pm
V, MC, Debit, $

IN 2002, Richard Paolini assumed control of this old business, formerly known as Weigle's Sausage & Meat Ltd. In 2008, he sold the Bridgeland location to Rocky Shermer, and it now operates as **Rocky's Meats & Delicatessen**. The Paolini influence is still felt in the southeast, where the remaining shop specializes in German and Hungarian smoked meats, salamis, cold cuts and links, along with a healthy collection of preserves. Lettering on many of the jars that line the shops are in Cyrillic script, so be prepared to translate or guess: chestnut puree, pickles, mustards, jams and syrups, sweet and hot paprika. The meat counter needs no translation, however. At the counter, witness a long choice but little beef—this is pork country. Choose from double-smoked bacon, smoked hambones, European white bacon, smoked and cured *kaiserfleisch*, smoked pork hocks and necks, *kassler*, *schinkenspeck*, and seductively soft-textured *lachs schinken*, with a mouth-feel akin to lox but made from cold-smoked pork loin. There is jiggly house-made headcheese, and *hurka*. Sausage hounds can wade through a wide choice of smoked and fresh-Hungarian or Mennonite farmers' sausages and Hungarian bratwurst, *landjaeger* and turkey smokies. Ask for help. The sausage lexicon can be as confusing as in any French cookbook—bratwurst is made and cooked fresh, but when smoked, it becomes Westphalian smoky. Salami is made in many textures and types, the best of which is the house version, dense, smoky and spiked with mustard seeds. Cold cuts, 14 varieties, include blood or beer, mushroom Lyoner, and paprika Lyoner. At *Links Deli* in the **Crossroads Market,** find a smaller selection. Ask about wild game processing.

- *House Specialties*: Hungarian and German smoked meats and sausages, preserves and wild game processing.
- *Also Available*: *Links Deli*, 1235–26 Avenue SE (**Crossroads Market**).

Polcan Meat Products & Delicatessen

Established: 1997 • Owners: Peter Kadlubowski & Sabina Wesierski
357 Heritage Drive SE (Acadia Shopping Centre)
Phone: 258•0228
Tuesday–Thursday 9:00 am–6:00 pm, Friday 9:00 am–7:00 pm
Saturday 9:00 am–5:00 pm
Debit, $

IT was 1983 when Sabina Wesierski, her now-deceased husband, and her brother Peter Kadlubowski arrived in Canada from Gdansk. The shop opened in 1997, and it has been busy ever since, the Polish flying as fast as the meats across the counter. I ask a few regulars for tips: they smile and say it's all good. Smoked and fresh sausages on offer include Krakow, Cabanos, Serdelki, *schinkenspeck*, blood or barley, juniper, Hungarian in two styles, Polish raw or dry, and turkey links. Look for in-house roast beef and pork, European cheeses, *kuchen*, and cheesecake. Shoppers wander deep aisles for herbal *tisanes*, dried mushrooms, baker's and cottage cheese, Polish butter and yoghurt, *kasha* and noodles, mackerel and herring, a plethora of cookies, and house-made frozen goods: *bigos*, cabbage rolls, tripe, pierogi. If it is a busy weekend, know what you want before you queue up, or ask your neighbours in the queue.

• *House Specialties*: Cabanos sausage, country style sausage, smoked meats, European cheeses, dairy and dry goods.

Regina's Fine Meats

Established: 1994 • Owner: Regina Marr-Fortier
1235–26 Avenue SE (Crossroads Market)
Phone: 861•8718 or 861•8719
Friday, Saturday & Sunday 9:00 am–5:00 pm
V, MC, Debit, $

REGINA Marr-Fortier, a rarity among the smokehouse fraternity, was raised in a family of German butchers in Hamburg. When Regina arrived in Canada in the mid-1970s, she was so dismayed by the lack of quality meat and smoked meats that she took up the family trade in earnest. She maintains a smokehouse at Red Deer Lake Meats southwest of Calgary, which supplies all her free-range meats. Provenance of her foods, from gate to plate, matters to Regina. Keep food pure, she says. In the 1980s, Regina held court at the **Blackfoot Farmers' Market**, then moved to **Crossroads Market** a decade later. She sells tons of bacon and bratwurst, her smoked meats are impeccable, and her sausages are mostly of pork, made in the German style, with a few exceptions: *chorizo* is smoked or fresh, Mexican twist is hottish compared to her *jalapeño* or Italian links. Try ham sausage, pencil-thin veal *debrazinger*, or the meaty, smoky double-smoked House specialties—pork ribs, pork hocks, whole chickens and pork picnic ham. Look for fresh pork, free-range birds and beef hung 25–30 days for maximum tenderness.

• *House Specialties*: Fresh and smoked meats—pork, poultry, sausages, beef.
• *Also Available*: On the menu at Diner Deluxe, Big Fish and Open Range.

Spolumbo's Fine Foods & Italian Deli

Established: 1992 • Owners: Mike Palumbo, Tom & Tony Spoletini
1308–9 Avenue SE
Phone: 264•6452
Store: Monday–Saturday 8:00 am–5:30 pm
Catering: Monday–Friday 8:00 am–4:00 pm
V, MC, AE, Debit, $

THE Spolumbo business—Italian sausages—is not complicated stuff, but it sure is good and, like most Italian food, it relies on quality to belie its unadorned presentation. Founders Tom and Tony Spoletini and Mike Palumbo still look like the CFL football players they once were, big and burly to the point of immovability, but their sheer size and physical presence is softened by genuine smiles and a benevolent interest in people. All three men are highly visible working owners of this bustling, casual deli and catering business that is the chief retail spot for their very fine sausages.

Tom married into an Italian family of restaurateurs. A year and a half of post-Stampeders brainstorming finally, simply, yielded the simple solution. Why not make sausage, Italian-style of course? A bit of kitchen wizardry, tinkering with the family recipe, and the company's first spicy link was created. Mike and Tom made sausages by night and sold sausages by day. Success has meant growth, including a federally inspected plant hulking invisibly behind the deli's cheery facade.

On-site, one deli case is filled with sliced meats, pickles, and cheeses—all the accoutrements of the deli lunch trade. The adjacent case is lined with tray after tray of premium sausage, a gentle reminder that here is the real *raison d'être* for Spolumbo's. These links are what you came for, so don't leave without them: mild or spicy Italian with fennel, chicken, sun-dried tomato and basil, *chorizo*, whiskey fennel spiked with Jack Daniels, *merguez* made with lamb and *harissa*, turkey with sage and pine nuts, chicken with roasted peppers—in all, 30 varieties. At least one is bound to sound like supper.

- *House Specialties*: Sausages in 30 styles, including sweet and spicy Italian, chicken and apple, lamb *merguez* and turkey in several flavours.
- *Also Available*: Widely available across the city, including **Canada Safeway** and **Calgary Co-op**.

www.spolumbos.com

Get What You Really Want to Cook

PORK in Canada is tender enough that any cut can be spit-roasted, grilled, broiled or sautéed. Red meat—lamb, bison, game and beef—is another question. Get the most for your money by matching meat cut to method of cooking: current labeling standards specify an appropriate cooking method for each cut in the display case.

Meat cuts that roast or spit-roast well may also grill well, depending on size: rib, standing and prime rib, top sirloin, strip loin and whole tenderloin, flank, all cut from the hind end of the steer. The front, shank, shoulder or chuck, and neck, are working muscles containing high proportions of connective tissue, or *collagen*, which requires slow cooking, or braising, in liquid until falling-off-the-bone tender.

- Tenderloin is the gold standard for many diners. This long tapered cut, positioned along the inside of the spine, is inert, so it is buttery-textured but bland. Roast it whole, or cut it into steaks to grill or sauté.
- Flank comes from the jointure of side and hind leg. Toothsome, lean and flavourful, it is the antithesis of tenderloin, with a pronounced one-way grain akin to fabric's warp. Grill or roast it over high heat to medium-rare, let it rest, and carve thinly against the grain.
- Skirt steak, from between the brisket and flank, is the diaphragm muscle, well-marbled and prime for quick cooking over direct heat to medium-rare.
- Standing rib, prime rib and strip loin roasts are cut from the ribcage, where minimal work keeps the meat tender-textured and supple.
- Rib-eye steaks, my preference, are cut from this area too. Grill, sauté or roast, depending on size.
- Top sirloin is located near the top of the hip joint, where some movement means more muscle. Good roasted. Some cooks may roast cuts from the round—eye, inside or outside—but I dislike their pronounced coarse grain.
- The chuck, or shoulder, short ribs and shanks of lamb, beef or bison are heavily muscled, less tender and ideal for braising. Poultry legs braise well too.
- Bone-in or boneless? The theory is that the minerals in bones make them effective heat conductors, but they are often honeycombed or hollow, which insulates and slows the transfer of heat. As a result, bone-in meats cook more slowly than boneless cuts; meats closer to the bone will be closer to rare.

SOUTHWEST

MacEwan's Meats

Established: 1986 • Owners: John & Lynne MacEwan
17, 9620 Elbow Drive SW
Phone: 228•9999
Tuesday–Friday 9:00 am–5:30 pm, Saturday 9:00 am–4:30 pm
V, Cheque, $

JOHN, Lynne and son Iain MacEwan run this Scottish-style family business. They specialize in British fare, supplying pubs and commoners alike with haggis, meat pies, black pudding and bacon cured in the English or Ayrshire style. MacEwan is not one to miss an opportunity. Ask him about haggis, and he will lay claim to making four tons in the month of January to celebrate Robbie Burns Day. Who is doing all that celebrating? Who is eating all that haggis? Fresh beef is on the counter and hook—AA beef, conventionally raised, hung at least 21 days, sold in freezer packs, as sides and hinds, and by the individual cut. Lamb, pork and hormone-free poultry are locally raised, as are autumn-only fresh natural turkeys, available by advance order only.

• *House Specialties*: Meat pies, haggis, Alberta beef, lamb and pork.

• *Also Available*: **Better Butcher, British Pantry**, Good Taste of Britain, **Heaslip Venture Meats Ltd., Second to None Meats.**

Missing Link Extraordinary Sausage

Established: 2005 • Owners: Mick & Deneise Sherlock
H6, 4421 Quesnay Wood Drive SW (Calgary Farmers' Market)
Phone: 277•6051
Friday & Saturday 9:00 am–5:00 pm, Sunday 9:00 am–4:00 pm
Debit, $

IT all started innocently enough. Mick Sherlock came home from grocery shopping in a fit of temper, frustrated with not finding the sausages he wanted at a local shop. "I'll just make my own," he said to his wife Deneise, and did. That first ten-pound batch did not last long as Sherlock's friends and colleagues asked to be "in" on the next batch. Soon enough, Mick and Deneise were eyeing plates full of sausages, and asking each other, "Why don't we try peddling sausage at the farmers' market?"

Mick filled a cooler with 55 pounds of sausages, and they took it to the **Cochrane Farmers' Market** in 2006. The cooler came home empty. It was not long before Missing Link's sausages were popular fixtures at three local markets, and Mick's repertoire evolved as he smartly paid attention to his clients' taste buds and feedback, switching from pork to exclusively chicken sausages. **Millarville Farmers' Market** was next, and the couple began to supply several restaurants and food shops, then opened at the **Calgary Farmers' Market** in 2007. Well en route to "serious" business status, Mick hand-cranks 1,000 pounds of sausage weekly, in over 30 styles. I am partial to the robustly flavoured Bombay, Moroccan and Three Amigos.

- *House Specialties*: Chicken sausages, seasoned in over 30 styles, including Bombay, Moroccan, Italian.
- *Also Available*: **Millarville Farmers' Market** (in season), **Boca Loca Fine Mexican Foods.**

Second to None Meats
Established: 2004 • Owner: Bob Choquette
3, 2100–4 Street SW (Plaza 2100)
Phone: 245•6662
Sunday & Monday 10:00 am–5:00 pm, Tuesday–Saturday 9:30 am–6:00 pm
V, MC, Debit, $

THIS impeccable shop is a dream come true for Bob Choquette after years in the meat cutting trade. The focus is on cut-to-order and local, naturally raised products. Shopping here is like a "best of the best" cook's ingredients menu, with possibilities to see you from breakfast to bedtime. Choquette sells Galloway beef, exclusively raised by Froehler Farms, of Strome, Alberta. All meat is wet-aged unless a customer specifically asks for dry-aged meat. Lamb oh such lamb, from **Ewe-Nique Farms**, pork from **Broek Pork Acres, Cunningham's Scotch Cold Smoking** cold-smoked fish, **Hotchkiss Herbs & Produce** vegetables in season, Maple Hill's British Columbia chickens and eggs. From Cortes Island, Brent "The Oysterman" Petkau's divine smoked oysters and Butterfly Brand's smoked scallops, caught with an environmentally sensitive, award-winning harvesting mechanism. Quèbecois Brome Lake ducks—off-the-bone breasts, duck fat and legs for confit, and whole.

Local processors get a chance to trumpet their wares too, from the Jam Lady's Zinfandel and garlic jelly, to **Janice Beaton Fine Cheese** tapenades, pestos and crackers, organic, fair trade beans roasted by **Cochrane Coffee Traders** and Saucy Lady sauces. Olive oils, pasta, and balsamic vinegar add the fillip to in-house value-added: steaks in marinade, spicing, and Cryovac-ing on request. Choquette is not a sausage maker, but sells **Valbella Meats/ Valbella's Deli & Cafe** links—custom-made from his house beef, smokies, wieners, pepperoni, bratwurst, and bangers. Fellow butcher Rocky Schermer of **Rocky's Meats & Delicatessen** makes lamb *merguez* and chicken sausages for the shop.

In 2008, Bob expanded his reach into the northwest when he purchased the butcher shop formerly known as **Rocky's Meats & Delicatessen** on Bowness Road NW.

- *House Specialties*: Galloway beef, local lamb and local products.
- *Also Available*: 4612 Bowness Road NW.

www.second-to-none-meats.ca

Best of the Wurst

SAUSAGES used to be the great unmentionables. In many cultures around the world, they were the thrifty butcher's way of using up trimmings. While they are still the thrifty way to use meat scraps, sausages have gone uptown. Modern sausage is cool, trendy, lean and good for you. Here are some worth trying:

- **Better Butcher's** Randy's bangers are indeed toothsome.
- **Bon Ton Meat Market's** pork breakfast sausages are mild and firmly textured.
- Airdrie's **The Butcher Shoppe** smoked turkey sausage deserves its gold medal status.
- **Edgar Farms'** garlic ring is good eaten out of hand.
- **Gour-Mart Meat Shop's** Mennonite smoked links, oh yum!
- **Heaslip Venture Meats Ltd.** makes links of cooked dark and light turkey seasoned with savoury, sage, and marjoram—available fresh or frozen.
- **Horizon Meats** makes four varieties of turkey sausage: Italian, natural, cranberry, and cognac-and-currants.
- **Hungarian Deli's** *letcho* is good sautéed, then stewed with onions and tomatoes.
- **Illichmann's Sausage Shop** makes a mean turkey hunter sausage, turkey smoky, and a standout bratwurst.
- **Jan's Meats & Deli's** ham sausage is dense, yummy and good for the grill.
- **Master Meats'** bison sausage with ginger and garlic is hot and reminiscent of jerky.
- **Missing Link Extraordinary Sausages** make a pukka Bombay chicken link.
- **Old Country Sausage Shop's** *andouille* is a standout.
- **Old Fashioned Meat Products & Delicatessen's** hickory-smoked Polish-style village sausage is meaty, wood-scented, aromatic and delicious.
- **Paolini's Sausage & Meats'** Westphalian (smoked) bratwurst is a smoker's lucky charm.
- **Polcan Meat Products & Delicatessen's** Krakow sausage—steamed or dry—is a Polish classic.
- **Regina's Fine Meats'** smoked *chorizo* is spicy and warm.
- **Rocky's Meats & Delicatessen** makes turkey sausage with Thai seasonings and a "regular" version seasoned with sage and pepper.
- **Spolumbo's Fine Foods & Italian Deli's** spicy Italian is the gold standard.
- **Valbella Meats/Valbella's Deli & Café's** *landjaeger* and *chimney-sticks* have been high on my list for decades.

NORTHWEST

Bon Ton Meat Market

Established: 1921 • Owners: Greg & Fred Keller
10, 1941 Uxbridge Drive NW (Stadium Shopping Centre)
Phone: 282•3132
Monday–Saturday 9:00 am–6:00 pm, Sunday 10:00 am–5:00 pm
V, MC, Debit, $

THIS carriage-trade market has had sawdust on its floors since 1921, and its current location expanded in 2004. Look for bow ties, real butcher twine, informed service and smiles. Display cases and freezers are full of meat pies, roasts (stuffed, tied and rolled), stuffed chicken breasts, frozen duck and stock, and sausages. This venerable butcher shop sells prime Alberta beef to take home and cook, but also a lot of hot, cooked meals, HMRs for folks on the hoof: beef ribs and pork ribs, BBQ chickens, and individual savoury pies, along with house-made salad. Fowl play here means frozen duck breast, boneless and skin-on, and whole frozen birds, all from Brome Lake, plus in-season fresh free-range **Winter's Turkeys** birds, whole and split in half for small households.

The owner has stocked the shelves with preserves and condiments to gild the proverbial lily. Keller and his staff don't attempt to re-invent the wheel with their food, but do put strict emphasis on service and quality.

• *House Specialties*: Alberta meats and poultry, value-added meats and HMRs, preserves and condiments.

Gour-Mart Meat Shop

Established: 1958 • Owner: Darrell Capune, Manager: Jonas Dorosz
64, 7930 Bowness Road NW (Bowness Shopping Centre)
Phone: 288•4696
Tuesday–Saturday 9:00 am–6:00 pm
V, MC, AE, Debit, $

THIS long-standing Bowness sausage house and butcher shop smells sweetly smoky inside from its on-site smokehouse. The shop is a family affair, and has a reputation among hunters as one of the best local locales for custom-cutting game. Provide provenance, call ahead, and ensure your game is clean and ready to process. Owner Darrell is a fourth generation butcher who acquired the shop and his education from his dad Fred, who bought the shop in 1968. Darrell also teaches meat cutting at SAIT "on the side." Check out the fine smokies in 16 styles, including Mennonite, bison, and several bird-based types, as well as 16 air-dried classics and a dozen varieties of fresh.

Half the business is fresh meat butchery of naturally raised Alberta beef and pork is free of MSG, chemical preservatives or additives. Little lamb sells in this blue-collar community except around early spring for Easter, so ask if you want Alberta lamb any other time.

For Christmas and Thanksgiving, advance order a Hutterite-raised free-range turkey from Granum Colony, or choose a goose. Hot lunch service of hearty dishes—chili, winter-only soups, salt and pepper ribs, meat pies and cabbage rolls—is supplemented by roast chicken and a freezer filled with in-house value-added dishes to take home: stuffed birds, marinated roasts and steaks. A small selection of condiments and cheeses are available.

• *House Specialties*: Fresh beef, custom game cutting and sausages, European smoked meats and sausages, HMRs and poultry.

www.gour-mart.com

Jan's Meats & Deli
Established: 1987 • Owners: Jan & Maria Igras
2436–2 Avenue NW
Phone: 270•8334
Tuesday–Friday 10:00 am–7:00 pm, Saturday 10:00 am–5:00 pm
Debit, $

JAN and Maria Igras arrived in Calgary in 1986. Their fabulous Polish smokehouse opened a year later, and still produces some of the city's best smoked goods—hot-smoked, sugar-cured wild salmon, European bacon, back bacon, ten types of smoked sausage, plus one fresh (*kashanka,* made with 80 percent *kasha*, pork and bacon), and a lovely array of pork *rouladen* stuffed with herbs and bacon or ground meats. The meat counter holds fresh AA beef and pork, all cut to order, free-range chickens and lamb on request. Look in the coolers and freezers for free-range eggs, baking cheese, *kefir*, beets and horseradish, herring, pickled or oil-pack wild mushrooms, *bigos*, and cheeses. There are syrups and jams, *kasha* and poppy seeds, breads and chocolate, mustards and sweets. Lovely!

• *House Specialties*: Fresh-cut AA beef, European sausages, smoked bacon and hams, European preserves and cheeses.

• *Also Available*: *European Deli* (**Crossroads Market**), **Rustic Sourdough Bakery.**

Master Meats
Established: 1976 • Owner: John Wildenborg
120–40 Avenue NW
Phone: 277•5002
Tuesday–Friday 9:00 am–5:30 pm, Saturday 9:00 am–5:00 pm
Debit, $

JOHN Wildenborg bought the business in 1999. Wildenborg's philosophy is that meat is the centre part of a meal, no matter how nice the potatoes. Bringing in some "exotic" meats gives this butcher and his clientele the chance to experiment with ostrich patties or buffalo sausage scented with ginger and garlic in addition to a healthy "freezer meat" business. Lamb is not a big part of his business, but if customers ask, he will bring in more. Look for **Winter's Turkeys**, some split in half, and excellent chickens from

Country Lane Farms Ltd. Look for a large line in sausages—spicy elk, turkey cranberry, bratwurst, hot Italian, popular cowboy sausage with smoky bacon—and some value-added meats, including shish kebabs of beef and pork. Bison is from **Carmen Creek Gourmet Meats**. He may be standing in one of the city's smallest shops, but cut and quality is number one—from AAA carcasses from Spring Creek Ranch.

 • *House Specialties*: House-made sausage and naturally raised AAA beef from Spring Creek Ranch.

www.mastermeats.com

Second to None Meats
Established: 2008 • Owner: Bob Choquette
4612 Bowness Road NW
Phone: 247•4004
Wednesday–Saturday 11:00 am–7:00 pm
V, MC, Debit, $
[see Meat & Game SW for Main Entry on p. 177]

Middle Eastern

THE FOOD OF THE MIDDLE EAST has been influenced by numerous peoples and influxes of civilizations. Borders have been smudged and smeared over centuries of travel and warfare. One can travel the Mediterranean basin and eat the same dishes called by many names. Berbers were invaded by Arabs, who transported their ingredients to other lands—Persia, Syria, Egypt, India, Spain—to infuse and flavour dishes as colourful as the landscape. Persians brought exotic spices like saffron, ginger, and nutmeg. The Syrian influence includes honey, almonds, and pistachios. Leaving Spanish Andalusia, Jews and Arabs fled the Christian conquest of the fifteenth century, melding sweet and savoury with bitter. African influences—from Algeria and Sudan—include spices and fruit.

Cities are adorned in multi-textured architectural details, geometrically inspired, garnished with intricate floral arabesques that serve as energy links toward unity. What looks busy can be deconstructed into intricate repeating geometric motifs. In medinas and *souks*, vendors are surrounded by baskets heaped with mounds and mounds of olives and spices, their pungent scents filling the narrow streets, their hues colouring the arched passages into alleys and buildings. Food is as complex as architecture and art, relying on a suave balance of sweet with savoury, just as art's underlying geometric structure provides a hidden order.

Calgarians do not have street markets, *souks* or medinas. But we have all of the Middle East's flavours and ingredients, brought to us by the new wave of immigrants, some fleeing war and poverty, others looking for new starts.

NORTHEAST

Almadina Grocery
Established: 2002 • Owners: Raya Sleiman & Moe Elwenni
5309 Rundlehorn Drive NE
Phone: 272•9696
Monday–Saturday 9:30 am–8:00 pm, Sunday 9:30 am–6:00 pm
V, MC, Debit, $

THIS tidy old building has an international clientele from Lebanon, Jordan, Syria, Egypt, Iraq, Iran, and Turkey. A busy meat market is at the rear, selling *Halal* beef, lamb, goat, and chicken. The lamb in particular is a big seller. Rices—aromatic *basmati* and short grain Egyptian—and dried pulses are accented by a plethora of preserves, from orange flower water to grape leaves and olive oils. Sweets abound, as in most Middle Eastern markets. Honey-comb, dates, *pomegranate molasses*, *halva*, rose syrup and *rose water*, apricots, are all classics of the Mediterranean basin, no matter what the nationality. Nuts too, and pumpkin seeds, along with a few cheeses are in the fridges. In the freezer, find **Thumbs Up Foods'** Serenna's snacks, filo, and *kataifi* for home bakers. Baked goods are from **Byblos Bakery, Village Pita Bakery & Mediterranean Food Store** and Shamsane Bakery.

• *House Specialties*: *Halal* meats, produce, preserves and dry goods.

Calgary Produce Market

Established: 2007 • Owners: Ahmed & Qamar Maqsood
1110, 4810 Westwinds Drive NE (Green Plaza)
Phone: 275•2414
Store: Monday–Sunday 10:00 am–10:00 pm, Meat Counter: 10:00 am–7:30 pm
V, MC, Debit, $

THE Pakistani family behind this shop stocks produce that reminds them of home—beautiful mangoes, *plantains*, eggplant, hot chilies, *deglet noor* dates. Find fresh leaves of spearmint and cilantro, and dried forms of the spices and herbs that form the backbone of Middle Eastern cuisine—*ajwain*, *mishiri*, cumin, coriander. Towers of lentils, sacks of rice and pulses, cane sugar, herbal teas, this tidy shop is expanding and re-organizing.

• *House Specialties*: Pakistani mangoes in season, produce, spices, pulses, meats.

Cedars Deli

Established: 1983 • Owner: Mohammed Omar
3103 Edmonton Trail NE
Phone: 233•2771
Monday–Saturday 10:00 am–7:00 pm
V, MC, Debit, $

IF you only come here for the *baklava*, judge it time well spent. Founded by Mary Salloum in 1983, this Lebanese business had several outlets in its heyday, including one in MacEwan Hall at the University of Calgary. Since its recent purchase by Mohammed Omar, in 2003, this location has alumni of the various former branches show up for a fix of good food. Prices are good, portions are generous, and the takeout clientele are happy. It smells good—always a good indication of a happy tummy time. Expect more than great *baklava*—*tzatziki, tahini, hummus, fatayer, falafel, shwarma,* and *donair,* as well as *spanakopita* and *kibbe*. A whole wheat pita option is always good. Corporate catering adds a courier delivery fee.

• *House Specialties*: Chicken *shwarma*, beef donair, *falafel, baklava*.

www.cedarsdeli.com

Chahine Supermarket

Established: 2002 • Contact: Nazem Chahine
1, 7196 Temple Drive NE
Phone: 590•2695
Monday–Saturday 10:00 am–8:00 pm, Sunday 10:00 am–7:00 pm
V, MC, Debit, $

THIS store's helpful Lebanese owner, Nazem Chahine, brings in a wonderful range of dried, candied fresh fruits, including Iranian dates so tender you'll eat half of them in the car. Check out the gorgeous candied fruit from Syria—they are not all what they seem—some are nuts, others are eggplant. Look too for pickled turnips the colour of beets. Grains and are in tidy bulk bins: large rounds of *Israeli couscous*, bulgur, Moroccan *couscous* and rice, spices, dried lemons, chickpea flour and lentils. Sweets play a major part in the Middle Eastern culinary palate, and syrups, jams and other condiments abound—from rose petal syrup to *pomegranate molasses*, date or carob syrup, grape molasses, fig marmalade, bitter orange jam, Morello cherry jam, and every conceivable style of mango—nectar, syrup, pulp, pickle and chutney. Olive lovers can choose among seven varieties in bulk. At the back, choose *laban* or *labneh*, and fresh *Halal* meat is in the cooler—beef, lamb, chicken, and goat by request.

 • *House Specialties*: Middle Eastern dry goods, preserves, condiments, *Halal* meats, cheeses and dairy from the Lebanon.

Hage's Mideast Foods & Halal Meats

Established: 1996 • Owners: Ria & Nagah Hage
212, 1440–52 Street NE (TransCanada Mall)
Phone: 235•5269
Tuesday–Friday 10:00 am–7:00 pm, Saturday–Monday 10:00 am–6:00 pm
Debit, $

MY favourite Middle Eastern market on the Eastside is spotlessly clean, and has an island of olives at its centre. Circumnavigate to taste and survey, then scoop out tubs of wrinkled black air-dried Moroccan, Lebanese black or green with or without *za'ataar*, colossal Kalamatas, fat green Sicilians. A tidy *Halal* meat market—Alberta AA or AAA beef, lamb, and goat on request, plus grain-fed chicken—sits opposite a thriving takeout counter. The back aisle of the store holds a mountain of fresh pita, bagged bulgur, a cooler with a good selection of Mediterranean cheeses and yoghurts, spices and syrups, grains and nuts. At the front, have lunch: ask for *hummus* to go, or stay in for the best *falafel* sandwich in the city, followed by Turkish coffee. The produce section is growing.

 • *House Specialties*: Middle Eastern dry goods, *Halal* meats, spices, preserves, oils, olives and deli.

Shaheen Grocery & Kabuli Naan

Established: 2007 • Owner: Ramin Nazari
105, 4655–54 Avenue NE
Phone: 293•0909
September–April: Monday & Wednesday–Sunday 10:00 am–8:00 pm
May–August: Monday & Wednesday–Sunday 10:00 am–9:00 pm
V, MC, Debit, $

IT smells right in this shop. Follow your nose and ears—the sharp slapping sounds of hands shaping dough will guide you to the goods. Walk in, turn left, proceed to the back, peer over the divide, and watch the guys loading the big oven with trays of rectangular hand-shaped *naan* in the Afghani style. These beautiful flatbreads are nearly three feet long, sprinkled with *baraka* and white sesame seeds, and are baked to a rich mahogany. On racks adjacent are stacks of *raute*.

An Urdu-Calgarian newspaper led me into this family business, the startup of an Afghan family of immigrants. In the centre of the room, shelving accommodates a range of products, from intricate geometrically patterned serving and eating dishes to green Lebanese olive oil in three-litre glass jugs. Tea from Dubai—Mahoud brand, in handsome tins—and dates from Iran, raisins in four colours, Pakistani rices, Bulchara dried plums, *rose water*, rice, bergamot preserves, and bulk-dried mulberries.

Upstairs, carpets! Take off your shoes and luxuriate in the feeling under your skin.

Downstairs, a *Halal* meat counter is coming. With or without the meat market, this store merits a detour. How many carpeted paths to heaven, rich with the scent of fresh baked bread, are there?

• *House Specialties*: Afghani flatbread, dry goods and Turkish carpets.
• *Also Available*: Wholesale arm under construction.

Village Pita Bakery & Mediterranean Food Store

Established: 1973 • Owner: Ismail-Abdel Rahman
208, 255–28 Street NE (Short Pants Plaza)
Phone: 273•0330
Monday–Saturday 8:00 am–6:00 pm, Sunday 8:00 am–5:00 pm
Debit, Cheque, $

NUTS stored in the cooler instead of on the shelf are a good sign that these folks know how to treat their food. Pita is sold by the truckload here, along with a few shelves of grape leaves, olive oils, and pickled vegetables, including turnips in brine, unexpectedly purple. Grains—rices, *freekeh*, *couscous* and bulgur—and pulses, dried or canned, are backbone ingredients of the Mediterranean kitchen. Sweets too, in prolific styles like *halva*, fruit preserves and syrups, dates in syrup, Phoenician honey, *tamarind* paste, unpitted dates. Cheeses in the fridge are all Mediterranean in origin if not in production—Bulgarian *kashkaval*, *halloumi*, unripened *akawie*, *nabulsi*, *baladi* and feta. But the draw is lunch to go—herbal, meat or spinach and feta pies

on pita, baked to order, folded or flat. Look in the cooler for 4" mini versions, along with *hummus, tabbouleh* and *baklava* to fill the gap between belly and belt.
- *House Specialties*: Nuts, pita, grains, preserves, sweets, dry goods, cheeses and pita pies.

SOUTHEAST

Green Cedars
Established: 1987 • Owner: Rochdi Sarout
Unit M, 4710–17 Avenue SE
Phone: 235•9983
Monday 9:00 am–8:00 pm, Tuesday–Sunday 9:00 am–9:00 pm
V, MC, Debit, $

THIS shop was formerly known as *Green Cedrus*, but was renamed Green Cedars in 2002. Half the store is devoted to dry goods, so look for the good stuff: *deglet noor* dates, locally made *injera* of *teff, preserved lemons* and pickles in the Mediterranean lexicon. Bulk bins of pulses and a wide collection of grains, nuts, bulk olives and some Mediterranean cheeses make it easy to almost one-stop shop. Buy an *ibrik* to make the coffee in, then buy the coffee. A small meat counter is stocked with lamb, chickens, a few cuts of beef and beef sausage.
- *House Specialties*: Dry goods, grains, nuts, olives, cheese and meats.

Pyramids Halal Products & Wholesale-Retail Mideast Market
Established: 2003 • Manager: Hisham & Samia Ali
Unit C, 1919–31 Street SE
Phone: 204•1754
Monday–Friday 10:00 am–8:00 pm, Saturday & Sunday 11:00 am–8:00 pm
V, MC, Debit, $

THE shop formerly known as Farwa has become this tidy but somehow sterile shop. It is worth a look-see, for olives and olive oil, fruit syrups and jams, herbal teas and sweets, and a nice line in Iranian and Tunisian dates. The meat market at the rear is clean and organized, stocked with fresh beef, chicken, goat and lamb. In the freezer, find *Halal* pepperoni pizza, Buffalo-style chicken wings, tilapia, mullet, sardines, and snapper. In the bulk bins, look for rices and grains, pulses and peas, spices and dried herbs.
- *House Specialties*: Condiments, dry goods, preserves, *Halal* meats and spices.

SOMAR Mediterranean Market
Established: 2006 • Owner: Suheil Shlah
17, 9250 Macleod Trail South (Macleod Plaza)
Phone: 252•2700
Monday–Saturday 10:00 am–8:00 pm, Sunday 10:00 am–6:00 pm
V, MC, Debit, $

THE Syrian-born owner is planning additions, including a *Halal* meat counter. The takeout counter features *shwarma* and *shish taouk*. Look in the freezer for *Halal* meats and *Halal* Armenian pizzas as well as filo and *kataifi* pastry for baking. Shelves carry a wide selection of sweets and dry goods, from fruit syrups to rose petal jam and *halva*, and from pulses to grains. The cooler has a reasonable selection of nuts, Mediterranean cheeses and dairy products, including *laban* and *labneh, akami* and *baladi*. The side counter has Lebanese olives in multiple colours.
• *House Specialties*: Mediterranean dry goods, *Halal* meats, cheeses, olives and preserves.

SOUTHWEST

Atlas Specialty Supermarket & Persian Cuisine
Established: 1999 • Owners: Amir, Satyar & Pari Khezri
1000–9 Avenue SW (Gibraltar Place)
Phone: 230•0990
Tuesday–Sunday noon–8:00 pm
V, MC, AE, Debit, $

EAT in the restaurant (unlicensed) or shop for a slim selection of Persian ingredients—*pomegranate molasses* and juice, *couscous* and rice, nuts and lentils, dates and dried figs, fruits and saffron, olives in bulk and in glass, olives oils from around the world.
• *House Specialties*: Persian dry goods, preserves and olive oils.
www.atlascalgary.com

Kalamata Grocery Store
Established: 1963 • Owners: Gus & George Kokos
1421–11 Street SW
Phone: 244•0220
Monday–Sunday 8:00 am–11:00 pm
Debit, $

IN his inner city market, founded by dad Jim (Dimitrios) and originally called Jim's Grocery, just south of the current location, Gus Kokos has shelves too crowded to see over, and a collection of cheeses that are sliced to order, including multiple choices of feta (Bulgarian, Macedonian, Canadian or Greek, in cow's, goat's and sheep's milk) and *Kefolitiri*. Ask that your *Kefolitiri* be sliced 1 cm thick, the perfect thickness for frying saganaki. Spices, oils, canned chickpeas, Iranian saffron, *preserved lemons, pomegranate molasses*, it is all here—somewhere. Ask Gus—he knows! Teas, coffees and spreads—from Yugoslavia to Iran and Iraq—syrups, preserves, Ajvar vegetable spreads (made from spices and peppers, onions and eggplant), 20 types of Turkish delight and chocolate bars...frozen filo, *kataifi, tiropita, kajmak*, stuffed filo and *kataifi* with sweet or savoury fillings, and European gyro kits (pita, *tzatziki* and gyro meat) to make it at home.

- *House Specialties*: Feta cheeses from the barrel, olives, dry goods, *spanakopita* and dolmades.
- *Also Available*: Wholesale to various city restaurants.

www.kalamata.com

Luxor Emporium & Café

Established: 1994 • Owner: Yasser Ramadan
937–7 Avenue SW
Phone: 282•0030 or Cell: 650•6588
Monday–Friday 8:00 am–10:00 pm, Saturday 10:00–10:00 pm
V, MC, Debit, $

FORMERLY located in Brentwood, Luxor has moved to the west end of downtown, downsizing in the process. The west end of the building is a sit-down café, and the east side is a small room with rice and lentils, cooler case, freezer and just enough room to turn around. The shelves are stocked with several flavours of Turkish delight (lemon, rose, or mint), and a few fragrant aromas—cardamom pods and *za'ataar, sumac* and *rose water*. The business caters as well.

- *House Specialties*: Egyptian and Middle Eastern dry goods, herbs and spices.

Shaganappi Grocery

Established: 1994 • Contact: Omar Najmeddine
3919–17 Avenue SW
Phone: 249•4200
Monday–Sunday 10:00 am–10:00 pm
V, MC, Debit, $

THIS well-stocked Westside Middle Eastern market carries all sorts of treasures. The Mediterranean diet emphasizes grains and pulses like *couscous*, lentils and chickpeas, but there is also a wide range of sweets to cook with, and they all seem to be available here. Shop for *pomegranate molasses*, wild Phoenician honey, rose jam, date syrup, and fig marmalade or bitter orange jam. Then choose some *deglet noor* dates—stuffed, whole or pitted—and *halva* or Turkish delight. If you still have room in your basket, add frozen and fresh *Halal* chickens or beef, and raid the deli counter for ready-to-eat *baba ganouj, hummus* and spinach pies with *za'ataar*. Finish up with olives, a tin of olive oil, some fresh herbs or immaculately ripened figs in season, coffee beans, rice or *couscous*, or fresh nuts from the cooler. Pickles include fluorescent purple turnips in beet juice, grape leaves in brine...and wonderful candied and dried fruits. Now that's shopping.

- *House Specialties*: Produce, cheeses, olives, dry goods and *Halal* meats.
- *Also Available*: Wholesale for businesses at Chinook Wholesalers, 119, 5718–1A Street SW.

West End Produce & Mideast Grocery
Established: 2003 • Contact: Getu Tessema
3916–17 Avenue SW
Phone: 246•3776
Monday–Sunday 10:00 am–10:00 pm
V, MC, AE, Debit, $

THIS relatively new Westside store has a cross-section of fetas, from Greece, Bulgaria and Canada, and a fairly comprehensive collection of Middle East-style cheeses, including *halloumi, kashkaval* and *vachekeval*. Shelves are filled with seeds and spices like *baraka* from Beirut, Syrian *mahleb,* and a good choice of nuts—pine nuts, walnuts and pistachios—wisely positioned in the cooler. On the shelves, find stacks of pita, canned and dried pulses, and grains—mostly *couscous* and rice. There's more bulk olives, some preserves from Greece (figs and oranges), Syrian and Turkish jams, Lebanese honeys, Turkish delight, nougats, *black* teas from Lebanon and Turkey.

- *House Specialties*: Turkish coffee, cheeses, spices, flatbread, dry goods and grains.

www.westendgrocery.com

NORTHWEST

A & A Foods & Deli
Established: 1984 • Owner: Jimmy Elrafih
1401–20 Avenue NW
Phone: 289•1400
Monday–Saturday 9:00 am–10:00 pm, Sunday 10:00 am–8:00 pm
Debit, $

THE hot and heady scent of roasting thyme and meat permeates this small store that claims the entire city as its neighbourhood. Houda Elrafih and her son Jamal (Jimmy), the wisecracking wizard in the battered cowboy hat, are the significant forces which propel this shop. Jimmy's maternal grandfather, Mohamed Chybli, came to Calgary from Lebanon forty-odd years ago and Jimmy remembers hanging out in his bakery in Brentwood Mall. "My grandfather was making multi-grain bread without preservatives long before it was cool, he was always the man."

Although it is Jimmy, second of eight siblings, who chats up the customers as they wait in line for the city's best *shwarma* and garlic sauce, it is his mother Houda who was instrumental in the birth of the business, setting the standard for their food in the family's first shop. Like most mothers, Houda dates the events in her life by the ages of her children. The year she opened her first store, she recalls her son Jimmy as an eight-year-old who threw snowballs at cars outside the deli. Now, as then, she serves pita-wrapped *donair* and *shwarma*, handfuls of pastry-encased spinach and feta *fatayer*, dollops of roasted eggplant *baba ganouj* or herb-dusted *tabbouleh*. The *shwarma*, topped with pungent garlic sauce, is tie-drippingly deliciously messily all-engaging: warm shreds of spit-roasted chicken thighs redolent of herbs and olive oil are topped with hot peppers, vegetables and garlic sauce inside a snugly wrapped pita round that inevitably splits and gushes. Yum, worth lining up for, and worth the stains.

The back of the building is where the Elrafihs have a few shelves of staples. Go for the takeout, and fill your basket while you wait with Egyptian brass mortars and pestles, aromatic apple tobacco, lemon *yerba maté*, dried hibiscus flowers, nuts, beans, coffee beans and grinders. For fun, buy a hookah. Or not. The flavours of Mediterranean cooking are warm and vibrant: mint-peppermint, not spearmint ("Too candy-ish," says Houda), the pungent camphor breath of cardamom and cumin, and the lemony snap of russet-coloured *sumac* and garnet *pomegranate molasses*. Don't stint on the olive oil, and get the really good stuff, says Houda.

• *House Specialties*: *Shwarma, falafel, hummus, tzatziki,* Mediterranean dry goods and preserves.
• *Also Available*: Mediterranea, 1304–4 Street SW, A&A Downtown, 213–6 Avenue SE.

Organics

THE MOVE TO ORGANICS REPRESENTS one of the biggest populist movements in food. From a counter-culture sub-genre of the hippy years, it has mushroomed, fed by fear as much as anything positive. Consumers have endured BSE, avian influenza, E. coli in salad greens, and genetically modified organisms (GMOs), all grim results of monoculture and industrial-style "commodity" agri-business.

Statistics Canada's 2006 census figures shows that of 229,373 farms in Canada in 2006, 6.8 percent were organic-uncertified, certified, or in-transition. Organic sales are forecast to account about 10 percent of all retail food purchases by 2010. That may sound like small potatoes, but organics have become such an economic force that supermarkets and retail giants want their slice of the organic garden plot too. This raises many questions that need answering.

Are organics and mass market food production mutually exclusive? What about provenance and accountability? Who sets standards for organic certification? How are standards checked? Who enforces compliance, especially offshore? At what point does it make more sense to buy local foods that are not produced organically instead of long-distance organically grown goods?

It seems obvious that foods produced organically should taste better, and that organic growing is a more sustainable method that does not pollute soil, groundwater, animals, people, plants or the atmosphere. Are organic foods really better for us than conventionally produced foods? Do they contain more nutrients?

To be certified organic, a producer must undertake a series of inspections by a professional inspector who represents a regulatory group. The organic movement began as a grassroots initiative, and there are many organizations that certify products as organic. Inspections are usually annual, and are mandatory to retain organic certification. The process costs dearly.

The common understanding of "organic" is confused by the fact that certifying organizations are not united. However, guaranteed provenance from birth to consumption is a common requirement.

Organic food—from animal sources—must be free of growth hormones and antibiotics, and must have been raised on organic feedstuffs, themselves grown without chemical fertilizers or synthetic pesticides, as certified by a variety of regulatory bodies. Thus, it is not only the animal but all its feed and supporting land that must comply. An audit trail is required as proof of compliance with the strict regulations set out by the certification body.

It is a similar story for organic food from plant sources—fruits, vegetables, oil seeds and grains.

Maybe the time has come for government grants to growers to retrofit their farms—to use sustainable energy sources like photovoltaic cells, alternative fuels and wind turbines—and look at new methods of raising our food. Or perhaps there should be grants to cover income loss during the 3-year transition to growing organically.

Food should be locally grown, raised and produced in an environmentally sustainable manner. The hidden costs and infrastructure that support a global food system are monumental. Seaways, train tracks, truck routes and runways, container ships and ferries, trains, trucks and planes and their fuel—we pay for it all in the cost of each pineapple, papaya, *plantain* and pomegranate.

The loss of rural communities as people leave agriculture for an urban life, the loss of arable land to urban settlement, the use of migrant workers and stoop labour, the loss of seed and plant varieties as businesses behind agriculture move into monocropping and selecting hardy plants that travel well but are tasteless…tally the cost in long-term damage to soil, water, air, people and the planet. It is too high.

The larger questions rise like cream. How to sustainably feed people? How small or large a farm is sustainable? How many families can a farm reasonably support? Can we return to locally grown food for more of our diet? Is food destined to remain a commodity or will it be dinner once again?

SOUTHWEST

Community Natural Foods
Established: 1977 • Operations Manger: Rob Eckstadt

1304–10 Avenue SW
Phone: 229•2383

202–61 Avenue SW
(Admiral Plaza)
Phone: 541•0606

Monday–Friday 9:00 am–9:00 pm, Saturday 9:00 am–7:00 pm
Sunday 10:00 am–7:00 pm
V, MC, Debit, $

SOUP to nuts, along with house, laundry and skin care, this store stocks one of the widest selection of organics in the city, and has a small book section and luncheon café as well. But Community is a frustrating experience for this shopper. Many of the 220 staff members are consistently uninformed about where to find things and what is in stock. However, the produce department at the 10 Avenue location is bright, clean, organized and filled with lovingly tended fruits and vegetables. Produce at the south location is not always so sweet looking. Produce is mostly organic, unsprayed, *transitional* or *biodynamically* raised, with an emphasis on local as it is available, in a rainbow from chard to Napa cabbage, kale to *bok choy*. Locally grown produce includes **Lund Organic Farm's** great carrots, and potatoes from **Poplar Bluff Farm**, but it never seems quite enough. A wide variety of winter squashes are countered by out-of-season imported greens—*mâche*, arugula, and mixed lettuces. Wheat grass—by the flat, or mung bean sprouts—by the ounce, add alternatives.

The bulk dried herb and spice section has a good turnover that assures freshness. The big bulk bins are a satisfying tour of grains, starches, flours and pulses. Coffee fans can choose from several fair trade and organic producers, and honey to sweeten it, from **Chinook Honey Company** in Okotoks. The store does not stock any jams (the word is strictly controlled in labelling to mean gelled fruit and sugar mixtures that contain a specific percentage of sugar) but it does have some good fruit spreads from a variety of companies, some organic and some conventional: Cascadian Farms' organic collection; and St. Dalfour's Mirabelle plum or Myrtille are good. Pickles too, from Saucy Ladies, in favourite Prairie styles—bread and butter or dill are crunchy-crisp.

This may be the rare meat market in town where ordering a Christmastime seasonal bird in advance is not a prerequisite of purchasing, due to the huge volume that waddles out under the wainscoting. Be warned, though, birds here are frozen, so plan for safe defrosting time in the fridge. Shoppers looking for the organically raised grass-fed beef of TK Ranch, **Hoven Farms** and Pine Terra from Peace Country can also buy **Winter's Turkeys** free-range or organic turkeys and sausages, and Bradner Farms chickens.

Sweets for the sweet? Predictably, what we found here was organic chocolate. Choose from chips, bulk bin chocolate of undeterminable provenance, or high-end fair trade Cocoa Camino, and Denman Island chocolate.

Look for these other fine locals: **Hotchkiss Organic Herbs & Produce** produce, Windy Ridge natural bison, High Country bison, Peace Country farmer Jerry Kitt's First Nature pork and turkey, Clint Black's ostrich from Delalta, **Edgar Farms'** produce, **Fairwinds Farm** yoghurt and feta, and **Vital Green Farms'** divine dairy products.

• *House Specialties*: Mostly organic produce, as local as possible, bulk dry goods, packaged goods, meats, dried and fresh herbs and spices, bulk grains and flours, body and baby care products, herbals and vitamins, books.
www.communitynaturalfoods.com

Planet Organic Market
Established: 2003 • Manager: Pat Tuft
100, 10233 Elbow Drive SW (Southwood Corner)
Phone: 252•2404
Monday–Friday 9:00 am–9:00 pm, Saturday & Sunday 9:00 am–7:00 pm
V, MC, Debit, $
[see NW Organics for main entry on p. 194]

NORTHWEST

Amaranth Whole Foods Market

Established: 1996 • Owner: Ken Klatt
7 Arbour Lake Drive NW
Phone: 547•6333
Monday–Friday 9:00 am–9:00 pm
Saturday, Sunday & Statutory Holidays 9:00 am–6:30 pm
V, MC, Debit, $

THIS is my preferred organics shopping spot, well lit and helpfully staffed. It has local organic breads from several bakeries (**Bernie's Bavarian Bakery**, Silver Hills, My Bakery, **Lakeview Bakery**), a wide range of oils and vinegars, and an extensive collection of grains, flours, starches and rices. Try the coconut oil for your next curry—it is yummy. Sweet teeth will marvel at their organic choices—sucanat, molasses, flavoured and maple syrups, cane and plantation sugars, stevia, brown rice syrup, honeys. Glass bottles of Avalon Dairy milk and whipping cream are a throwback to another era but **Vital Green Farms** dairy products are just as treasured. Shelved stocks include propylene and glycol-free deodorants and wonderful botanically derived skin care products. **Cochrane Coffee Traders**, Earth's Choice, and Amazon Trading Co. coffees are all organic. Organic, honey-sweetened, and sugar-free preserves are visible choices—behind the plain label of Zebroff's organic jams, made in Cawston, British Columbia, is deep fruit flavour. Or pick up a jar of Crofter's fruit-juice-sweetened jams, and look in the refrigerator for Bubby's kosher vinegar-free sauerkraut and dills. Best bird bets include **Winter's Turkeys** fresh free-range and fresh organic turkeys, and Bowden free-range chicken. Meat-eaters can select Olson's High Country Buffalo and TK Ranch beef, and round out their plates with **Hotchkiss Herbs & Produce** greens, **Poplar Bluff Farm** produce and Judy G's gluten-fee pizza—all local goods. Customer service is paramount here, and it shows.

• *House Specialties*: Bulk dry goods, celiac and gluten-free products, 100 percent organic produce (local as available), natural and organic meats as local as possible.

www.amaranthfoods.ca

Planet Organic Market

Established: 2006 • Manager: Michael Kelner
110, 4625 Varsity Drive NW (Shaganappi Village)
Phone: 288•6700
Monday–Friday 9:00 am–9:00 pm, Saturday & Sunday 9:00 am–7:00 pm
V, MC, Debit, $

SOME fine-looking produce is on display at Planet Organic's small but succinct produce department—gorgeous fresh herbs, fat golden beets in fall, yummy cherries in summer. More: fat, fresh shiitake mushrooms, sleek zucchini, and winter requisites—kale and cabbage, red cabbage, leeks, squashes. Peruse the centre shelving for "the rest". It is all there, somewhere, but the staff could be more helpful. There are numerous choices to be made among the fair trade organic coffees, the flours, and the bulk bins of refrigerated nuts. Both locations have a strong local commitment. Find meat and game from **Winter's Turkeys** and **Hoven Farms**, cold-pressed oils and grains from **Highwood Crossing Farm Ltd.**, cheese and yoghurt from **Sylvan Star Cheese Farm** and **Fairwinds Farm**, and vegetables from **Poplar Bluff Organic Farm** and **Hotchkiss Herbs & Produce**. The deli at the entrance offers samples of HMRs and ready-made meals. This is good food, by and large, with real flavour. Try it if you are too busy to cook.

- *House Specialties*: Organic local produce, dry goods, meats, HMRs.
- *Also Available*: 100, 10233 Elbow Drive SW (Southland Corner).

www.planetorganic.ca

Sunnyside Market
Established: 1997 • Owners: Pat Guyn & Patty Nowlin
10, 338–10 Street NW
Phone: 270•7477
Monday–Wednesday 9:30 am–7:00 pm, Thursday & Friday 9:30 am–8:00 pm
Saturday 9:00 am–7:00 pm, Sunday 10:00 am–6:00 pm
V, MC, AE, Debit, $, Calgary $

SOMEONE has a sense of humour in this jam-packed tiny neighbourhood shop. Among its incredibly diverse range of products, we found Ben & Jerry's ice cream beside the frozen Soy Dream. You can't take yourself too seriously!

Meats regularly stocked include selections from local stalwarts **Hoven Farms, Sunworks Farm** and **Winter's Turkeys**. From the coast, try amazingly wonderful tinned line-caught wild salmon and tuna. This is the source of one of the city's best selections of organics, exhibiting solid support of local growers of produce and vegetables from **Blue Mountain Biodynamic Farms, Gull Valley Greenhouse, Hotchkiss Herbs & Produce, Poplar Bluff Farm**, and Galimax-delivered vegetables from **Broxburn Vegetables & Café**.

From the valleys west, try Martin Rothe's biodynamic fruits from Oliver, British Columbia, Oso Negro coffee roasted in the Kootenays, Kootenay Kitchen Krackers (a dense *spelt* and rye cracker), and jars of Zebroff jams, fruits and honey.

Made-in-Calgary goods on the shelves include bread from **Prairie Mill Bread Company**, Pure's cookies and crackers, **Highwood Crossing Farm Ltd.**'s oils and grains, Tres Marias *tortillas*, **Fairwinds Farm** cheese and yoghurt, and dairy products from **Vital Green Farms**.

Culled foods are donated to Food Not Bombs, an ad hoc group that feeds the homeless from a local kitchen.

- *House Specialties*: 90 percent organic produce, much of which is local, bulk dry goods, meats, dairy.

www.sunnysidemarket.ca

All-Natural, Organic, or Certified Organic?

- *All Natural*: According to the Canadian Food Inspection Agency (CFIA), the use of the word "natural" on meat, poultry, and fish products is not acceptable unless the animal product is raised without any human intervention. This means no vaccinations, antibiotics, medication, veterinary drugs, hormones, direct-fed microbials, or formulated feeds. In Canada, most commercially raised animals receive some kind of vaccine, and are given feed with added vitamins and minerals. In naturally raised herds, animals requiring human intervention must be separated or "culled" from the herd and sold as conventionally raised meat.
- *Organic/Certified Organic*: The Government of Canada is working to regulate the use of the terms "Canada Organic" on agricultural products. The proposal sets the federal government atop the pyramid, with the CFIA acting as the competent authority. Existing accreditation and certification bodies would be integrated with the system, provided they meet the prescribed requirements. This labelling measure is designed to ease international market access and protect consumers against deceptive and otherwise misleading labelling practices.
- Following are some online sources of information about organics. Of these, the O'Mama Report from the Organic Trade Association is probably the most accessible and useful and the site for the Centre for Science in the Public Interest is fascinating. Healthy surfing!

- <www.ocia.org> for the Organic Crop Improvement Association (OCIA).
- <www.scc.ca> for the Standards Council of Canada (SCC).
- <www.usda.gov/wps/portal/usdahome> for the United States Department of Agriculture (USDA).
- <www.organicconsumers.org> for the Organic Consumers Association.
- <www.theorganicreport.org> for the O'Mama Report from the Organic Trade Association.
- <www.centerforfoodsafety.org> for the Centre for Food Safety.
- <www.cspinet.org> for the Centre for Science in the Public Interest (CSPI).
- <www.goingorganic.ca> for the Going Organic Network of Alberta.

Personal Chefs & Caterers

PERSONAL CHEFS DO THE SHOPPING and then cook in your kitchen, leaving hot meals, refrigerated dishes, or frozen meals in their wake. It is like letting a tidy genie out of the bottle.

Who wouldn't want a personal chef? Double-digit "must-do" lists and crosstown traffic snarls, hockey playoffs and management meetings all erode life at home. The result is dining decisions too often made while hungry and staring blindly into the fridge after a hectic day. The appeal of a personal chef is apparent to many—double-income earners, with and without kids, people with allergies or dietary intolerances, the elderly, new parents, and professionals tired of restaurants and dining out.

A personal chef is not necessarily a private chef. A private chef usually has an exclusive contract with one family, while a personal chef almost always has more than one client. Once a week, once a month, or somewhere in between, the personal chef goes to the client's home and cooks a number of specifically tailored dishes, packages them, and stores them in the fridge or freezer. The client simply follows the reheating or finishing instructions provided by the chef.

Most personal chefs will schedule a preliminary meeting to establish a client's dietary needs, likes and dislikes, as well as to establish schedules and budget. Some chefs have access to professional kitchens, and cook there instead of in the client's home. Some shop, others don't. Most personal chefs offer five main dishes per week multiplied by the number of persons in the household. Some provide special meals for children. Some leave a hot meal in the oven on delivery day. Ask for what you need. Menus are custom-tailored to likes, dislikes, and often take into account any allergies or sensitivities. Variants include frequency of visits, menus, delivery dates, building access, costs and availability of side dishes. Ask for specifics. Good food and skilled hands are expensive, and time is at a premium. Expect to pay for the privilege having of a personal chef. Rates vary.

Caterers bring food to your office, gallery, or home. Most food is prepared in their professional kitchens. Some assembly, cooking, finishing, plating or presentation may be done on-site, or the business may deal only in assembled trays, picked up or delivered to your door or office. Many caterers operate in Calgary, with a wide range of specialties and specifics, including the size of gatherings they can accommodate. Some chefs have a storefront or deli, where clients can also acquire meals-to-go. (See Make 'n' Take/HMRs.) Others also function as personal chefs—the line is fluid, so ask if you are unsure.

Ask for what you need, and be specific about rentals, dishes, deliveries, staffing charges, menu options, linens, serving dishes, beverage service and food styles. Get a detailed quote, and do not haggle. Nor try to cut costs by reducing the staff your caterer suggests as a requisite number—you will regret it. Book far ahead if you are hiring a wedding caterer, and remember that stress has a price. Many caterers do not cater weddings because they are the most stressful events on most families' calendars.

Once your caterer or personal chef has arrived, remember that this is a skilled professional, not a nanny, servant, cleaner or confidant. Show him or her the kitchen (clean, with fridge and counter room), access, and other relevant spaces, keep the dog at bay, answer and ask all pending questions, then give her room to work her magic. Pay the bill promptly, and tip exceptional service.

CITY WIDE

Dine In Personal Chef Service

Established: 1999 • Owner: Elizabeth Sawyer
Phone: 701•3463 • E-mail: elizabeth@dine-in.ca
Hours by Appointment
Cheque, $

INITIALLY, Elizabeth Sawyer hauled her cook's toolbox and gear from house to house as an itinerant. Now she cooks in her certified professional kitchen and does deliveries, usually on a two-week rotation. Her low-fat, healthy down-home style is also available with a variety of dietary spins: low-carb or gluten-free, vegetarian, Italian, you-name-it. Sawyer, a former caterer, does desserts on request, and still caters occasionally.

• *House Specialties*: Personal chef services with menus to accommodate dietary limitations.

Inter-Course Chef Services

Established: 2006 • Owner: Patrick Dunn
Phone: 880•4207 • E-mail: patrick@inter-course.ca
Hours by Appointment
PayPal, Cheque, $

THIS private caterer and chef is better known in the classroom as "The Thai Guy" in recognition of his depth of knowledge in the cuisine of Thailand. One of the rare chefs who both bakes and cooks, Dunn has worked as a chocolate-maker at **Bernard Callebaut Chocolaterie** and is both a grad of the **SAIT Polytechnic** apprenticeship program and of the pastry program at Le Cordon Bleu in Ottawa. A keen rock climber and mountaineer, his travels to Nepal and Thailand gave him a larger viewpoint of the world, a good look at Mount Everest, and an enduring appreciation for Thai food. His company offers classes and private dinners, in a knife-edge balance of knife skills, aphrodisiacs and sexy couples cooking, with a turn at team-building in between.

• *House Specialties*: Private catering, classes and corporate team building.
• *Also Available*: Scheduled and private classes at **Talisman Centre** and **The Cookbook Company Cooks**.

www.inter-course.ca

Judy Wood Cuisine

Established: 1998 • Owner: Judy Wood
Phone: 542•6117 • E-mail: butterandcream@telus.net
Hours by Appointment
Cheque, $

CHEF Judy Wood is a classically trained bilingual chef with a long history in Calgary restaurants, from opening chef at Buchanan's Chop House prior to the 1988 Olympics, to operating her own bustling business, Savoury Café from 1998–2003. She is consulting chef to **Mise En Place**, has a regular gig with Global TV (*The Saturday Chef*, 8:15 am on Channel 7), and participated in the successful *"Dishing"* cookbooks with ten other Calgary women food professionals. Wood is a popular teacher at **Willow Park Wines & Spirits**, and has been an integral instructor at **The Cookbook Company Cooks** local classes and cooking camps overseas. She offers private chef and catering services, all delivered with her trademark French approach, attention to detail, and self-deprecating wit.
- *House Specialties*: Private catering and chef sevices, specializing in bistro-style modern and classic French fare.

King Brisket Boy

Established: 2005 • Owner: Dave Thurgar
Phone: 510•0000 • E-mail: eatbbq@kingbrisketboy.com
Hours by Appointment
V, MC, Cheque, $

AUTHENTIC and delicious southern-style BBQ has been a mouth-watering, finger-licking fact in Alberta since 1994, with the formation of Rockin' Ronnie's Butt Shredders. The Butt Shredders went on to well-documented victories, educating hungry Calgarians in the subtleties of barbecue along the way. The latest incarnation, Dave Thurgar's King Brisket Boy, is a graduate of Rockin' Ronnie's late-night school of good coals. Thurgar competed as a Butt Shredders team member before heading out on his own with his portable smoker. He is justifiably proud of his long association with Ronnie Shewchuk, Amo Jackson and Kathy Richardier—the Butt Shredders' founding members. Thurgar is proud to have been a part of winning Calgary's BBQ on the Bow Grand Championship and Grand Championship Reserve, the Canadian National Grand Championship at Whistler, and two showings at the prestigious Jack Daniels Invitational BBQ championship in Lynchburg, Tennessee, on the grounds of the famous bourbon distillery.

Thurgar cooks what he competes with, putting your money where his mouth is, including award-winning rubs and sauces. All dishes are cooked s-l-o-w-l-y in his mobile custom smoker, using Okanagan apple wood and oak whiskey barrel staves. His specialties include beef brisket, pulled pork, pork ribs, chicken, sausages, dark amber ale beans, creamy tidewater coleslaw, peach or berry crisp. Dave is a **SAIT Polytechnic** grad, and is Calgary Health Board approved and licensed by the City of Calgary.

• *House Specialties*: Custom mobile catering of slow-cooked southern-style BBQ, specializing in beef brisket, pulled pork, pork ribs, and chicken. **www.kingbrisketboy.com**

Los Sabores de México • Flavours of Mexico Ltd.
Established: 1997 • Owner: Norma Schmill de French
Phone: 283•6384 • E-mail: mexicocuisine@shaw.ca
Hours by Appointment
Cheque, $

NORMA Schmill de French, born in Mexico, was trained in Mexico and Canada. She caters to corporate and private clientele, but in home venues only, not in downtown offices. She teaches classes as well, to illustrate the refinement and affordability of Mexican cuisine. Norma prefers cocktail parties to dinners, and her classes are hands-on in the client's home kitchen, using only ingredients that are available locally. Norma was involved at **Boca Loca Fine Mexican Foods** as initial consulting chef and production consultant, making salsa and *tamales*, and teaching the store's classes until 2004. Private culinary tours to Mexico for on-site cooking classes can be arranged.
• *House Specialties*: Private caterer and teacher, providing meals, hands-on classes and culinary tours to Mexico.

Manna Catering Services
Established: 1998 • Owner: Chris Halpin
Phone: 616•8008 • E-mail: email@mannaonline.com, chrishalpin@shaw.ca
Hours by Appointment
Cheque, $

CATERER Chris Halpin does cocktails and dinners, with custom-designed menus that are an opportunity to explore cuisine. He specializes in "urban" food that hangs together with French flavours and ethnic overtones, with a strong suit in plating and visual display, as one would expect of a man whose day job is art consultancy. Halpin believes that food should not require deconstruction in order to be eaten.
• *House Specialties*: Private custom catering, offering cocktails and dinner service, serving "Frenchified ethnic fusion."

Meta4 Foods
Established: 2006 • Owner: Eric Giesbrecht
Mailing Address: 70, 9000 Wentworth Avenue SW, Calgary, Alberta T3H 0A9
Phone: 616•6164 • E-mail: chefmystic@meta4foods.com
Hours by Appointment
Cheque, $

META4 Foods seeks to inspire, connect, energize and operate as a force for constructive change. Chef-owner Eric Giesbrecht's food philosophy is to bring the mystery of existence to the forefront of the awareness of everyday life, thus the company slogan, "Mid-Wifing the Mystery with Meal as Metaphor." Working as a personal chef reinforces his belief in the power of interpersonal interaction as a key to the pleasure of food.

Giesbrecht works as a private chef, caterer, and consultant, offering intimate dinner parties and private cooking lessons in a variety of ethnic styles, specializing in fish—backyard lobster boils and oyster parties. With training and experience in classical French cuisine, specializing in seafood and shellfish, Giesbrecht also operates a wholesale shellfish business which delivers premier quality oysters, mussels, and clams to Calgary's top restaurants and individual bivalve lovers. Order Friday for the following week delivery of Brent "The Oyster Man" Petkaus's Cortesan Gem oysters, clams, and mussels, shipped direct from Cortes Island. Giesbrecht's "hot hands" twice earned him the title of Calgary's speediest oyster shucker, and he finished fourth in the Eastern Canadian shucking championships in 2004. He is also an instructor at **The Cookbook Company Cooks** cooking school.

• *House Specialties*: Personal chef and private catering services, specializing in shellfish (wholesale and catering), consulting and classes.

www.meta4foods.com

Pennache

Established: 2003 • Owner: Joanne Penn
Phone: 829•2433 • E-mail: chef@pennache.com
Hours by Appointment
V, MC, Cheque, $

THIS self-taught world traveller grew up in her mother's professional kitchen. After a career in teaching tech software, she followed her passion into food. A member of both the Canadian and US Personal Chef Associations, Penn shops, and cooks on-site once a week, leaving behind a small gift (flowers, brownies), and meals—frozen or chilled, as required. She is committed to providing home-cooked meals that bring families together at the dinner table. She cooks in a modern fusion genre that encompasses comfort, often in her trademark spicy Indian or Mexican preference, like cranberry-glazed pork loin or Texican shredded pork burrito.

• *House Specialties*: personal chef services, specializing in cross-cultural and comfort cuisine.

www.pennache.com

Saffron Personal Chef Services

Established: 2001 • Owner: Dean Mitchell
Phone: 850•5008 • E-mail: saffron.chef@telusplanet.net
Hours by Appointment
V, MC, AE, Cheque, $

DEAN Mitchell has a restaurant background and cooks dinners in two Calgary seniors' residences. He also offers independent personal chef services, specializing in cooking for allergy and dietary restrictions within a home-style framework of meals. He designs menus to fit, with deliveries as required by appointment. Dean is a member of the Calgary Academy of Chefs & Cooks, and holds the Canadian Culinary Federation's highest professional designation, Certified Chef de Cuisine (CCC).

• *House Specialties*: Personal chef service accommodating allergy and dietary home-style fare.

www.saffronpersonalchef.com

Savour the Flavours
Established: 2001 • Owner: Mike Pruden
Phone: 630•3582 or 279•0879 • E-mail: mike@savourtheflavours.com
Hours by Appointment
Cheque, $

SERVING "good old home-style cooking or creative gourmet," Pruden is a personal chef who calls himself a "personal culinary designer." He likes to accommodate any diets, from low carb to celiac, within a heart-smart style that does not include butter or whipping cream. He shops, arrives every two weeks, and offers specialized catering on request—dinner parties, hors d'oeuvre, and in-home culinary instructional classes too.

• *House Specialties*: Personal chef services featuring dietary and heart-smart fare, as well as diet-sensitive catering and in-home classes.

www.savourtheflavours.com

Suppertime Solutions Personal Chef
Established: 2003 • Owner: Susan Simonelli
Cell: 890•2659 • E-mail: smh3@shaw.ca
Hours by Appointment
Cheque, $

SUSAN Simonelli loves Thai and Indonesian food, but she is also adept at Italian and Moroccan, her current flavour fave. She loves cooking for others so they find good meals when they come home, and finds herself smiling on a "cook day" while peeling potatoes or simmering vegetables. A little gift is left for her clients, and she specializes in health-conscious cooking that accommodates family limitations or allergies. Simonelli belongs to both the Canadian and U.S. Personal Chefs' Associations.

• *House Specialties*: Personal chef services specializing in healthy family food, heart-smart or diabetic, vegetarian and ethnic dishes that include Moroccan, Thai and Indonesian flavours.

NORTHEAST

Darryl Bennett, Chef for Hire
Established: 2000 • Owner: Darryl Bennett
2442–23 Avenue NE
Phone: 285•4924 or Cell: 819•3279 • E-mail: chefhire@telus.net
Hours by Appointment
V, MC, AE, Cheque, $

CORPORATE work keeps Darryl Bennett's burners hot, but he continues to acquire clients as a personal chef. Specialized menus span it all—gourmet, gluten-free and allergies, and everyday comfort "Mom" fare that Bennett calls North American home-style. His catering encompasses all of the possibilities: weddings, social events, corporate breakfasts, including continental "box" breakfasts—to go or delivered—and on-site customized omelet stations, hot lunches—delivered and set up for easy service, office delivery of cold platters comprising antipasti, sandwiches, cheeses and fruit, dinners for romantics, and elegant house parties. Bennett's mobile service travels to galleries, office towers, and homes.
• *House Specialties*: Personal chef and catering service in gourmet, gluten-free or allergy fare and North American home-style cuisine.
www.chefforhire.ca

EthniCity Catering
Established: 1998 • Manager: Ebtisam Tamraz
Back Door, 1308 Edmonton Trail NE
Phone: 537•8809 • E-mail: via website
Hours by Appointment
V, MC, Cheque, $

SINCE 1988, the Centre for Newcomers (formerly the Calgary Mennonite Centre for Newcomers at 125, 920–36 Street NE) has helped to ease the transition for new immigrants. The Centre offers settlement aid, employment and language support to new families. In 1998, the Centre added work training and kitchen experience, starting EthniCity Catering with seed money from the Calgary Foundation and the United Way. Now, the kitchen's thriving catering business teaches the practicality of cooking along with applied lessons in the English language.

Ebtisam Tamraz, the kitchen manager, estimates the number of women who have passed through the kitchen since 2000 at upwards of 30. The changing staff of 12 may hail from China, the Philippines, Iraq, Syria, Egypt, India, and Albania, with languages to match. The women stay for between 3 and 6 months—depending on how well they absorb English, learn transferable skills in a team environment—and then move on to school or employment in the food service industry. The immigrant women—wives, sisters, mothers and daughters—who work at EthniCity are all deeply appreciative of the fact that they now live in a peace zone. Delivery (of food, and perhaps peace) can be arranged.

• *House Specialties*: Private catering of authentic East Asian, South Asian, Mediterranean, Latin American appetizers and main courses.
www.ethnicitycatering.ca

SOUTHEAST

Great Events Group

Established: 1982 • Contacts: Lindsay Chadderton & Walter Tomandl
7207 Fairmount Drive SE
Phone: 256•7150 (Catering), 256•9344 (Office) • E-mail: info@greateventsgroup.com
Monday–Friday 8:00 am–5:00 pm
Consultations by Appointment
V, MC, Debit, Cheque, $

THIS big, big, big family business is vertically integrated, offering one-stop shopping for catering—from renting cutlery or marquee tents to the unofficial "test kitchen" in Cravings restaurant downstairs. You have likely enjoyed their fare writ large at the Jubilee Auditorium, local art galleries, or Spruce Meadows. The range of scope and size possible is monumental: from steak and beans to "Flavours" boutique cooking, office lunch deliveries, or on-site catering for 1,500 people.

• *House Specialties*: Corporate, private, office catering, rentals.
• *Also Available*: Spruce Meadows, RR#9, Spruce Meadows Way SW.
www.greateventsgroup.com • www.officegourmetcatering.com

La Table du Chatelain Cuisine & Catering

Established: 2004 • Owner: Jean-Paul Chatelain
221 – 62 Avenue SE
Phone: 271•9442 • E-mail: jeanpaul@tableduchatelain.com
Hours by Appointment
V, MC, AE, Debit, Cheque, $

AS a private chef and off-premises caterer, originally from Montreal, and trained in northern France, Chatelain cooks what he knows—fine dining in the classic style. His goal is to create special parties, not necessarily day-to-day fare. Expect meals that span *amuse-bouche* to *mignardaise*. House-made *boeuf bourguignon* is one classic signature dish and chocolate mousse needs little explanation in Jean Paul's hands.

• *House Specialties*: Private chef and catering, offering classic French fare, from cocktails to dinners, corporate and private, including weddings.
www.tableduchatelain.com

See Catering • Catering Inc. • A Gourmet Affair

Established: 2006 • Owner: Charlie See
1415–38 Avenue SE
Phone: 253•4944 (See Catering) • E-mail: chef@seecatering.com
Phone: 999•8448 (Catering Inc.) • Phone: 253•2829 (A Gourmet Affair)
Hours by Appointment
V, MC, Cheque, $

CHEF Charlie See spent his formative years with European chefs, cooking in the Rocky Mountains, at Num-ti-Jah Lodge at Bow Lake, and for Canadian Mountain Holidays. See cooks uncomplicated meat-based bistro-esque fare.

A partnership with his brother, former Department of National Defence (DND) chef, Brian See, has manifested a long-held plan that offers support to those in need of a professional kitchen. The kitchen space, Catering Inc., can be rented by food professionals—chefs and pastry chefs—to develop and launch a business around a food service idea. The Ogden-area space is still rough around the edges, but the idea is a sound one. In the building proper, a dedicated bakeshop and a savory kitchen, complete with storage, refrigerator and freezer space, are available for rent by the hour, day, week or month. A tightly designed mobile catering kitchen, a galley on wheels, is ideal for movie-sets, off-premises or "off-the-beaten-track" events, and is available for rent.

- *House Specialties*: Catering, co-op kitchen for chefs, homemade bread, themed menus or traditional European style fare, mobile kitchen for rent.

www.seecatering.com • www.agacatering.ca

Finding a Personal Chef

INTIMATE services like personal shopping and personal training are legitimized by their presence in the yellow pages. Personal chefs have not yet achieved that status in Calgary. Check out the following websites, and be aware that not all personal chefs are members of any umbrella organization.

- <www.cdnpca.com> for the Canadian Personal Chefs Association (CPCA).
- <www.uspca.com> for the United States Personal Chefs Association (USPCA).
- <www.personalchefalliance.com> for the Personal Chefs' Alliance.
- <www.personalchef.com> for the American Personal & Private Chef Association.

SOUTHWEST

Copper Pot Creations

Established: 2003 • Owners: Chris & Crystal Niddrie
11229–30 Street SW
Phone: 585•4717 • E-mail: info@copperpotcreations.com
Store: Monday–Saturday 10:00 am–6:00 pm, Catering: Hours by Appointment
V, MC, AE, Debit, $

COPPER Pot Creations was started in 2003 by a husband-and-wife-team. Chef Chris Niddrie, born and raised in Calgary, has more than a decade of culinary experience. A **SAIT Polytechnic** professional cooking grad, he is a Certified Chef de Cuisine (CCC)—the highest professional culinary recognition and accreditation in Canada provided by the Canadian Culinary Federation. He is also accredited by the Calgary Academy of Chefs and Cooks.

The catering business serves private and corporate clients, offering cocktails and dinner buffets, corporate lunches downtown (delivery included), online ordering and delivery within Calgary and area. Delivery is free to Southside communities in the deep south, where their storefront is located.

In addition to the catering company, the pair produces Home Meal Replacements (HMRs). Their child-size meals are sold frozen and can be ordered online or purchased at their storefront, which opened in late 2006.

They focus on local and naturally raised meats and wild fish, using **Second to None Meats** as their source, **Poplar Bluff Organic Farm** vegetables, pork from **Broek Pork Acres**, lamb from **Ewe-Nique Farms**, and **MacKay's Ice Cream** for desserts. Entrees are individually portioned and frozen, and include side dishes and soups. In the summer, meals can be bought BBQ-ready, marinated, or frozen. A line of condiments and sauces using local ingredients is coming soon.

- *House Specialties*: Catering services, children's fare and HMRs, using local and natural foods.

www.copperpotcreations.com

Devour Catering Inc.

Established: 1997 • Owners: Torin & J'Val Shuster
10, 4604–37 Street SW
Phone: 242•0046 • E-mail: info@devourcatering.com
By Appointment: Tuesday–Saturday 9:00 am–5:00 pm
V, MC, Debit, $

THE food style at this busy catering shop is self-described as creatively European-influenced with a strong affection for the unpretentious. The business has a strong flair for visual presentation and staging, befitting J'Val's background in production design with Alberta Theatre Projects. Chef Torin has a Slovak family background, and was interested in baking and food from an early age, chopping vegetables in a Chinese restaurant at age 15. His training at Canadian cooking schools has informed Torin's work—he leans to classic

modern fare, drawing on French and Italian traditions and simple flavours.
- *House Specialties*: Private catering of French and Italian fare, traditionally inspired, with contemporary execution. Staging and presentation are strong suites.

www.devourcatering.com

Haifa Delicatessen & Caterers • Kavin's Kosher Meats
Established: 2005 • Owners: Denise & Ivor Kavin
Bays 8 & 9, 3109 Palliser Drive SW
Phone: 238•0525 • E-mail: haifadeli@shaw.ca
Monday–Thursday 9:00 am–6:00 pm, Friday 9:00 am–2:00 pm
Sunday 9:00 am–2:00 pm
V, MC, Debit, $

THIS shop and deli was certified *kosher* in 2005. The Jewish owners, Yorkshire-born Denise and South African Ivor, met in Canada in 1999. Ivor missed some of the South African meat dishes of his homeland, so he started to make *biltong, dry wors, boerewors* and *sosaties.*

Denise is a very good cook indeed and she keeps the deli case full: turkey and chicken schnitzel, chopped liver, chopped herring, *rugala,* cabbage rolls, Polish sausages, smoked meats, potato *knishes* and *latkes, baba ganouj,* smoked salmon, coleslaw in vinaigrette, *borek* stuffed with vegetables or mushrooms, chopped and fried fish, good soups. Most desserts are brought in from Montreal.

The shelves are full of *kosher* fare, from canned fruit and spices to South African fish paste made from mackerel. (Ivor says it is the best on toast with a coffee chaser.) Cooks can carry away soup mixes and *matzo,* balsamic vinegar and honey, *bamba* and *bissli,* kosher gum, pickles, herring, tomatoes and horseradish, American rennet-free cheeses (sealed to keep *kosher*), Passover foods and dry goods. *Kosher* chicken and beef are fresh or frozen.
- *House Specialties*: *Kosher* catering, South African value-added meats, deli, meats, dry goods and sweets.
- *Also Available*: *Kosher* catering at local hotels.

www.haifadeli.ca

Indulge Catering
Established: 1997 • Owners: Eric & Sharon Day
Studio 3, 5524–1A Street SW
Phone: 229•9029 • E-mail: order@indulgecatering.com
Hours by Appointment
V, MC, AE, Cheque, $

THIS pair offers mostly corporate catering, served downtown, in office towers. Book for sandwiches, stand up receptions, dinners that are buffet or sit down, or breakfasts with omelet stations. All foods are prepared in the company's signature "upscale eclectic" style. Clients can peruse menus and order online. House-made dessert is the extra carrot.
- *House Specialties*: Corporate downtown catering.

www.indulgecatering.com

Infuse Catering • Forage Foods

Established: 2001 • Owners: Wade Sirois & Jaclyn Labchuk
3508 & 3510–19 Street SW
Phone: 269•3902 (Infuse) and 269•6551 (Forage) • E-mail: via websites
Infuse Catering: Hours by Appointment
Forage Foods: Monday–Friday 2:00–7:00 pm
V, MC, Cheque, $

WADE and Jaclyn's Infuse Cuisine Group Ltd. is home to Infuse Catering and Forage Foods. They have a deep sense of connection to regional cuisine, and support local growers and producers almost exclusively in all their culinary endeavours. Sirois attended Slow Food's Terra Madre in 2006 as part of a contingent of Albertan chefs. He loves to try his hand at many things from scratch, and has made his partner share office space with "mother" vinegars, sourdough starters, ripening homemade cheeses, and other aromatic experiments.

The catering arm provides stylish and modern fare, from "dishes to tents, DJs to big bands, centrepieces to sofas." Arrange hors d'oeuvres or sit-downs, private or corporate, in fields, offices, art galleries, or private homes. Just ask. The catering business uses house-made cordials and breads, and the company's overriding mandate is to use 70 percent local ingredients, often sourced directly from the producer.

Next door, at Forage Foods, local food is made into "farm to fork foods to go," a retail version of fast Slow Food that hopes to make eating well, and locally, a convenient act in the city's most densely populated neighbourhoods, Marda Loop and Garrison Woods. Retail shelves at Forage Foods are stocked with local goods, like **Highwood Crossing Farm Inc.** canola oil, **Chinook Honey** honey and honeycomb, and **Edgar Farms** pickled asparagus.

Hot meals to go or frozen meals to take home, in one to two person portions, feature an array of local producers: **Wapiti Ways** frozen meals, made with elk—chili, stew, meatloaf and meatballs with porcini cranberry cream sauce, **Sunworks Farm** roasted chicken, **Gull Valley Greenhouse** tomatoes in sauce and salsa, and **Broek Pork Acres** pork in meatloaf, meatballs or roast shoulder.

- *House Specialties*: Catering with local foods, HMRs featuring local producers, dishes available frozen, fresh and hot, local ingredients.

www.infusecatering.com • www.foragefoods.com

Red Tree

Established: 2001 • Co-owners: Susan Hopkins & Aaron Creurer
2129-33 Avenue SW
Phone: 242•3246 • E-mail: susan@redtreecatering.com
Monday–Friday 10:00 am–7:00 pm, Saturday 10:00 am–6:00 pm
V, MC, Debit, $

OPENED in 2001, this busy catering and elegant food-to-go shop in Marda Loop is the brainchild of co-owners Susan Hopkins and Aaron Creurer, both grads of **SAIT Polytechnic**. Look for adventurous and gorgeous dishes, in their popular "funky retro with a twist" style of cooking. Artist-painter Creurer designs gorgeous windows. Step inside to see pretty food-to-go and HMRs, shelves bursting with a growing collection of selectively chosen condiments, and carefully chosen tableware, plates and platters. The condiment collection includes truly elegant indulgences, like house-made candied grapefruit rinds in slivers and wedges. HMRs can be picked up at the shop—order in advance for large volumes. Local products on sale include **Brassica Mustards**, and the kitchen uses meat and game from **Carmen Creek Gourmet Meats, Hoven Farms, Sunworks Farm**, and **Valbella Meats/Valbella's Deli & Café**, and grains from **Grainworks Inc.** House specialties include braised bison short ribs, portobello *tortilla* cake, pasta platters and "grazing" trays for lunchtime sharing.

A Northside retail shop and bakery opened in 2007, stocking both shops with baked goods. Try a sweet breakfast loaf or sourdough *boule* on weekends, along with ciabatta, baguettes, and artisan breads through the week. Tarts and ice creams from **Nectar Desserts** supplement in-house baked tortes, cookies, cakes and squares.

- *House Specialties*: Caterers of elegant, funky-modern and retro fare, HMRs, local products and preserves.
- *Also Available*: 1245 Kensington Road NW.

www.redtreecatering.com

NORTHWEST

Red Tree

Established: 2007 • Co-owners: Susan Hopkins & Aaron Creurer
1245 Kensington Road NW
Phone: 242•3246 • E-mail: susan@redtreecatering.com
Tuesday–Friday 10:00 am–7:00 pm, Saturday 10:00 am–6:00 pm
Sunday 12:00 am–6:00 pm
V, MC, Debit, $
[see SW Personal Chefs & Caterers for main entry on p. 209]

Food Organizations

WITHIN OUR CITY AND PROVINCE, there are many thoughtful, committed organizations involved in wide-ranging aspects of food. Some are nonprofit, working in invisible kitchens, feeding the homeless and disadvantaged. Others plant urban community gardens or advocate a slower life. They recognize that if all are to eat, and eat well, societal changes are imperative.

Opinions vary as to how meaningful change occurs. Governments believe in "top down," as legislated by bureaucrats and elected officials. Grassroots activists believe in action by and for the people, movements impelled by issues that come close to home. Few actions are as intimate as putting food into our mouths—for eating is a sacred act cloaked in dailiness. However, many of us have forgotten this, and take our abundance for granted. Even as we debate the ethics and issues surrounding how we raise our food, and debate the complexities and weaknesses of our food systems, we forget to consider the weak links in our society. Why are there hungry children in such a wealthy city? Why are there families and individuals struggling to put food on the table? When did we forget to take care of each other? Why can't we cook? The societal implications of self-absorption and isolationism are evident: hungry kids, homeless shelters, food banks. The simple act of eating together can begin to restore the sacred, but it takes will and small beginnings to change how things are. As Margaret Mead observed, "Never doubt that a small group of thoughtful, committed citizens can change the world. Indeed, it is the only thing that ever has." Here are some groups and organizations that are actively heeding Mead's words.

Alberta Food Processors Association (AFPA)
Established: 1974 • VP, Training & Development: Janet Henderson
100, 4760–72 Avenue SE
Phone: 201•1044, Ext. 22 or 201•3657

THIS not-for-profit organization exists so that the wheel need not be re-invented each time a person or company wants to turn a food idea into a marketable product. AFPA provides its members with a number of services, industry connections, marketing knowledge, labelling and nutritional requirements lingo, PR smarts, workplace safety guidelines, food safety, Hazard Analysis and Critical Control Points (HAACP) training, and systems development. AFPA attends to up-and-coming chefs' development with the Stan Ballard Apprenticeship Fund, awarded to Albertan culinary students to support their educational opportunities. A consumer-oriented website provides member businesses with a window to potential buyers.
www.afpa.com • www.preparedwithpride.com

Calgary Drop-In & Rehab Centre

Established: 1961 • Executive Director: Dermot Baldwin
423–4 Avenue SE
Phone: 263•5707

IN a kitchen not far from the Bow River, a petite, birdlike woman in professional cook's whites is one of three chefs who make 3,500 meals a day at the Calgary Drop-In & Rehab Centre. "I feel I am doing something worthwhile here, not just making money for some business," Cindy McPhee says. "We feed people who need feeding." She counts herself as one of the lucky survivors, and is glad to make a contribution to the community that supported her through her own tough times. Calm and no-nonsense, she works small miracles with what she is given, and does not tolerate violence or disruption. Her staff is made up of volunteers—who fill the plates inside the locked kitchen—and the centre's clients—who serve the plates in the dining room. The dining room is crowded. One of the last people to climb the stairs and hand in her meal ticket is a woman I spotted walking alone beside the Centre Street bridge.

It is hard to view the scene at the Drop-In Centre as anything but tough. The Centre's Executive Director, Dermot Baldwin, quotes a May 2006 civic census, citing over 3,600 homeless people in the city, with a 15 percent increase in homelessness annually. On Baldwin's office walls, a portrait of Mother Teresa and a poster of the Dalai Lama share space with photos of his kids and his clients. Compassion and kindness are all that contradict the life he witnesses first-hand—an ugly, violent and cruel world, where drugs, illness, human frailty, homelessness and hunger are normal.

The Centre is the least selective of all the aid organizations in the city. By the time its clients have fallen through the cracks and arrive at its doors, they are, without exception, at a desperate place of last resort.

The Centre opened in its current Bow River location on September 11, 2001 but dates back to 1961—in a variety of forms and locations—and provides temporary sleeping accommodations, meals, counselling, training, limited longer-term accommodation and hope to 1,100 lost souls, in a total of five locations around the city. It is funded by both provincial and municipal government, the United Way, as well as corporate and private donations. More than 8,500 clients pass through its doors annually, dealing with addictions, violence, mental illness, tough transitions, and the bitter dregs of life gone terribly sour. Art therapy, computer training, and woodworking skills are available to those who demonstrate willingness to rebuild a life.

The kitchen and dining room are at the heart of the building. Next to a safe and secure place to sleep, Baldwin says, food is the most important thing the centre offers its clients.

After dinner, the young woman from the bridge is sitting on the curb. She is not alone, and I fear for her safety and survival. A meal is not the only need of the fallen.

www.cdics.com

Calgary Horticultural Society

Established: 1908 • President: Gabrielle Kaufmann
208–50 Avenue SW
Phone: 287•3469
September–June: Tuesday–Friday 9:00 am–4:00 pm, Saturday 9:00 am–1:00 pm
July & August: Tuesday, Wednesday & Friday 9:00 am–4:00 pm
Thursday 9:00 am–8:00 pm

CANADA's urban agriculture has included shared gardens since the early 1900s. Community gardens offer people—from diverse cultures and socio-economic groups—a chance to interact together while growing vegetables, fruit, herbs, and flowers.

The Calgary Horticultural Society is powered by volunteers, including Ruth Anne Rudack, who acts as a liaison officer for the society and community gardeners around the city. Rudack says, "Calgary's oldest community gardens date back to 1974, but community gardens and more green space still need a champion at City Hall. With high land values and so many competing demands for unused open space, does a vacant strip of land become a basketball court or a garden?"

A community garden can be almost any size. Each plot is rented for the growing season—by individuals, families, or groups—for a nominal fee. Gardeners all contribute to maintenance and seasonal cleanup. It is a small but vital way to share, and can lead to a sense of community that extends beyond the soil to the table. A booklet, "How to Start a Community Garden," is available through the CHS office.

Beyond community gardens, the CHS encourages gardens of all shapes and sizes, in recognition of the healing and unifying power of soil and seeds. We all eat, and we all can tend edible plants in our yards instead of mowing lawns that guzzle water. A vegetable patch can make a difference, one seed at a time.

www.calhort.org

Calgary Inter-Faith Food Bank Society

Established: 1982 • Chief Executive Officer: James McAra
5000–11 Street SE
Phone: 253•2059

CALGARY'S inter-denominational food bank opened in 1982, established at that time by three leaders of the faith in response to the economic downturn in the oil and gas sector.

The mandate is simple: feed people who are hungry. In 2006, 94,689 clients were served with more than 38,000 hampers—an average of 165 hampers per day. Forty-two percent of those fed by the food bank were children.

The organization is housed in a huge warehouse that has more in common with a supply depot than a cathedral or a kitchen. At the front of the building, potential clients are screened, then move on to receive their food from a conveyor belt. At the back, row after row of huge boxes—two months' supply of food in case of a civic emergency—are stacked six high, and forklifts and more conveyor belts are the tools of choice. One wall is brightened by half a dozen murals, painted by volunteers—children and art therapy groups.

Groceries are not a luxury, but the food bank is a stopgap measure. Each hamper contains groceries for five to seven days—core ingredients deemed vital, from peanut butter to pasta. If people need more than three hampers, they are referred to agencies for help in addressing underlying issues.

In an offshoot program called Hampers for the Homeless, hampers containing ready-to-eat foods and snacks are distributed to nearly a dozen street agencies. The food bank's Food Link program also provides food to other agencies in and around the city, and the bulk food distribution program directs food to other food banks across Alberta, Saskatchewan, and British Columbia.

Every year the organization needs $13 million worth of food and $3.5 million in cash for its programs. Donations of time—90,000 hours annually—translates into the equivalent of 55 full-time jobs.

CEO James McAra talks in terms of community—the civic community and the dedicated people who confront hunger daily without blinking or losing faith. He sees our current urban lifestyle as one of fostering isolation, taking us away from community, faith-based groups, city organizations, and family. Nevertheless, he is hopeful, despite dwindling church congregations, and the "not in my back yard" (NIMBY) approach to life. He believes a new type of community is stepping up to ask, "How can I help?"

Helping our neighbours will alleviate the fear that has sent children, young mothers, old folk and families into isolation. "Build a community one step at a time. Hold a BBQ, meet your neighbours, meet their dog, say hi," he suggests. "Our government has missed the boat. Better business does not necessarily equal better living, and more money does not equate to more life value. Our infrastructure is broken."

Until the system is fixed or changed, when people are hungry, the food bank feeds them. No "run" will empty the vaults. If ever the bank empties of donations, the staff goes grocery shopping.

www.calgaryfoodbank.com

Calgary Meals On Wheels

Established: 1965 • Executive Director: Lou Winters, Director of Operations: Bill Storey
3610 Macleod Trail SE
Phone: 243•2834
Monday–Friday 7:30 am–3:30 pm

L IVING alone as an aging person is not easy. This is where Calgary Meals on Wheels drives into the neighbourhood, providing clients with part of the means—sustenance—to maintain their independence within their own homes for as long as is possible to effect with dignity.

At 6:15 each morning, the first cadre of Calgary Meals on Wheels staff and volunteers are in the kitchen, preparing meals for 700 clients. The diners won't be eating at fancy linen-lined white tablecloth settings in deluxe dining rooms. They won't be sipping vintage champagne. More likely, they will be drinking water to wash down their daily meds and eating alone at the kitchen table of the family home.

The important thing is that they ARE eating at home. The visible purpose of this charitable organization is to provide affordable and nutritious meals to seniors and the disadvantaged. The underlying mandate is to help people remain independent and in their homes for as long as possible. "We are an aging society, but we cling to our independence," says Lou Winters, executive director of Calgary Meals on Wheels. At present, over a period of a year, 1,800 clients receive meals delivered by Calgary Meals on Wheels volunteers— 400,000 meals annually, with projections of one million meals by 2015. Winters says that the actual need would probably double these figures.

The elderly are not the only beneficiaries. Each day, 216 bag lunches go to the **Calgary Drop-In & Rehab Centre**, where they are distributed to the working homeless. Each week, 835 servings of hearty soup go to eight high-risk elementary schools. A program called "Magic Meals," offers a selection of frozen entrees to house-bound clients who order in advance for home delivery.

Established in Calgary in 1965, an annual contingent of more than 650 volunteers (75 pairs of hands daily) contribute time and effort to Calgary Meals on Wheels—through cooking, packing meals into insulated boxes, transporting the boxes to supply depots, or driving one of 65 delivery routes. More than 50 percent of the meals prepared are special diets, to accommodate allergies, cultural sensitivities or textural alteration for medical reasons. A nutritionist and a dietary technologist ensure that menus meet nutritional guidelines established by the *Canada Food Guide*.

Every client receives a hot meal and a bag lunch, filled with soup (which can be reheated) or salad and sandwich, and what operations manger Bill Storey calls "nighttime survival supplies"—fruits and house-baked desserts. Friday deliveries are sufficient to last through the weekend.

Anyone who is concerned can advocate for the service—a family member, friend, medical support person, homecare worker. Service fees are essentially means-tested, based on client income. Seventy-seven percent of the service's clients are 75 years of age, or older, and mostly on fixed incomes. Paying clients cover only one-quarter of the program's cost; the remainder is subsidized. The organization has an annual budget of $2.5 million, and receives funding from the city's Family and Community Support Services and from the United Way.

Calgary Meals on Wheels is relocating to bigger premises in the spring of 2009, and needs more than $8 million dollars for its expansion.

www.mealsonwheels.com

Community Kitchen Program of Calgary
Established: 1995 • Community Development Coordinator: Janice Nicolay
3751–21 Street NE
Phone: 538•7380
Monday–Friday 8:00 am–4:00 pm

IN collaboration with Neighbour Link, the Community Kitchen Program of Calgary has created and implemented many initiatives designed to feed hungry and disadvantaged people of all ages in a dignified and respectful manner. Founder and CEO Marilyn Gunn is the dynamic leader—a conscience for the city. She spearheads half a dozen programs that help those in need of food and education.

The Community Kitchen Program offers affordable access to fresh produce, and volunteers assist families in need with planning and making nutritious meals in an economic and time-effective fashion.

- Tummy Tamers is a summer feeding program, an outreach to children in high need communities.
- Souper Stars goes into schools and teaches kitchen confidence along with how to select and prepare healthy food. Group dynamics, social skills and positive self-image grow with good nutrition.
- Calgary's Cooking is a mobile unit that feeds kids in the Park & Play program during the summer.
- The Good Food box program is a centralized buying club that distributes nutritious and affordable food boxes.
- Spinz Around is the rescued food program, collecting still-edible food from other agencies and food businesses and spinning it around to those in need.

In the works: a new on-site training kitchen to host workshops and training programs for students, where cooking classes as well as information about making healthy food choices will be offered.

www.communitykitchenprogram.com

Dine Alberta

Established: 2002 • Network Development Specialist: Marlene Abrams
Alberta Agriculture & Food
Main Floor, Provincial Building
4709–44 Avenue, Stony Plain, Alberta T7Z 1N4
Phone: (780) 968•3519

ALBERTA Agriculture & Food's annual Dine Alberta celebration of local fare showcases all that is grand about homegrown. The festival of local food started as an annual month-long, restaurant-based dining event, putting local fare on restaurant plates across the province. It continues to support growers and producers, foster enduring and synergistic relationships between chefs and growers, and inform consumers about where to find great Alberta-grown food year-round. Online, a searchable database lists Alberta growers, what they grow, and when it is available. Diners can also check an online listing of restaurants and caterers across the province who feature Alberta-grown ingredients on their menus. The next step for Dine Alberta is providing consumers with information about culinary and agricultural tourism around the province, highlighting farm visits and festivals, farmgate sales, farmers' markets and self-guided tours.

www.dinealberta.ca

Feed the Hungry

Established: 1993 • Contact: Toni Palmiere
Mailing Address: c/o Pastoral Centre, 120–17 Avenue SW, Calgary T2S 2T2
221–18 Avenue SW (St. Mary's Cathedral Hall)
Phone: 218•5532
Sunday 3:30 pm–5:00 pm

FOR many of us, Sunday dinner is sacred, embellished with memories of friends and relations, rituals and hospitality interwoven into the fabric of family. For others, Sunday is the day set aside for worship. Saint Mary's Cathedral Hall is home to both, making a practical sacrament of service, community, and sharing from its weekly dinner for those without sufficient resources.

In 1993, the Catholic Charities, an agency of the Roman Catholic Bishop of the Diocese of Calgary, began a monthly dinner program for hungry families and individuals. The program has become a weekly occurrence. In 2008, Feed the Hungry celebrates its 15th anniversary of feeding an average of 700 diners each week.

Feeding 700 people inside of two hours is no accidental occurrence, but the result of many years' honing of method and system. Some volunteers are a reliable constant, committing themselves to weekly or bi-weekly attendance. Of those to whom much is given, much is expected, says one.

Volunteers who have come to serve their community laugh as they work, setting mugs on trays, buttering buns, slicing desserts and vegetables, or helping in the kitchen, serving and clearing. The hall looks like a dining room, with over thirty tables set for dining. At 3:00 pm, coordinator Toni Palmiere takes up a microphone and briefs her charges with what to expect and how to conduct themselves. By 3:30 pm, the doors are open, and guests walk into the hall. Some have been queued for hours. One young man in jeans and hoodie composes a rap as he waits for dinner: "You seem to be mistaken, In what you call forsaken..."

The cost of dinner each week—$4,000—and the people to set up, prepare and serve it—about 110—is underwritten by sponsors who commit their business, organization, family or friends to a Sunday service a year in advance.

Palmiere enforces safety: no kids under the age of 13 may go to the washrooms alone; men serve the VIP (Very Inebriated Persons) tables, guests may not hoard food or drink, and may have as many servings as they can consume, but only one plateful at a time. After eating dinner, homeless diners queue up for one of 100 hampers that are given out each week in collaboration with the **Calgary Inter-Faith Food Bank.**

In 2007, in collaboration with Elizabeth House, Feed the Hungry began an new initiative in teaching young mothers—aged 14 to 25—how to shop for groceries and cook together. "Eating well is not a privilege, but a right," Palmiere says. "The needs of hungry children ripple through the community. I want all the pebbles, so we can make a wave."

Feed the Hungry takes place 47 or 48 Sundays of the year.

www.rcdiocese-calgary.ab.ca

Growing Food Security in Alberta (GFSA)
Established: 2002 • Project Coordinator: Susan Roberts
Project Assistant, Community Building Resources: Angie Dedrick
Phone: (780) 987•2002, Ext. 1 • E-mail: info@foodsecurityalberta.ca

THE GFSA is an ad hoc grassroots network that brings together individuals and organizations—ranchers, university faculty, health professionals— interested in rural food literacy. Part of the goal is to assist rural communities in developing vibrant and sustainable roots. The health and economic viability of rural Alberta is a litmus test for our agriculture and food systems, says project coordinator Susan Roberts.

Food security is the currently popular three-dollar phrase for the simple concept of abundance: ensuring that all have access in a dignified manner to safe, nutritious, affordable and appropriate food and know how to prepare it. Roberts is a fan of cooking classes. She calls them highly effective tools that blend skills and socialization. The seeds sown yield a harvest of equitable wealth generation, environmentally aware food production and community wellness.

Seeing the big picture inherent to food security—how food is produced, processed, distributed, and purchased or recycled—means we recognize the major role of food, one that is often underestimated simply because of its ubiquitousness. The Slow Cities movement, which had its inaugural meeting in Orvieto, Italy in 1999, and is an offshoot of the global **Slow Food** movement, is a good example of food security and quality of life moving to the top of the list of civic priorities.

Food policies can positively influence agriculture and food production through encouraging consumers' support for local food producers, farmers' markets, and food processors. Inherent advantages include reducing our reliance on imported foods that are transported long distances at significant cost, often with unknown provenance and with little or no track record of safety or assurance against adulteration. Food policies can encourage the development of better neighbourhoods through the astute placement of grocery stores that are accessible on foot or by bicycle. A bike ride to the store for milk is as local as it gets, and is relatively simple to achieve.

Food policies address hard and often hidden truths about modern life: child hunger, the enduring and growing presence of food banks in Canada, the availability of free and low-cost meals for the disadvantaged, food recovery programs, the existence of community kitchens offering an affordable, friendly location to cook and socialize (the prime functions of any kitchen!).

Towns and cities are first and foremost the dwelling places of human beings. Quality of life is gauged by many things, including how we eat. In a cityscape, this means encouraging urban agriculture—green spaces, school and community gardens, and rooftop gardens. We all have a stake in food. Think globally. Act locally.

www.foodsecurityalberta.ca

Inn From the Cold Society

Established: 1997 • Executive Director: Diana Segboer
106, 110-11 Avenue SE (Centre 110)
Phone: 263•8384
Office Hours: Monday–Friday 9:00 am–4:00 pm (on call 24/7)

INN From the Cold celebrated its tenth anniversary in 2007, and is the only Calgary organization that provides the opportunity for homeless families to remain together, giving first priority to families, then to single women. Until 2008, ad hoc inns provided hot meals, shelter and beds, shower facilities, companionship and cookies to homeless families in Calgary seven nights a week, every night of the year. In 2008, the society successfully purchased Centre 110 and converted the building to provide suitable accommodation for families, and sleeping space for between 80-100 individuals. There is zero tolerance for drugs and alcohol, and potential clients suffering from mental illnesses are referred to other agencies. "Children are involved," Executive Director Diana Segboer says simply. "Our clients must prove four days' sobriety." Unaccompanied minors are referred to any number of other agencies, including Avenue 15, Exit Outreach, the Boys and Girls Club, and the Back Door.

According to Segboer, the greatest social issue facing Calgary is the serious lack of affordable housing. The average period of time that families rely on Inn From the Cold is three to six months although, in some cases, it can take longer to effect enduring positive change. Inn From the Cold stays in contact with client families for two years, offering support, an outreach worker's willing ear, groceries, or referrals to other agencies.

Segboer's staff of 12 works hard to remember that what is broken may not mend quickly. "We measure our clients' success in small ways, and we measure progress, not perfection," says Segboer. Progress has many faces, depending on the spectrum of issues that initiated the downward spiral which resulted in a state of homelessness. Any movement forward is positive: into affordable housing, into a stable mental space, into an open acknowledgement of underlying issues, into treatment if warranted. Rewards are tangible: seeing a family reunited, seeing an addict clean up and move on, seeing families find housing and come back to volunteer at the church that stood by them.

Her staff is bolstered by volunteers who cook meals for the families and provide hospitality. In 2006, more than 3,800 volunteers contributed time, hope and help to 310 homeless families in the program. The Centre holds Mother Goose sessions for children and parents, and provides a computer lab with online access to assist with job searches.

The existence of Inn From the Cold illuminates a larger problem, a societal one, limned by the lives and needs of its weakest members.

www.innfromthecold.org

L'Arche Cakewalk

Established: 2007 • Executive Director: Peggy Loescher
307–57 Avenue SW
Phone: 571•0155

CAKE Walk is a fundraiser for L'Arche Calgary, part of the International Federation of L'Arche, founded in 1964 by Jean Vanier in response to the needs of people with developmental disabilities to find a valid place in society. The organization focuses on the creation of homes for developmentally disabled adults, mostly seniors. These homes function as places of growth and acceptance where healthy relationships with others are fundamental. The foundation believes that every person is unique and has a right to become the best they can be mentally, physically, emotionally and spiritually.

For Cake Walk, local pastry chefs and bakers create beautiful cakes. The towering architectural edifices, wacky flora and fauna, and romantic hearts on display are all edible. Each is a tangible and edible illustration of the theme of "Love is for everyone," a perfect agenda for a fundraiser and organization based on inclusion. The winner receives Natalie's Cake Cup, a crystal vase named in honour of the late founder of Cake Walk, Natalie McLean.

Funds raised at Cake Walk contribute to L'Arche's day program—which provides art classes and music therapy—as well as the upkeep of the family-style homes of the organization's developmentally disabled members, where they are able to live with dignity and loving support. The cakes—each is big enough to feed dozens—are mostly earmarked for donation to the Alberta Children's Hospital, Mary Dover House, the Mustard Seed and Alberta Adolescent Recovery Centre.

The goal in selecting a cake-based fundraiser is fun, pure and simple, combined with creating an inclusive event. Not much is as fun as cake!

www.larchecalgary.org

Slow Food Calgary

tablished: 2000 in Calgary • Calgary Convivium Leader: dee Hobsbawn-Smith
Further information and tickets for all events available at either:

The Cookbook Company Cooks	*Janice Beaton Fine Cheese*
722 – 11 Avenue SW	*1017 – 16 Avenue SW*
Phone: 265•6066	*Phone: 229•0900*

SLOWER living—and a better life—is the goal of this global movement. Slow Food began in 1989 in Italy, and now lists thousands of members in dozens of countries. Slow Foodies espouse local, authentic, handmade foods, sustainable and fair production, and support of producers and growers.

The protection of regional and traditional cuisines and the restoration of pleasure—particularly the pleasures of the table—are underlying goals. A figurative Ark of Taste supports the survival of endangered plants, animals, and artisanal food production methods at risk of extinction because of the industrialization of our food supply.

In 2004, Slow Food inaugurated Terra Madre, called by many "the United Nations of food," in Turin, Italy. This biennial gathering of 5,000—farmers, breeders, fishers, traditional food producers, and cooks—convenes to exchange views, experiences, and ideas toward the development of small-scale sustainably raised food and communication networks. It is an ambitious, inclusive program that seeks to change the world, one bite at a time, welcoming the experiences and stories of Third World cooks as well as celebrity chefs from developed nations. Cooks occupy the honourable middle ground, advocating for growers on the plate, putting food into the mouths of all.

Slow Food is personal. Feeding the people we love is an intimate sacrament clothed in dailiness, and Slow Food honours growing, cooking, and eating food, restoring "culture" to "agriculture." Cultures are defined by cuisine as much as by any other art, and our eating habits speak volumes.

Slow Food Calgary hosts events—both educational and social—year-round on a monthly basis, and they are open to members and non-members alike. The annual showcase event is an autumn harvest celebration held outdoors in Rouge restaurant's historic garden. Feast of Fields hosts several hundred people, and partners 30 of Calgary's leading food professionals with local food growers and producers. Live music is provided by local talent. Tickets to Slow Food events are available at **Janice Beaton Fine Cheese** and **The Cookbook Company Cooks**. Memberships are available online.

• *Key Events*: Feast of Fields in September, and Roots & Shoots in March.

www.slowfoodcalgary.ca

Bow Valley & Beyond

OUTSIDE CALGARY, in every direction, small towns are growing more rapidly than yeast in a warm kitchen. As the populations and buildings rise, so do the stores—and crops in nearby fields—to serve them.

Urban and rural residents have an uneasy coexistence. Some municipalities annex land without giving thought to who will grow our food once the cities and towns have paved all the good soil. Some recognize the value of farms and farming.

Within this section, the mix is as widespread as poems and proverbs. Look for specialty retailers, food processors, farmers, ranchers and growers. Some are urban, others are rural. Some rural residents will welcome your visit, and the opportunity to engage in farmgate sales. Please remember that these are family businesses, and call ahead.

Points North

BOW VALLEY AND BEYOND: POINTS NORTH includes entries for the following communities: Airdrie, Blackfalds, Bowden, Caroline, Carstairs, Didsbury, Elnora, Innisfail, Lacombe, Olds, Ponoka, Red Deer, Sundre and Sylvan Lake.

AIRDRIE

CHAINS (BIG & SMALL)

Calgary Co-op
2700 Main Street, Airdrie
Phone: 912 • 3700
Monday–Sunday 8:00 am–10:00 pm
Pharmacy: 912•3703
Monday–Friday 9:00 am–9:00 pm
Saturday, Sunday & Holidays 9:00 am–6:00 pm
Liquor Store: 912 • 3708
Monday–Saturday 10:00 am–10:00 pm, Sunday 10:00 am–8:00 pm
Gas Bar: 912 • 3711
Monday–Friday 5:30 am–10:30 pm, Saturday & Sunday 7:00 am–10:30 pm
V, MC, AE, Debit, Cheque, $
[see Chains (Big & Small) for main entry on p. 39]

Canada Safeway

505 Main Street (Tower Lane Mall), Airdrie
Phone: 948•4838
Monday–Sunday 8:00 am–11:00 pm
Pharmacy: 948•3361
Monday–Friday 9:00 am–9:00 pm, Saturday 9:00 am–6:00 pm
Sunday 10:00 am–6:00 pm
V, MC, AE, Debit, $
[see Chains (Big & Small) for main entry on p. 43]

Real Canadian Superstore

300 Airdrie Road, Airdrie
Phone: 945•2361 or 945•2318 (Customer Service)
Store Hours: Monday–Sunday 8:00 am–11:00 pm
Pharmacy: 945•2335 & Optical: 945•2347
Monday–Friday 9:00 am–10:00 pm, Saturday 9:00 am–7:00 pm
Sunday 9:00 am–6:00 pm
Liquor Store: 945•2340
Monday–Saturday 10:00 am–10:00 pm, Sunday 10:00 am–8:00 pm
Gas Bar: 945•2337
Monday–Sunday 7:00 am–10:30 pm, Sunday 8:30 am–10:00 pm
V, MC, Debit, $
[see Chains (Big & Small) for main entry on p. 47]

FARMGATE SALES

Purple Ridge Farm

Established: 1985 • Owners: Jean & Marvin Peterson
RR#2, Site 5, Box 2, Airdrie
Phone: 948•7735
July–September: Hours by Appointment
Cheque, $

JEAN and Marvin Peterson, their daughter Colleen, and their grandson have spent more than a quarter-century in the Airdrie region. They are in their second decade of farmgate market gardens sales, growing without herbicides or pesticides. Saskatoons and raspberries are either u-pick or custom-picked. Ask for red-skinned *sangre potatoes*, one of three varieties of potato they grow, or four types of carrots, turnips, chard and peas. Phone ahead to ensure that produce and people are available.

• *Directions*: Phone ahead for precise directions.
• *House Specialties*: Berries, potatoes and other vegetables.
• *Also Available*: **Airdrie Farmers' Market.**
www.purpleridge.ca

MEAT & GAME

The Butcher Shoppe

Established: 1995 • Owners: Tracy & Brian Hauck, Kolin Friske
705 Main Street (Towerlane Mall II), Airdrie
Phone: 948•9572
Monday–Friday 8:00 am–6:00 pm, Saturday 9:00 am–5:00 pm
Sunday 11:00 am–5:00 pm
V, MC, AE, Debit, $

IF I lived in Coventry Hills, Harvest Hills, Beddington, or anywhere deeply north within Calgary, I would drive north for ten minutes, along Harvest Hills Boulevard until it became Range Road 13, and head east on Big Valley Springs Road into Airdrie to shop for my meats at this spacious and impressive shop. Brian is the butcher with 30 years behind him, Tracy runs the front. Immaculately trimmed ultra-lean beef is what you get. A specialized line of gluten-free sausages is ensured by meticulous cleaning of machinery before each run of gluten-free products. Sourcing matters: AA and AAA beef, an almost exclusive supply of hormone- and antibiotic- free beef from Spring Creek Ranch, pork from one farmer, toothsome and deeply flavourful poultry from **Country Lane Farms**, bison from Canadian Rangeland near Rimbey— hormone free and grass finished. That ain't all. Duck is from Brome Lake, in parts and whole on request, and **Winter's Turkey** is the bird of choice for holidays and high days. Local lamb, too. An in-house smoker fills the shop with warm smoky smells. Ask for smoked pork and beef ribs, smoked salmon and check out 30 varieties of smoked sausage. In 2007, this shop won the **AFPA** provincial championship for its smoked goods. Try the gold medal-winning smoked turkey sausage. This is a serious smokehouse.

Half the business is value-added: meats are rolled, seasoned, wrapped, skewered, marinated, and mostly raw, stuffed chicken breasts are filled with *cordon bleu* variations, and there are grill-ready kebabs. Ready-to-eat meals are substantial—lasagna with ricotta and spinach, cabbage rolls and shepherd's pie, meatballs and meatloaf, and house-made salads and dressings. Add a few cheeses, or four-legged buddy food—smoked dog bones and house-made dog food, pig ears and high protein dog biscuits. Shelves are full of treats for their two-legged friends too, from chocolate to condiments, breads to rice crackers, and gluten-free pancake mix. Trend trackers may like to know that *Toro* magazine (out of Toronto) rated Brian's steaks among the top four countrywide in 2006, and *The Food Network* has filmed the meat-cutting life of Brian. This "shoppe" merits a major detour.

• *House Specialties*: Gluten-free sausages, Spring Creek beef, local products, HMRs and in-house smokehouse.

BLACKFALDS

FARMGATE SALES

Ladybug Organic Gardens & Bed & Breakfast

Established: 2000 • Owners: Wes & Jeannette Jones
Box 2298, Blackfalds
Phone: 782•0301
Hours by Appointment
$ only

A second career for Wes and Jeanette Jones after mixed cattle and grain farming has led to this certified-organic market garden in a new location, where Jeannette tills four acres, with one staffer and dogs to help. The garden grows Saskatoons, strawberries, raspberries, heirloom vegetables, pumpkins, peas and garlic. U-pick is by appointment. Pre-picked is drop-in, but call to ensure someone is about. Bring a picnic. Sweeten your table with house-made wild chokecherry syrup and jelly, strawberry jam—with or without sugar, and add zest with garlic jelly, pickled garlic and carrots, or salsa.

Jeannette also has a B&B, a trio of rooms, friendly and cozy, to offer respite from hustle-bustle city life, with trail strolls. Eat local, Jeannette says.

• *Directions*: Highway 2A north past Blackfalds. East 2 kilometres (road curves) on Calgary & Edmonton (C&E) Trail tothe first stop sign. East again for 2.3 kilometres on Lakeside Sargent Road. Turn north at Range Road 270 for 2.2 kilometres. Look for the sign on the east side of the road.

• *House Specialties*: Strawberries, raspberries, heirloom vegetables, peas, preserves and garlic, B&B.

BOWDEN

FARMGATE SALES

Pearson's Berry Farm & Gordo's Foods

Established: 1969 • Owners (since 2003): Duane & Deb Mertin
(purchased from long-time farm owners Len & Joyce Pearson)
Site 24, Box 1, RR#1, Bowden
Phone 224•3011
Farm Hours: July–August only: Monday–Sunday, 10:00 am–6:00 pm
V, MC, Debit, Cheque, $

THE farm and the orchard are still the solid ground beneath this flourishing family business. The Saskatoon berry trees date back to 1969, when founder Len Pearson planted them, and they are ready to harvest in the brief summer window of mid-July to mid-August, as dictated by Mother Nature. The berries are available as u-pick and we-pick. The chokecherries are now used exclusively for the family's value-added products, and are not available for public harvesting. The pie is exactly the same as it was when Joyce Pearson's team of hard-working women made it. In fact, there may be more berries in it now, and the crust is just as good. Exemplary butter tarts are available at the farmgate store and refreshment stand, as well at at the family's stall at the **Calgary Farmers' Market**. Both locations are under the direction of new owners Duane and Deb Mertin. They sell baked and berry-based goods under the Pearson label as well as their Gordo's line of seasonings and seasonal beverage concentrates. Try wintertime hot cider, or summertime lemonade concentrate with a berry blast of flavour. Gordo's line of grilling and basting sauces might be your cuppa, of which the Greek blend is the bread and butter of that side of the business. The Pearson's line features preserves, syrups, and spreads (the Saskatoon and chokecherry syrups are lovely), and of course pies or pie filling—if you'd rather bake your own, and those butter tarts.

- *Directions*: From QE II, west on Highway 587 for 27 kilometers to Range Road 40. Turn north on Range Road 40 and drive 1 kilometer. The farm entrance is on the east side of the road, with signage on the roadside along the way and at the farmgate.
- *House Specialties*: Pies, preserves, fruit-based beverages.
- *Also Available*: **Calgary Farmers' Market**, the Festival of Crafts at the Calgary Roundup Centre, **Tutti Frutti**, **Wild Rose Brewery**, Gordo's sauce line at **Sobey's**, and syrups, spreads, and pies at Heritage Park, and various coffee bars.

www.pearsons.ca • www.homestylebeverages.com

CAROLINE

FARMERS' MARKETS

Caroline Farmers' Market*
Established: 1975–77 • Contact: Jennifer Larsen
5103–48 Avenue (Kurt Browning Complex), Caroline
Phone: 722•3531
May–mid-September: Friday 1:00 pm–3:30 pm
$ only

CARSTAIRS

FARMGATE SALES

Blue Mountain Biodynamic Farms

Established: 1977 • Owner: Kris Vester
RR#2, Carstairs
Phone: 337•3321 • E-mail: vesterkh@yahoo.ca
Hours by Appointment
$, Calgary Dollars

KRISTIAN Vester, is a second-generation Alberta-born farmer of Danish-German extraction, who developed his interest in sustainability while in junior high school. Now in his early 30s, he believes that *biodynamic* practices make the most sense. "Consider how the planet turns energy into other feasible forms of energy," he advises. The farm is certified organic and leaves 35 acres in native pasture. At the farmgate, look for herbs and greens, root crops, eggs, house-milled flours and grains—triticale, rye, oats, and wheat. Ask about pork for your freezer.
* *Directions*: North on Highway 2 (QE II) to Carstairs overpass. West 12 kilometres on Highway 580 through Carstairs, (or from Highway 2A, through Carstairs it is 8 kilometres). Look for signs on the south side.
* *House Specialties*: Biodynamically raised vegetables, grain, pork, goats.
* *Also Available*: **Farm Fresh Organics Home Delivery Ltd, Green Market, SPUD, Sunnyside Market.**

PERSONAL CHEFS & CATERERS

The Homestead Chef

Established: 2003 • Owner: Gord Johnson
PO Box 847, Carstairs
Phone: 337•2665 • E-mail: gord@thehomesteadchef.com
Hours by Appointment
V, MC, Cheque, $

THIS Carstairs-based cook, possessor of a "self-taught cooking degree," feeds folks from Olds to Calgary. He offers catering and personal chef services and classes, working from his approved mobile kitchen in a trailer, heading to hay fields, sports fields, rodeo infields, and every field in-between. "Meals in Minutes," a recent addition to his services, are weekly menus that range from Asian to mac 'n' cheese. Clients can "peruse and choose" from Thai, Indian, and Italian flavours, or opt for flame-roasted, wood-fired outdoor grilling. Johnson says he is not a specialist, nor a big Atkins fan, and he cooks mainstream meals.
* *House Specialties*: Personal chef service and off-site catering services, specializing in East Indian, Thai, Italian, and "Meals in Minutes."
www.thehomesteadchef.com

DELBURNE

FARMGATE SALES

Twisted Willow Berry Farm
Established: 1968 • Owners: Marion & Ed Sanders
Box 236, Delburne
Phone: 749•2026
July–September: 9:00 am–dusk
Cheques, $

MARION and Ed Sanders, owners since 1968, have been growing berries since 1990, and they planted raspberry canes in 2005. In addition, they grow strawberries, rhubarb, blackcurrants, carrots, beans, peas, and potatoes. U-pick, or we-pick. This farm, set in gently rolling country, has a picnic area and horseshoe pitches. Recent additions include hardy cherry trees developed at the University of Saskatchewan in Saskatoon, and both Saskatoons and chokecherries are expected to be in production by 2010.
- *Directions*: North on Highway 2 (QE II) to Highway 595 overpass. East 40 kilometres on Highway 595 (Delburne Road). North 3.2 kilometres on Range Road 234. East 1.2 kilometres on Turnpike Road 382. Look for signs and the farm on the north side of the road.
- *House Specialties*: Vegetables, fruit, and berries.

DIDSBURY

FARMERS' MARKETS

Didsbury & District Farmers' Market
Established: 1985 • Manager: Laura Krebs
1702–21 Avenue (Didsbury Curling Club), Didsbury
Phone: 335•4252
July–September: Wednesday 6:00 pm–8:00 pm
$ only

ECKVILLE

FARMGATE SALES

Staniforth Summerberry Farm
Established: 1915 • Owners: Margo & Gordon Staniforth
RR#3, Eckville
Phone: 746•3681
Hours by Appointment
Cheque, $

MARGO and Gordon Staniforth are third-generation farmers who tend a thorny patch of raspberries in rainbow colours—red, yellow, and black—the latter a cross of blackberries and red raspberries. "Black raspberries have that yummy blackberry texture and flavour on hardy raspberry canes," says Staniforth. A longtime jam-maker, she also grows red and blackcurrants, all u-pick, and 6,000 new strawberry plants which are custom-pick only. This pesticide-free grower's future might include a commercial kitchen, where she can produce what she calls "the natural next step"—jams, jellies, and IQF (individually quick frozen) berries for sale.

• *Directions*: North on Highway 2 (QE II) to Innisfail. West 12 kilometres on Highway 54. North 14 kilometres on Highway 781. West 10 kilometres on Turnpike Road 380. North 0.5 kilometres on Range Road 24. Look for signs. Staniforth Summerberry Farm is the first driveway on the east side.
• *House Specialties*: Berries.
• *Also Available*: **Sylvan Lake Farmers' Market.**
www.staniforthfarm.com

ELNORA

FARMGATE SALES

DNA Gardens
Established: 1976 • Owners: Dave & Arden Delidais
Phone: 773•2489 or (866) 687•5268
Box 544, Elnora
Office: Monday–Friday 8:00 am–4:30 pm
Nursery, May–September: Monday–Sunday 9:00 am–5:00 pm
V, MC, AE, Debit, Cheque, $

THIS farm and orchard with a Saskatoon patch that dates back to 1976 is more than three-decades old and is owned by Dave and Arden Delidais. The company does tissue cultures and has a test orchard. Once there, gardeners will find much to discuss. Ask about indigenous berries, hardy cherries bred by researchers at the University of Saskatchewan, dryland fruit and Zone-2-hardy honeyberries. Breeding experiments with hardy cherries began on the prairies in 1940. Six varieties of *Prunus cerasus* cherry trees were released in 2004. I have a young pair thriving in my sunny front yard, and am waiting for cherries. The shop also sells juices, pies, and jams.

- *Directions*: North on Highway 2 (QE II) to Innisfail and Highway 590. East 52 kilometres on Highway 590, crossing Highway 21, to Range Road 230, then turn south for 1 kilometre, and look for signs on the west side.
- *House Specialties*: Fruit trees, hardy berry shrubs, juices, pies, shrubs.
www.dnagardens.com

INNISFAIL

FARMERS' MARKETS

Innisfail Farmers' Market*
Established 1993 • Manager: Linda Jensen
5804–42 Street (Twin Arena), Innisfail
Phone: 224•3247
May–September: Thursday 10:00 am–1:00 pm
$ only

FARMGATE SALES

Cakadu Heritage Lamb
Established: 1993 • Owners: Linda & Denis Jabs
RR#1, Site 15, Box 2, Innisfail
Phone: 728•2398
Hours by Appointment
Cheque, $

DENIS and Linda Jabs have been raising Barbados Black-bellied sheep, a heritage breed that dates back to 1627, since 1993 on their chemical-free farm. The breed is a "hair" sheep, free of lanolin, its meat milder than sheep in woolly jackets, and is an antecedent of the Katahdin line, introduced into the pedigree for their high fertility rates. Their flock now numbers 800. I guess that fertility rate is true! Denis appreciates their wild instincts, that his flock is not easily led like more docile domesticated breeds.

At the farmgate, frozen lamb is available cut and wrapped, year-round, but if you want to start a flock, you can purchase breeding stock on the hoof. Call for an appointment, and expect a wait of two weeks for custom cutting of whole animals. The Jabs offer delivery with a minimum order.

- *Directions*: North on Highway 2 (QE II) to Innisfail. West 29 kilometres on Highway 54, through Innisfail, to Range Road 25. North to just before Turnpike Road 364. Cakadu Heritage Lamb is the last house before the crossroads on the east side.

- *House Specialties*: Barbados Black-bellied lamb, frozen for meals, or breeding stock.
- *Also Available*: On the menu at Brava Bistro, **Infuse Catering/Forage Foods**, La Chaumière, and **Route 40 Soup Company** in Turner Valley.

Edgar Farms (Innisfail Growers)

Established: 1987 • Owners: Doug & Elna Edgar
RR#3, Innisfail
Phone: 350•0659 or 227•2443
mid-May–mid-September: Farmgate store open during daylight hours
$ only

INNISFAIL Growers is a five-family co-operative: Doug and Elna Edgar of Edgar Farms, John and Cory Buyks of Upper Green Farm, Bev and Les Carson of Claremont Farm, Blaine and Leona Staples of **The Jungle**, Shelley and Rod Bradshaw, Peter Edgar and Stan Mills as joint owners of Beck Farms.

Elna Edgar and her family are Alberta's largest producer of green asparagus. The first crop was planted in 1986, harvested in '89, and made commercially available to the public in '96. The family has added 5 acres a year to bring their asparagus field up to 17 acres. They also grow peas and beans, and sell the stellar produce of the rest of the co-operative at their farmgate, along with the Edgars' frozen Red Angus beef and garlic sausage. Be warned—asparagus may be done by June's end—call ahead and ask. Edgar Farms has a self-serve honour system counter for pre-picked produce from the Innisfail Growers, notably Beck Farms' Nantes carrots and **The Jungle**'s greens and berries. The good news is that the Edgars' daughters, for whom the patch was first planted, are settling on the farm to raise their families, thanks to the prolifically producing asparagus patch. In 2008, the Edgars received the Innovation in Agriculture Award of Distinction, presented by Alberta Chambers of Commerce, for "outstanding achievement in providing innovative solutions...to agriculture...."

- *Directions*: North on Highway 2 (QE II) to Innisfail. West at South Innisfail overpass, (Exit 365) on Cottonwood Road for 10 kilometres. Look for the sign on the south side of the road.
- *House Specialties*: Asparagus, Red Angus beef, beans and peas.
- *Also Available*: **Bearspaw Farmers' Market, Calgary Farmers' Market, Cochrane Farmers' Market, Grassroots Northland Farmers' Market, Hillhurst-Sunnyside Farmers' Market, Innisfail Farmers' Market, Lacombe Farmers' Market, Millarville Farmers' Market, Olds Farmers' Market, Red Deer Farmers' Market**, and **Sylvan Lake Farmers' Market**. A Saturday truck delivers to Glennifer Lakes Resort (since 1993), as well as on the farms of Innisfail Growers.

The Jungle (Innisfail Growers)

Established: 1897 • Owners: Leona & Blaine Staples
RR#3, Innisfail
Phone: 227•4231
Summer: Monday–Saturday 8:00 am–8:00 pm
Spring: Check website • Fall: Hours by Appointment
Debit, Cheque, $

BLAINE and Leona Staples, their three sons, and a team of Mexican workers farm 15 acres on a picturesque farm that acquired its name from Leona's great-grandfather when he purchased it more than one hundred years ago. Dig-your-own potatoes, pick strawberries, spinach and hydroponic lettuce, zucchini, root veggies, winter squashes, as well as corn, pumpkins, cucumbers and flowers. Look in the farmgate shop for pickles and jams, including **Edgar Farms'** fabulous pickled asparagus, flowering baskets and bedding plants in season. Call ahead to learn what is ready. Recently the family planted 50 honeyberries, a sturdy fruiting Siberian honeysuckle shrub. The gorgeous strawberry patch, augmented by rows of raspberries and greens, is the prime draw to the farm. On-farm events include a July Strawberry Festival and the Scarecrow Festival on Thanksgiving weekend—with hayrides, a corn maze, and a bale maze. An on-site farm store sells other goods from members of Innisfail Growers.

- *Directions*: North on Highway 2 (QE II), and 6 kilometres past Innisfail. West 2.5 kilometres on Old Pole Road. Look for signs and the driveway on the north side of road.
- *House Specialties*: Strawberries, greens, berries, vegetables.
- *Also Available*: **Calgary Farmers' Market, Grassroots Northland Farmers' Market, Hillhurst-Sunnyside Farmers' Market, Millarville Farmers' Market** as well as on the farms of Innisfail Growers.

www.thejunglefarm.com

LACOMBE

FARMGATE SALES

Bles-Wold Dairy & Bles-Wold Yoghurt

Established: 1994 • Owners: Tinie Eilers & Hennie Bos
RR#5, Lacombe
Phone: (403) 782•3380
Friday 12:30 pm–3:30 pm
Cheque, $

TINIE Eilers and Hennie Bos operate Alberta's first licensed farm yoghurt business. Tinie started the company in the kitchen after they emigrated from Holland in 1994, making yoghurt for her diabetic sister Martine, using her brother's Dutch recipe. "Why not make a bit more and we could sell it?"

asked her husband Hennie. Tinie took the resulting yoghurt to local farmers' markets for a year. The markets proved a useful product development tool, revealing that Canadian palates prefer sweeter, thicker yoghurts in a wide choice of flavours. The yoghurt appeared on Lacombe shelves in 1997. Now, the family produces 4000 litres of all-natural yoghurt weekly, no colours or artificial flavours added, the Danish culture laced with probiotic bifidus and acidophilis.

- *Directions*: North on Highway 2 (QE II) for 4 kilometers past the Highway 12 overpass (Lacombe-Bentley turnoff). West 6 kilometres on Range Road 27. Be cautious as you cross the QE II highway! Look for signs and access on the south side of the road.
- *House Specialties*: Yoghurt.
- *Also Available*: **Calgary Co-op**, **Community Natural Foods**, **Nutter's Bulk & Natural Foods** in Canmore and Okotoks, **Planet Organic Market**, **Sobey's/IGA**, **Sunworks Farm**, **Sylvan Star Cheese Farm** in Sylvan Lake, and on-site at the farmgate.

www.bles-wold.com

OLDS

FARMERS' MARKETS

Olds Farmers' Market*

Re-established: 2003 • Manager: Denise Rice
5116–54 Street (Olds Cow Palace), Olds
Phone: 556•3770
May–September: Thursday 4:00 pm–6:30 pm
$ only

FARMGATE SALES

Buffalo Horn Ranch

Established: 1994 • Owners: Peter & Judy Haase
RR#2, Site 7, Box 7, Olds
Phone: 556•2567
Year Round • Hours by Appointment
Summer: V, MC, Cheque, $, Winter: Cheque, $

NORTHWEST of Calgary, in the foothills, Peter and Judy Haase tend the country's largest pure plains bison herd. Bison acquired in 1994 have changed their lives from teacher and photographer, to Slow Food members, attending Terra Madre 2006 in Turin, Italy. This showplace ranch has hosted Slow Foodies, agriculture students, and visitors on the annual *City Palate* "Foodie Tootles." They sell natural bison—antibiotic-free, without growth hormones and available by the portion—wrapped and frozen, as well as freezer packs, bison bacon or ham, sausage, and jerky.

- *Directions*: North on Highway 2 (QE II) to Olds. West 27 kilometres through Olds on Highway 27. North 3 kilometres on Range Road 4. The ranch access is on the eastside of road.
- *House Specialties*: Naturally raised bison.
- *Also Available*: Year-round limited selection at *Eagle Hill Co-op*, RR#1, Bowden, <www.eaglehillcoop.com>, and during the summer at **Cochrane Farmers' Market, Bearspaw Farmers' Market, Grassroots Northland Farmers' Market** and **Hillhurst-Sunnyside Farmers' Market** in Calgary. In off-market seasons, the Haases will deliver—for free—to Calgary and Cochrane advance orders valued at $100.00 or more.

www.buffalohornranch.ca

SUNDRE

FARMERS' MARKETS

Sundre Farmers Market*
Established 1991 • Manager: Judy Bysterveld
6101–2 Avenue NW (Sundre Curling Rink), Sundre
Phone: 638•2231
May–September: Friday 5:00 pm–7:30 pm
$ only

FARMGATE SALES

TLC Farm Katahdins
Established: 2005 • Owners: Carl & Tracy Hooch-Antink
RR#2, Site 3, Box 36, Sundre
Phone: 638•3173 • E-mail: hooch@davincibb.net
Hours by Appointment
Cheque, $

CARL and Tracy Hooch-Antink raise Katahdins, a hair sheep without lanolin, with resulting mild meat. They also keep a sheep guardian canine, a large Maremma, so phone first for directions. Their naturally raised lamb is available at the farmgate, and Calgary delivery can be arranged. Order whole animals, share a side with a friend, or buy individual cuts at the market. Be prepared to pay in advance for whole animals.
- *Directions*: Phone ahead for precise directions.
- *House Specialties*: Lamb.
- *Also Available*: **Bearspaw Farmers' Market** in Calgary, and **Sundre Farmers' Market**.

www.tlcfarm.ca

SYLVAN LAKE

FARMGATE SALES

Sylvan Star Cheese Farm

Established: 1999 • Owners: John & Janny Schalkwyk
RR#1, Site 6, Box 31, Red Deer
Phone: 340•1560
May–October: Monday–Saturday 10:00 am–6:00 pm
Winter: Monday–Saturday 10:00 am–5:00 pm
Debit, $

JOHN and Janny Schalkwyk's award-winning Gouda (pronounced "how'da," with a guttural, bone-in-the-throat coughing "H"), is available at the farmgate store near Sylvan Lake and at the **Calgary Farmer's Market**. At the farmgate shop, peek past the shop's rear door to the racks filled with rows and rows of wheels of Gouda aging like fine wine. Cheese making is not a simple process. Those racks represent a significant investment in time and patience, and go a long way toward explaining the high cost of aged cheese. Cheese shrinks as it ages, losing mass as moisture content drops. It takes time to make that leap to immortality.

After 25 years of cheese making in the Netherlands, John and Janny followed their son to Canada, where more land is available to farmers than in densely-populated Holland. Farming is harder in Holland, John says, complicated by costly living and stringent regulations. In Holland, manure disposal has become a big issue, and dairy farmers may only keep one cow per acre of land. While the ratio is slightly higher in Canada, Canadian dairy farmers are required to have agreements with farming neighbours regarding the removal and distribution of their manure.

House-made standouts are the robust, aged Gouda and unsalted butter. Only housemade cheeses are for sale on the farm, but a goodly gathering of things Canadian are available at their **Calgary Farmers' Market** cheese stall: *Du Village de Warwick* and *Le Chevalier* triple creams, *Bleu Bènèdictin* and *Ermite*, Village Cheeses from Armstrong, Alberta-made Edelweiss, and Woolwich Dairy's good Ontario goat cheeses. They also stock a few imports—Spanish *Manchego*, raw milk *Tilsit*, Greek *Kefelotiri*. In 2006, Sylvan Star's Extra Aged Grizzly Gouda placed fourth in international competition. It also won Gold at the 2006 Canadian Dairy Farmers' Cheese Grand Prix. In late 2008, they will open a new production facility on the farm, with a larger retail space and a viewing gallery to oberve milk's transformation into cheese.

- *Directions*: From QE II, west on Highway IIA for 10 kilometres. North on Range Road 10 for 400 metres.
- *House Specialties*: Award-winning Gouda, butter.
- *Also Available*: **Calgary Farmers' Market, The Cookbook Company Cooks, Janice Beaton Fine Cheese**, Red Deer Farmers' Market, **Say Cheese Fromagerie, Sylvan Lake Farmers' Market**, and the **Bison Mountain Bistro & General Store** in Banff.

FARMERS' MARKETS

Sylvan Lake Farmers' Market*

Established: 1990 • Manager: Crystal Loewen
49 Avenue & 50 Street (Railway Park Promenade), Sylvan Lake
Phone: 887•3461 or Cell: 350•2639
May–September: Friday 4:00 pm–7:30 pm
$ only

Points East

BOW VALLEY AND BEYOND: POINTS EAST, includes entries for the following communities: Brooks, Chestermere Lake, Dalemead, Drumheller, Rosemary, and Strathmore.

BROOKS

FARMERS' MARKETS

Brooks Farmers' Market*

Established: 1994 • Contact: Bonnie Spragg
Lake Newell Road (Kinsmen Rodeo Grounds), Brooks
Phone: 378•3277
May–October (Thanksgiving): Thursday 3:00 pm–7:00 pm
$ only

CHESTERMERE LAKE

BAKERIES

Sugar Flowers & Elegant Cakes

Established: 1996 • Owner: Kate Fielder
129 Westchester Way, Chestermere Lake
Phone: 273•3626
Hours by Appointment
V, Cheque, $

KATE Fielder has been baking for more than 40 years, the last 12 in Chestermere Lake, in the highly specialized niche of wedding cakes. Her contemporary style often features the sugarwork flowers and whimsical figurines which Kate teaches **SAIT Polytechnic** culinary students how to make in her role as a guest instructor. Details are Fielder's signature—sugar flowers that match the bride's bouquet, sugarwork beading to mimic the patterns of a bride's wedding dress, and elegant piping in metallic or white finishes. She likes the detailing, and she likes meeting the wedding family, especially the brides. Both take nerves of steel and patience. Her Chestermere Lake kitchen, entirely nut-free, produces 15 mix-and-match cakes and fillings, the most popular of which is pink champagne. Fielder is fond of her tropical-style pineapple and coconut cake filled with mango passion fruit filling, but the house's "Millennium Cake," made to honour the turn of the millennium, continues to be popular because of its subtle blend of roasted coffee and chocolate, with white chocolate filling and chocolate buttercream.

- *House Specialties*: Custom-made wedding cakes made in a nut-free kitchen: 15 flavours including Millennium Cake, "fruits of the forest," raspberry ripple and tropical.

CHAINS (BIG & SMALL)

Canada Safeway

100, 135 Chestermere Station Way, Chestermere Lake
Phone: 410•9700
Monday–Sunday 8:00 am–11:00 pm
Pharmacy: 410•9626
Monday–Friday 9:00 am–9:00 am, Saturday 9:00–6:00 pm, Sunday 10:00–6:00 pm
V, MC, AE, Debit, Cheque, $
[see Chains (Big & Small) for the main entry p. 43]

DALEMEAD

FARMGATE SALES

Winter's Turkeys

Established: 1991 • Owners: Corinne Dahm & Darrel Winter
Box 321, Dalemead
Phone: 936•5586 • E-mail: darrel@wintersturkeys.ca
Hours by Appointment
Cheque, $

I have a special fondness for Darrel and Corinne. My restaurant, Foodsmith, was their first restaurant client in 1992. They produce amazingly good turkeys. Turkey is in Darrel Winter's blood. His dad started a flock of turkeys in 1958, and sold his birds direct to meat markets, and privately to consumers. Darrel and his wife Corinne Dahm took over in 1977. Since, they have scratched out a pioneering turkey run with loyal fans, their fresh and frozen birds roosting in restaurants, independent meat markets, and food stores. As well as selling full-flavoured, free-range (hormone- and antibiotic-free) turkeys for the "big bird" holidays, Winter keeps a certified-organic flock. He has branched out into value-added turkey fare that can be found in local health food stores—turkey pastrami, 4 kinds of smokies, salami, and turkey jerky.

- *Directions*: East on Highway 22X for 18 kilometres past city limits to Range Road 273. Turn south for 1.5 kilometres to Township Road 224. Turn east for 1 kilometre. The farm is on the south side of the road.
- *House Specialties*: Free-range and organic turkeys.
- *Also Available*: **Amaranth Whole Foods Market, Bon Ton Meat Market, Canada Safeway, Community Natural Foods, Calgary Co-op, Heaslip Venture Meats, Horizon Meats, Master Meats, Planet Organic Market, Rocky's Meats & Delicatessen, Second to None Meats,** and **Sunnyside Market,** and the **Griesser Spoon Custom Catering/Railway Deli, Nutter's Bulk & Natural Foods** and **Valbella Meats/Valbella's Deli & Café** in Canmore.

www.wintersturkeys.ca

DRUMHELLER

FARMERS' MARKETS

Drumheller Farmers' Market*
Established 1987 • Manager: Susan Keddie
555 Highway 10 (Greentree Mall), Drumheller
Phone: 823•8955
May–October: Saturday 9:30 am–12:30 pm
with special Easter, Canada Day, and Christmas Markets
$ only

FARMGATE SALES

Sun Valley Farm
Established: 1987 • Owner: Rhona McIver
Box 692, Rosedale
Phone: 823•9191
July–September: Monday–Sunday 8:00 am–8:00 pm
V, MC, Debit, Cheque, $

FOR more than 20 years, Rhona McIver has grown raspberries, Saskatoons and strawberries (if the deer don't eat them!) in the badlands near Drumheller. She says that the deer prefer berries to u-pick or custom-pick vegetables, greenhouse tomatoes, bedding plants, hardy perennial flowers, or spring annuals.

- *Directions*: East on Highway 1. North on Highway 9, through Drumheller. East 12 kilometres on Highway 10.
- *House Specialties*: Berries, tomatoes, perennials.
- *Also Available*: **Drumheller Farmers' Market.**

ROSEMARY

FARMGATE SALES

Spragg's Meat Shop

Established: 2002 • Contact: Bonnie & Greg Spragg
438 Centre Street, Rosemary
Phone: 378•3800 • E-mail: gbspragg@eidnet.org
Monday–Friday 10:00 am–6:00 pm
V, MC, Debit, $

IT began with a birthday gift of piglets, and has become a free-range pork shop and processing business. In 2002, Bonnie Spragg purchased 3 little pigs for her husband. From that modest start, Spragg Farms now raises approximately 300 hogs to market weight—as well as weaner pigs—on 200 acres of irrigated land, sown to include barley, wheat and fava beans, all of which are ground into food for growing piggies. Spragg's Meat Shop opened in November 2005 in Rosemary. Greg and Bonnie do it all—raise the hogs, process, and direct-market the meat.

The piglets do not receive any antibiotics or growth stimulants in their feed or by injection, their tails are not docked, and they graze and wander in an outdoor life. Happy pigs are easier to raise and handle, fed on sunlight, fresh air and pasture, and they make damn fine eats! Buy a side or a pair of chops or buy some bacon, a party-size pork dinner roast, or a whole pig. Order online.

• *House Specialties*: Pork and cured pork products.
• *Directions*: East on Highway 1 to Bassano. Continue eastwards 22 kilometres on secondary Highway 550 to Rosemary. The shop is at the corner of Railway Avenue and Centre Street. Watch for signs.
• *Also Available*: **Brooks Farmers' Market** and **Millarville Farmers' Market**.

www.spraggsmeatshop.com

STRATHMORE

BOOZE

Bumbleberry Orchard Ltd. & Fieldstone Fruit Wines

Established: 1998 • Contact: Elaine & Marvin Gill, Lorraine & Glen Ellingson
RR#1, Site 6, Box 19, Strathmore
Phone: 934•2749
July–August: Monday–Sunday 10:00 am–6:00 pm
September–mid-October: Friday–Sunday noon–5:00 pm
mid-October–June: Hours by Appointment
V, MC, Debit, Cheque, $

ELAINE and Marvin Gill and their partners Lorraine and Glen Ellingson operate this "natural" farm, following biological ionization principles—calcium needs to be 6× potassium levels, phosphorus must be 3× potassium levels—to avoid invading insects that are attracted to stressed plants which are low in sugar. It's all an interlocking relationship. This is the home of Alberta's first farmgate fruit winery, established in 2005. "The days of growing a raw product and making a living are gone. In agriculture, being on the edge means you better make something value-added." So says Marv Gill. He was right. Their berries, planted with an eye to the future, are now used in their house-made fruit wines. In July 2006, their farmgate store released their inaugural vintage, 12,000 bottles of Alberta-grown, cottage-industry fruit wine under the label of Fieldstone Fruit Wines.

Winemaker Dominic Rivard, who has prior experience with both fruit wines and grape wines, is in charge of producing a dry Saskatoon table wine, and four sweet wines, made from raspberries, strawberries, and wild black cherries (formerly known as chokecherries), plus a new table wine, Prairie Cherry, a unique blend of three Alberta cherry varieties, Carmine Jewel, Rose, and Evans.

Berries grown here include strawberries, raspberries, chokecherries, and Saskatoons, available frozen in the off-season, u-pick or, if ordered in advance, we-pick. Lorraine makes pies, preserves, and wine jelly. Kids are welcome—there is lots of room to run. It is wise to call ahead to confirm availability for u-pick/we-pick, and advance ordering is mandatory for large orders. Picnic areas and two gazebos in the centre of the fields are available for visitor use.

• *Directions*: East on Highway 1 to Strathmore. South 10 kilometres on Highway 817.
• *House Specialties*: Berry and fruit wine, u-pick berries.
• *Also Available*: Select Alberta wine stores. (check their website).

www.fieldstonefruitwines.com

CHAINS (BIG & SMALL)

Calgary Co-op
320–2 Street, Strathmore
Phone: 934•3121
Monday–Sunday 8:30 am–8:00 pm
Pharmacy: 934•6632
Monday–Friday 8:30 am–8:00 pm, Saturday & Sunday 10:00 am–6:00 pm
Liquor Store: 901•0852
Monday–Wednesday 10:00 am–9:00 pm
Thursday–Saturday 10:00 am–10:00 pm, Sunday 10:00 am–6:00 pm
Gas Bar: 715 Wheatland Trail • Commercial Cardlock: 421 Ridge Road
Phone: 934•3044
Monday–Friday 5:00 am–10:00 pm, Saturday & Sunday 6:00 am–10:00 pm
V, MC, AE, Debit, $
[see Chains (Big & Small) for main entry p. 39]

IGA
221–4 Avenue, Strathmore
Phone: 934•4512
Monday–Saturday 8:00 am–9:00 pm, Sunday 8:00 am–6:00 pm
V, MC, AE, Debit, $
[see Chains (Big & Small) for main entry p. 49]

FARMERS' MARKETS

Strathmore Farmers' Market*
Established: 1997 • Manager: John Goodman
120 Brent Boulevard (Agricultural Society Exhibition Grounds), Strathmore
Phone: 901•0477 (Office) or 618•7094 (Manager)
June–mid-September: Friday 3:30 pm–7:30 pm
$ only
www.strathmorefarmersmarket.ca

FARMGATE SALES

Serviceberry Farms
Established: 1988 • Owners: Grace Fedak
RR#2, Site 23, Box 15, Strathmore
Phone: 934•2412
Hours by Appointment
$ only

THIS family-run business has been owned by Grace Fedak since 1984. It enjoyed its first serious strawberry harvest in 1988. Serviceberry Farms is committed to environmentally friendly conservation practices such as IPM (integrated pest management) and shelterbelts. Four fields are used in rotation. Each year, there is a planting field, a picking field full of strawberries, and two fallow fields. U-pick and custom-picking are offered for strawberries, and some vegetables—potatoes, carrots, peas, beans and beets.
- *Directions*: Drive east on Highway 1 and turn north 1.6 kilometres beyond the junction of Highway 1 East and Highway 24. Watch your odometer, as the road is unnamed and unsigned. Drive north 5.6 kilometres. The farm is the second driveway on the east side.
- *House Specialties*: Strawberries, saskatoons, vegetables.
www.serviceberryfarms.com

Points South

BOW VALLEY AND BEYOND: POINTS SOUTH, includes entries for the following communities: Black Diamond, Claresholm, DeWinton, Fort Macleod, Glenwood, High River, Lethbridge, Millarville, Nanton, Okotoks, Pincher Creek, and Turner Valley.

BLACK DIAMOND

FARMERS' MARKETS

Black Diamond (Foothills Country) Market*
Established: 1996 • Contact: Doreen Lesko
206 Government Road SE, Black Diamond
Phone: 933•7478
May–September: Saturday 10:00 am–2:00 pm
$ only

KITCHENWARE

Provenance

Established: 2007 • Owners: Jill Marsh & Heath Waller
202–1 Street SW, Black Diamond
Phone: 933•8862
Hours by Appointment
V, MC, Debit, Cheque, $

WHEN I drove out to the foothills to examine a newly installed Mugnaini wood-burning oven from Italy, I thought I knew what to expect—maybe just a taste of pizza and flatbread. Then Canadian distributor Jill Marsh and her daughter Heath Waller served an array of rustic dishes—lamb shank, pizza, roasted peaches on cream—all intensely flavoured and lightly scented with the undertone of woodsmoke. Now I am rethinking my backyard design to make room for an outdoor oven. These wood-fired indoor or outdoor ovens are a European tradition that has caught on globally. Restaurateurs like Alice Waters at Berkeley, California's Chez Panisse have Mugnaini ovens, and the Culinary Institute of America (CIA) offers "ancient cookfire classes." In Australia, rustic "cob" ovens of many makes are creating heatwaves. The ovens come in a variety of sizes, and weigh hundreds of kilograms. Their exteriors can be personalized with stone or brick or an artist's whim. Make room.
• *House Specialties*: Mugnaini ovens.
www.livingedgeco.com

CHAMPION

FARMGATE SALES

Ewe-Nique Farms

Established: 1992 • Owners: Bert & Caroline Van de Bruinhorst
General Delivery, Champion
Phone: 894•5262 (LAMB)
Monday–Saturday: Hours by Appointment
Cheque, $

THIS Dutch-descended family has been tending sheep since 1997. Their free-range, antibiotic-free lamb raised here are crossbred Suffolks, and the flock size fluctuates from 150 to 450. Bert's new, large facility on their new farm is now in use for cutting and packaging the meat after it returns from the High River processing plant. Lamb is available either fresh or frozen.
• *Directions*: South on Highway 2 just past Parkland. Head east 30 kilometres on Highway 529 toward Champion. Then south 6 kilometres on Highway 23. Finally west 5 kilometres on Township Road 144. The farm is on the north side of the road.

- *Also Available*: **The Better Butcher, Rocky's Meats & Delicatessen, Second to None Meats**. A presence at the **Grassroots Northland Farmers' Market** and **Hillhurst-Sunnyside Farmers' Market**, is dependent upon time and the availability of farm labour. On the menu at The Belvedere, Calgary Petroleum Club, Il Sogno, Moti Mahal, Muse, and St. Germain.
www.ewaniquefarms.com

CLARESHOLM

FARMERS' MARKETS

Claresholm Farmers' Market*
Established: 1993 • Contact: Barb Uhl
4918–2 Street East (Indoors, Claresholm Arena), Claresholm
Phone: 625•2595 (Arena) or 625•2298 (Barb Uhl)
July–early September: Wednesday 3:00 pm–6:00 pm
$ only

COALHURST

FARMGATE SALES

Broek Pork Acres
Established: 2000 • Contact: Allan & Joanne Vanden Broek
Box 791, Coalhurst
Phone: 381•4753 • E-mail: ajvandenbroek@telus.net
Monday–Saturday Year Round: Hours by Appointment
$ only

THE Vanden Broek family raises pork, including a heritage breed called Berkshires that is highly favoured by chefs and consumers alike for its great flavour and texture. In 2007, they opened their own processing facility on the farm. Their animals are pastured, and do not receive any growth hormones, antibiotics, or animal by-products. Order by e-mail or phone, and arrange for sides, freezer packs, or a whole animal for the backyard rotisserie. They offer a 10 percent discount on farmgate sales.

- *Directions*: South on Highway 2, then turn east on Highway 3. Drive through Fort Macleod, and turn east onto Kipp Road also known as Range Road 225. Cross the tracks, drive north for 8 kilometres, cross Township Road 104, and turn into the drive 1 kilometre north on the west side of the road. If you reach Highway 519, you have gone 1 kilometre too far north.
- *House Specialties*: Pork in freezer packs, as whole animals or sides.
- *Also Available*: **Infuse Catering/Forage Foods**, Lethbridge Farmers Market, **Rocky's Meats & Delicatessen, Second to None Meats** and on the menu at Bistro 2210, River Café, St. Germain and others.
www.broekporkacres.com

DEWINTON

FARMGATE SALES

Saskatoon Farm

Established: 1987 • Owners: Paul & Karen Hamer
RR#1, DeWinton
Phone: 938•6245 or (800) 463•2113
Year Round: Monday–Sunday 9:00 am–5:00 pm
V, MC, Debit, $

O N the site of an ancient buffalo jump, at the junction of the Sheep and Highwood Rivers, Paul and Karen Hamer established a greenhouse and nursery, a bison herd grazing on the range, 50 acres of Saskatoon berries, a café and a general store that sells jams, honeys, jellies, syrups, pies, and even sausage and buffalo burgers seasoned "à la pemmican" with Saskatoons. Buy a tree, buy the makings of an orchard, buy u-pick or pre-picked berries or buy jam, buy lunch or the makings of lunch, it's a breath-taking 600-acre site. Spend an hour or take the whole day.

* *Directions*: South on Highway 2 (Macleod Trail) 19 kilometres from 22X. Alternatively, follow the Deerfoot Trail extension (which joins Highway 2 at its intersection with Highway 552), and continue 8 kilometres south on Highway 2. East 3 kilometres on 338 Avenue (opposite a prominent locomotive, railcars and railway station display.) Watch for the signs. 338 Avenue dead ends at the farm.
* *House Specialties*: Saskatoon berries, jams, preserves, and pies, buffalo sausage, trees and shrubs.

www.saskatoonfarm.com

FORT MACLEOD

FARMGATE SALES

Driview Farms

Established: 1977 • Owners: Janet & Gerrit Van Hierden
Box 1123, Fort Macleod
Phone: 553•2178 • Email: driview@telus.net
Hours by Appointment
Cheque, $

J ANET and Gerrit Van Hierden started farming in 1977, and began direct marketing their lamb in 2001, with fresh lamb available year-round. The flock is currently around 650 head. Buy whole animals, custom cut, and specialty cuts like crown roast and saddle, then try lamb sausage, *merguez*, and experimental English-style "bangers." Their lamb is highly favoured by chefs for its exceptional tenderness, mildness, and flavour. The family also raises hormone- and antibiotic-free cattle, and sells beef sides, whole carcasses and freezer packs.

- *Directions*: South on Highway 2 to Fort Macleod. From Fort Macleod, continue southward 4.5 kilometres on Highway 2. West 1 kilometre at Turnpike Road 84. South 2.5 kilometres on Range Road 260. Driview is the second farm on the east side of Range Road 260.
- *House Specialties*: Lamb and beef.
- *Also Available*: **Millarville Farmers' Market** seasonally, and delivered to Calgary without a delivery charge so long as you meet Gerrit somewhere on his weekly delivery route each Tuesday. On the menu at Calgary Golf and Country Club, Divine, Divino, Glencoe Golf & Country Club, La Chaumière, Murrieta's West Coast Bar & Grill, Muse, Red Water Rustic Grill, River Café, Rouge, Teatro, and Wildwood.

www.driviewfarms.ca

Fairwinds Farm

Established: 1999 • Owners: Ben & Anita Oudshoorn
Box 953, Fort Macleod
Phone 553•0127
Monday–Saturday, Hours by Appointment
Cheques, $ only

BEN and Anita Oudshoorn started as operators of a home dairy in 1998, when they began milking a dozen goats for Natricia Dairy. They expanded the flock and production and by 2001, they were making yoghurt. Natricia Dairy closed down and so, after moving to their current location near Fort Macleod in 2003, the Oudshoorns added *chèvre* and feta to their production list, and are currently experimenting with additional "hard" cheeses. They are also considering making ice cream with the excess milk from their 300 does—but be patient! The farm and livestock were recently certified organic.

- *Directions*: South on Highway 2, 36 kilometres beyond Claresholm. East 1 kilometre on Range Road 264. Be careful crossing Highway 2's dual carrigeway! On Range Road 264 drop into the valley, turn left onto the driveway before the bridge, but do not cross the creek. Watch for signs marking the gateway.
- *House Specialties*: Goats' milk yoghurt and cheeses.
- *Also Available*: **Amaranth Whole Foods Market, Community Natural Foods, Planet Organic Market, SPUD, Sunnyside Market, Sunterra Market** (at West Market Square) and **Sunterra Marketplace** (at Shops of Britannia), as well as the menus of select restaurants.

GLENWOOD

FARMGATE SALES

Room2Grow

Established: 1993 • Owners: Heather & Norman Dodd
Township Road 55, Glenwood
Phone: 626•3223 or Cell: 892•3223
April–October: Monday–Sunday 8:00 am–8:00 pm
November–March: Tuesday–Thursday 9:00 am–5:00 pm
$ only

HEATHER and Norman Dodd are lifelong farmers. They raise Simmental cattle, sold frozen, cut and wrapped by the piece, roasting chickens and turkeys in season and, by advance order, farm eggs, and pesticide-free produce too: greenhouse tomatoes and cukes, u-pick strawberries, u-pick or we-pick Saskatoons, cut flowers, Nanking and Evans cherries, fresh or jammed, and house-made pickles. It's usually windy, so wear a hat when you visit!
- *Directions*: South on Highway 2 through Fort Macleod. Head south out of Fort Macleod on Highway 810 for 40 kilometres (7 kilometres north of Glenwood). East 0.25 kilometres on Township Road 55.
- *House Specialties*: Beef, poultry, berries, vegetables, cut flowers, cherries, jams, pickles.

www.nhdsimm-rm2grow.com

HIGH RIVER

CHAINS (BIG & SMALL)

Sobeys

98 Centre Street SE, High River
Phone: 652•5515
Monday–Sunday 9:00 am–9:00 pm
V, MC, AE, Debit, Cheque, $
[see Chains (Big & Small) for main entry p. 49]

FARMERS' MARKETS

High River Farmers' Market

Established: 1985 • Coordinator: Cynthia Farrow
228–12 Avenue SE (Bob Snodgrass Recreation Complex), High River
Phone: 652•4042
mid-June–early September: Thursday 4:00 pm–7:00 pm
$ only
www.highriver.ca

FARMGATE SALES

Highwood Valley Ranch

Established: 1974 • Owners: Ralph & Jacquie Nelson
RR#2, High River
Phone: 652•7477
Hours by Appointment
Cheque, $

I T is easy to cultivate a sense of place when your family has deep roots. Ralph and Jacquie Nelson live on one of the region's prettiest ranches, where Ralph's family has lived for decades. They raise and sell hormone- and antibiotic-free Angus beef. Advance order only frozen cuts—by half or whole carcass—at the farmgate.

- *Directions*: South on Highway 2 to Highway 23 overpass at High River. West on Highway 23 into High River and 88 Street. South 3 kilometres to 562 Avenue. West 6.8 kilometres to 24 Street. North 2.5 kilometres down a hill to the house, set back in the trees. There are three cattle guards to cross.
- *House Specialties*: Frozen beef, by sides and half.
- *Also Available*: Wild Horse Bistro in Black Diamond and, occasionally, River Café in Calgary.

LETHBRIDGE

FARMGATE SALES

Broxburn Vegetables & Café

Established: 1994 • Owners: Paul & Hilda de Jonge
RR#8, Site 26, Box 16, Lethbridge
Phone: 327•0909
U-pick, June–Frost: Monday–Saturday 8:00 am–6:00 pm (call for availability)
Store & Café: Monday–Saturday 9:00 am–4:00 pm
Debit, $

P AUL and Hilda de Jonge have been farming since 1994 and market gardening since 1995, with 80 acres—12 acres in fruit and vegetables— and a 90,000 square foot (2 acres) greenhouse heated by coal and sunlight. They are blessed with a longer growing season than Calgary due to lower elevation, and rely on integrated pest management (IPM) to control insects. Expect two types of strawberries—June and ever-bearing—starting in mid-June right through until the first frost in September (although the frost can arrive as early as late August but also not be seen until mid-October), raspberries from mid-summer to freeze-up, Saskatoons, black and redcurrants. Vegetables available include bell and hot peppers, 3 kinds of tomatoes, butter lettuce, long English and gherkin cucumbers. Festivals on the farm include a strawberry festival and a pumpkinfest. Their on-site farm store (since 2002) has a thriving café. It serves strawberry pie well worth the road trip.

- *Directions*: South on Highway 2, through Lethbridge. East 5 kilometres on Highway 3. South 1 kilometre on Broxburn Road.
- *House Specialties*: Strawberries, currants and other berries, tomatoes, peppers, cucumbers, lettuce, strawberry pie.
- *Also Available*: On the menu at local restaurants, including River Café, as Calgary chefs have learned the value of Broxburn vegetables and fruit, buying through distributor Rudy Knitel of Galimax Trading Inc.

www.broxburn-vegetables.com

MILLARVILLE

FARMERS' MARKETS

Millarville Farmers' Market*

Established: 1982 • Contact: Donnette Montgomery
Box 68 (Millarville Racetrack), Millarville
Phone: 931•2404
mid-June–early October: Saturday 8:30 am–noon
Christmas at Millarville occurs annually in November
Friday 10:00 am–8:00 pm, Saturday & Sunday 10:00 am–5:00 pm
$, Debit machine on site

WEEKEND early birds who enjoy a picturesque drive to the foothills will probably love strolling through Millarville's 180 stalls, which has a strong contingent of craftspeople and artisans, farmers—including Gerrit van Hierden's incomparable lamb from **Driview Farms** in Fort Macleod—and made-in-Alberta cooks, including **Missing Link Extraordinary Sausage** sausages. The largest outdoor market in the province celebrated a quarter-century in 2007 and teamed up with the Priddis and Millarville Fair to observe the fair's centennial in the same year.

- *Directions*: South on Highway 2. East on Highway 22X. South 14 kilometres on Highway 22 to Millarville. East 1.6 kilometres on Highway 549.

www.millarville.ab.com

NANTON

CHAINS (BIG & SMALL)

IGA

2107–20 Avenue, Nanton
Phone: 646•5691
October–March: Monday–Friday 9:00 am–8:00 pm
Saturday & Sunday 9:00 am–6:00 pm
April–September: Monday–Friday 9:00 am–9:00 pm
Saturday & Sunday 9:00 am–7:00 pm
V, MC, Debit, Cheque, $
[see Chains (Big & Small) for main entry on p. 49]

FARMGATE SALES

Paradise Hill Farm

Established: 2000 • Owners: Tony & Karen Legault
Box 1390, Nanton
Phone: 646•3276
April–November: Monday–Thursday 8:00 am–4:30 pm, Friday 8:00 am–noon
Evenings & Weekends, Hours by Appointment
Cheque, $

Tony and Karen Legault have spent many years working at getting farmers' market-quality tomatoes into Alberta supermarkets, and are pleased that they have cracked the market at **Calgary Co-op** and several other venues. "A local product is from a neighbour, so keep the dollars in the neighbourhood and buy local," says Tony. The farm is located south of Calgary and east of Nanton, along Mosquito Creek's picturesque, back-bending oxbow curves. Buy their pesticide-free, vine-ripened tomatoes at the farmgate, or try spicy dried tomato chips Cajun style.

- *Directions*: South on Highway 2 through Nanton. East on Township Road 162 (28 Street) for 3.5 kilometres. Watch for signs.
- *House Specialties*: Tomatoes.
- *Also Available*: **Calgary Co-op, High River Farmers' Market.**
  www.paradisehillfarm.ca

OKOTOKS

CHAINS (BIG & SMALL)

Sobeys

700 Cornerstone at 201 Southridge Drive, Okotoks
Phone: 938•3439 or 995•4088
Monday–Sunday 8:00 am–10:00 pm
Pharmacy: 995•4123
Monday–Friday 8:00 am–9:00 pm
Saturday 10:00 am–6:00 pm, Sunday 10:00 am–5:00 pm
Postal Outlet: 995•0919
Monday–Friday 8:00 am–10:00 pm
Saturday 9:00 am–6:00 pm, Sunday 10:00 am–5:00 pm
V, MC, AE, Debit, Cheque, $
[see Chains (Big & Small) for main entry on p. 49]

FARMGATE SALES

Chinook Honey Company • Chinook Arch Meadery

Established 1995 • Owners: Cherie & Art Andrews
RR#1, Site 14, Box 12, Okotoks
Phone: 995•0830
March 31–December 23: Wednesday–Saturday 10:00 am–5:00 pm
Sunday & Monday noon–5:00 pm and most Holidays
January 12–March 30: Thursday–Saturday 10:00 am–5:00 pm
V, MC, Debit, Cheque, $

CHERIE and Art Andrews started the honey business in 1995 as a stress-buster for Art. Now the business hosts 250 hives and a bee-based value-added shop (since 2004). Their lobbying resulted in successful amendments to Alberta legislation governing the new business of cottage fruit wineries so that it now includes mead. The couple was recognized with a $10,000 Farm Renewal/Makeover Scholarship from Alberta Agriculture for innovative thinking and creative approaches to diversification and growth.

When you visit the farm, spend time watching the observation hive. It is a fascinating look into the murderous world of drones and queens, their complex communication patterns and societal structures. Then shop! The store carries a wide range of honey, *apitherapy* products—including propolis and royal jelly, honey-based body care products, candles and amazing honey ice cream made in High River with **Kayben Farms'** blackcurrants.

Art and Cherie have branched out into value-added beverages, and are Alberta's first mead-makers, under the label of Chinook Arch Meadery. Their inaugural vintage of mead (one of humanity's most ancient of alcoholic beverages) is available at the farmgate and by delivery on request to individuals in Calgary as of May 2008. The first release of 350 litres of traditional mead in 750 mL bottles, augmented by a limited release of buckwheat and black currant versions, is scheduled to be followed by a release of spiced mead, called metheglin, and fruit-infused mead, called melomel, in November. Half of each bottling is being held back for aging.

- *Directions*: South on Highway 2 onto 2A into Okotoks, through the centre of town to the intersection of Highway 2A and Highway 7. West about 3.5 kilometres on Highway 7 to 16 Street West. South 0.5 kilometre on 16 Street West. Chinook Honey Company is the first farm on the right. Look for the blue buildings.
- *House Specialties*: Honey and honey products, apitherapy, and mead.
- *Also Available*: Honey available at Divine in Okotoks, and **Nectar Desserts** in Calgary.

www.chinookhoney.com

Kayben Farms

Established: 2000 • Owners: Claude & Judy Kolk
RR#2, Site 2, Box 60, Okotoks
Phone: 938•2857
May–September: Monday–Friday 9:00 am–6:00 pm, Saturday 10:00 am–5:00 pm
May–June Only: Thursday & Friday 9:00 am–8:00 pm
V, MC, Debit, $

FROM a test plot of 300 blackcurrant plants in 2000, the orchard has grown to 20 acres and 25,000 shrubs. The orchard includes newly planted strawberries, with raspberries to come in 2008. Other services keep this energetic couple and their three daughters busy: a handsome new garden centre, a tree and shrub nursery, landscaping service, and a growing line of wonderful house-developed, value-added products. They all feature black-currants—in vinaigrette, dessert topping, jam and jelly, meat baste and glaze, fresh and frozen fruit (whole and pureed), with new products being added each year. The best of the lot is an assertive, thirst-cutting "punch base" made of unsweetened black currant juice. Enjoy u-pick or custom-picked berries, and pack a picnic to enjoy in the picnic area near the "look-only" fish pond. Walking trails are under construction, and food service will arrive— perhaps—in the coming years, depending largely on availability of staff.

- *Directions*: South on Highway 2 for 3 kilometres past the Okotoks overpass (Highways 552 & 2A). West 0.5 kilometre on 306 Avenue. South 1.2 kilometre on 32 Street East. The Sales Garden Centre is on the east side of the road. There is a blue u-pick sign out on Highway 2 providing further assistance with route-finding.
- *House Specialties*: Blackcurrants, u-pick or we-pick, value-added products including punch, preserves, vinaigrettes, and chutneys, nursery plants and shrubs, landscaping service.
- *Also Available*: **Chinook Honey Company, Community Natural Foods, The Cookbook Company Cooks, Route 40 Soup Company, Sobey's/ IGA** and Terra Cotta Dudes in Black Diamond.

www.kayben.com

KITCHEWARE

A Touch of Italy (ATOI), Okotoks

Established: 1984 • Owner: Victoria Lecce
94 Elma Street, Okotoks
Phone: 938•0488
Tuesday–Friday 10:00 am–6:00 pm, Saturday 10:00 am–5:00 pm
V, MC, Debit, $

THIS lovely bungalow is filled with opera arias and a more extensive collection of high-quality specialty foods—from a global pantry—than its Calgary offspring. Look for Callipo tuna in olive oil, Mas Portell oils and vinegars from Spain, Barilla and Paese Mio pasta and gnocchi, Illy and Mauro coffees, but also British and Scottish imports too. To be expected are Italian-made Alessi—handsome espresso pots and cups. Waring electricals (blenders, toasters, immersion wands, countertop toaster ovens) are the brand of choice, along with some very good pots, pans, and cocottes made by Le Chausseur, Le Creuset and Emile Henri. Knife selection is to-the-point—Global, Wüstof Trident, Henckel, including a mezzaluna—but if you do not see the style you like, ask for a boo at the catalogue. Cutting surfaces are Epicurean's wood fibre composite, and hand tools are mostly Rosle's fine German-made line, but Silpat and Zyliss are tucked in between and behind the gaskets and gadgets. Seven shelves hold some very carefully chosen food, art and cookery books. Tabletop serving dishes from Fitz & Floyd, and some lovely linens to accent them are on display, in a changing array of colours. Victoria keeps oil-packed anchovies and wedges of Parmigiano-Reggiano in the fridge—ask if you need either. These two rooms are soon to be expanded into four, but Victoria does not expect to move into ranges, electric coffee makers or more pots. For those, seek out the Bridgeland store in Calgary.
- *House Specialties*: Imported global pantry products including Italian oils and pastas, kitchen tools and pans, books and tableware.
- *Also Available*: 8, 606 Meredith Road NE, Calgary.
www.atouchofitaly.net

ORGANICS

Nutter's Bulk & Natural Foods

Established: 1982 • Manager: Leanne Taborski
Bay 9, 900 Village Lane, Okotoks
Phone 938•1740
Monday–Friday 9:00 am–6:00 pm, Saturday 10:00 am–5:00 pm
V, MC, AE, Debit, $

THIS small shop contains 75 percent organic goods, and yet it is being overhauled to reduce its present focus on bulk sweets in favour of placing a greater emphasis on cooking ingredients, including a growing section of baking and fair-trade ingredients. The bulk bins are indeed the heart of the store, holding 13 kinds of dried beans, extensive seeds and nuts, flours, grains and *maltitol*-sweetened chocolate and candy, and many snacky things, including fruit and nut mixes. Gluten-free and wheat-free ingredients, and Kinnikinnick's frozen baked goods, and Nanton-made Terra Cotto gluten-free mixes, are available as well. **Highwood Crossing Farm Ltd.**'s grains, oils and mixes are the only other local product, but this baker was thrilled to find unbleached parchment paper by the roll. The fridge is small, and holds both flax and hemp oil but not much else. A bigger fridge is coming, but until then, cold selections are minimal. Good alternative cleaning products for the kitchen are available too, for post-cooking tidiness.

- *House Specialties*: Organic ingredients, bulk ingredients, gluten-free and wheat-free ingredients, and some local products.
- *Also Available*: 900 Railway Avenue, Canmore.

www.nutters.com

PINCHER CREEK

FARMGATE SALES

Bloomin' Inn

Established 1996 • Owners: Colleen & Francis Cyr
Box 1346, Pincher Creek
Phone: 627•5829
Monday–Sunday, Hours by Appointment
V, MC, Debit, Cheque, $

COLLEEN and Francis Cyr and their daughter Jenny (the farm's 4th generation) make their living on the year-round sales of farm products, without the fallback of off-farm income. Their "Pantry" is actually an in-house farm store, selling High Country Meats, honey, fruit juice, wine, pickles, salsa, jams and jellies. Look for local crafts, dried flowers, and Christmas arrangements, antiques, kitchen graniteware and farmhouse crocks. The family tends gardens, and raises natural hormone-free beef, pork, chicken, lamb, and eggs. There is a picnic area, and it is possible to arrange farm tours and retreats.

- *Directions*: South on Highway 2 to Fort Macleod. West on Highway 3 to Highway 785. South 4 kilometres to Tower Road. East 4 kilometres on Tower Road, following the signs for 1.5 kilometres, turning south and then west.
- *House Specialties*: Chicken, beef, and lamb, condiments, jams and preserves, kitchenware, garden and farm tours. Year-round B&B and home-baked goods.

www.bloomin-inn.com

TURNER VALLEY

MAKE 'n' TAKE MEALS/HMRs

Route 40 Soup Company

Established: 2002 • *Owners: Mark & Lanny Klaudt*
146 Main Street, Turner Valley
Phone: 933•7676
Monday–Thursday 11:00 am–5:00 pm
Friday & Saturday 11:00 am–4:00 pm, 5:00 pm–8:00 pm
V, MC, Debit, $

CHEF Mark Klaudt and wife Lanny own a cute and charming café, Route 40 Soup Company, in Turner Valley. Mark's booming voice and big personality fill his funky dining room. His wraps, especially the five-spice pork and the *chipotle* beef, are amazingly good. And don't leave without sampling the home fries, a multicolour tumble of perfectly crisp spuds. Soups and house-made condiments are the notable take-away business. Browse among seven types of soups refrigerated in 1-litre jars. They are semi-condensed and need to have liquid added. Mark's mainstays include butternut squash with piri piri, apple and peanut, roasted cauliflower with *ancho* chili (an outstanding, robust, wonderfully wow soup), and organic French lentil and *preserved lemon* (I add duck to this one in my own kitchen). All are gluten-free, vegetable-stock-based, and made without animal products. Yes, that also means no butter. There are some seasonal variants wrapped around the mainstays. Of note, as the year unwinds, are port and caramelized red onion, stinging nettle, asparagus, and broccoli with toasted almond soup.

If you like preserves of a unique bent, check out Mark's great green tomato chow or blood orange, kumquat and pansy flower jelly. The latter is a pretty one that uses local edible flowers in a semi-sweet style that is good with cheese or on toast. I like the house BBQ sauce, made of *ancho* chili and sweet maple, used in-house on Portobello mushroom ravioli. Find other good local condiments here, including **Kayben Farms** black currant jelly. Also of note, and for sale on request, is the house 5-spice blend. And if you call ahead, the kitchen will make a whole meal to go.

- *House Specialties*: Preserves, condiments and soups to go, using local products.
- *Also Available*: **Millarville Farmers' Market** in season, AG Country Food Market, Diamond Centre Mall, Main Street, Black Diamond.

www.route40.ca

Points West

BOW VALLEY AND BEYOND: POINTS WEST includes entries for the following communities: Banff, Canmore, and Cochrane.

BANFF

BAKERIES

Wild Flour Artisan Bakery & Café
Established: 2005 • Manager: Jenna Dashney
101, 211 Bear Street (Bison Courtyard), Banff
Phone: 760•5074
Monday–Sunday 7:00 am–7:00 pm
V, MC, Debit, $

JENNA Dashney <www.butterchik.com> might be the freshest breeze to blow into Banff since the last Chinook. This hired gun pastry whiz kid has cooked since age 15 around the globe and across Canada, from Ottawa to Sooke Harbour House. She has taken on the bakery for owner/architect Peter Poole of Arctos & Byrd. Dashney might talk rapidly, but her brain keeps up, and so does her sense of place. It means she has embraced an organic and environmentally responsible business—as befits the residents of this environmentally sensitive building—and custody of a wood-fired Le Pagnole oven (nicknamed "the sleeping buffalo").

Look for daily and weekly breads, gluten-free scones, *brioche* buns, and from-scratch organic, artisanally crafted sourdough breads, *croissants* and sweet goods—all served in a funky environment.

Recently launched is a summer and autumn "regional cuisine and culture market" in the courtyard outside the door of the Wild Flour. It happens on Thursdays, and features the tenants of the courtyard, along with live music and art, as well as organic produce from **Blush Lane**.
- *House Specialties*: From-scratch organic artisan breads all from sourdough starters, *croissants*, baked goods, house-made soda and iced tea.
- *Also Available*: Glacier Lily, Banff's Indulgence Parlour, 104, 211 Bear Street (just across Bison Courtyard). Go there for Wild Flour's house-made sorbets, dairy-free *gelato*, ice cream from scratch, organic Kicking Horse coffee, hand-crafted candies, taffies, and fruit jellies.

www.wildflourbakery.ca

BOOZE

Banff Wine Store

Established: 1986 • Owner: Marc Saumur
Lower Level, 302 Caribou Street, Banff
Phone: 762•3465
Monday–Sunday 10:00 am–11:00 pm
V, MC, AE, Debit, $

T HIS well-stocked basement enclave conducts informal in-house tastings, with always a bottle or two open for customers. Staffers are trained by the International Sommelier Guild (ISG) or through the self-taught school of life, although most of them have extensive restaurant backgrounds, and can talk knowledgably about food and wine pairings. It is relevant to recall that Banff is an international tourist destination, so the global approach to selling wine includes a healthy Canadian section. It gives visitors a chance to see and taste what is made domestically. In addition, the shop tends to Mediterranean-style wines, from the south of France, Spain, and Italy. The New World, especially Australia, is only barely secondary. This shop shares access to a direct source import license, so many bottles are exclusive.
 • *House Specialties*: Service, selection, availability of exclusive products, with Canadian, Mediterranean (French, Spanish, Italian) and Australian wines at the forefront.

CHEESE

Bison Mountain Bistro & General Store

Established: 2006 • Owners: Ryan & Camilla Rivard
213, 211 Bear Street (Bison Courtyard), Banff
Phone: 762•5550
October–May: Monday–Friday 11:00 am–6:00 pm
Saturday & Sunday 10:00 am–6:00 pm
June–September: Monday–Friday 11:00 am–7:00 pm
Saturday & Sunday 10:00 am–7:00 pm
V, MC, AE, JCB, Debit, $

R YAN Rivard is nobody's fool, and he took full advantage of his years spent learning cheese lore while at **Janice Beaton Fine Cheese.** He has launched from that base, smartly setting up a cheese shop as part of the main-floor general store in the thriving Banff business he co-owns with his wife Camilla. Upstairs is one of Banff's best casual dining spots, but downstairs, tuck into the cheese counter to take away the Bow Valley's finest cheeses.
 Shelves contain good in-house processed condiments, including a dynamite smoked tomato ketchup, and several mustards. If you tilt toward sweet or like Philippine-style classic banana sauce, you may enjoy the banana

curry mustard. Otherwise, maybe the curried pumpkin ketchup. Look for meals to go—many made with locally-raised ingredients, frozen soups, marinated ready-to-cook meats (kebabs of chicken or beef), bison cuts, lamb shank braised and ready to eat, sandwiches for picnics, and pasta sauces. It is all produced under the eye of executive chef Grant Parry. Look for the June–September market in the Bison Courtyard on Thursdays, (noon–5:00 pm) featuring the organic produce of **Blush Lane**.

- *House Specialties*: Raw milk cheeses, seasonal local vegetables, sandwiches and soups, house condiments, HMRs.
- *Also Available*: Wholesale cheese services to Bow Valley restaurants, including **Fuze Fine Dining** and Num-ti-Jah Lodge.

www.thebison.ca

COOKING SCHOOLS & CLASSES

Fuze Finer Dining

Established: 2005 • General Manager: Anthony Chalmers
Upstairs, 110 Banff Avenue (Clock Tower Mall), Banff
Phone: 760•0853
School & Class, Hours by Appointment
V, MC, Debit, $

CLASSES take place in a handsome open kitchen adjacent to the restaurant and its kitchenware shop (stocked with Paderno and select lines, including a house line of spices). All classes are private events, booked in advance and only upon request, for a minimum of 10 guests. General Manager Anthony Chalmers says classes are mostly corporate team-building and spousal programs, but private groups may book chef Gary Dayanandan's unique fusion flair as well. Designer Ron Yakymyshyn (It's About Time Interior Design) has designed a glass-walled presentation kitchen outfitted with Thermador four-burner stove and a pair of flat panel monitors. Classes run for 2.5–3 hours, in daytime or evening time slots, in both demo and hands-on format, with full meal, recipe handouts, and a glass of wine. Take home the apron.

- *House Specialties*: Classes in fusion cooking, spousal programs, team building, kitchenware.

www.fuzedining.com

CHAINS (BIG & SMALL)

Canada Safeway
318 Marten Street, Banff
Phone: 762•5378
Monday–Sunday 8:00 am–11:00 pm
Pharmacy: 762•5370
Monday–Friday 9:00 am–9:00 pm, Saturday 9:00 am–6:00 pm
Sunday 10:00 am–6:00 pm
V, MC, AE, Debit, $
[see Chains (Big & Small) for main entry on p. 43)

CHOCOLATE & SWEETS

Chocolaterie Bernard Callebaut
111 Banff Avenue (Harmony Lane Mall), Banff
Phone: 762•4106
June 1–Thanksgiving: Monday–Saturday 10:00 am–9:00 pm
Thanksgiving–May 31: Monday–Saturday 10:00 am–7:00 pm
Year Round: Sunday 11:00 am–7:00 pm
V, MC, AE, Debit, $
[see SE Chocolates & Sweets for main entry on p. 60]

CANMORE

BAKERIES

Gourmet Croissant
Established: 2005 • Owners: Yasmina, Ifel, Thomas & Clara Costa
1205 Bow Valley Trail (Bow Valley Professional Centre), Canmore
Phone: 609•4410
Monday–Saturday 7:30 am–4:30 pm
V, MC, Debit, $

THIS Parisian family has settled happily into Canmore, to the joy of *croissant* and pastry fans in the Bow Valley. Ifel's croissants are without doubt the best for a hundred miles, so get yours! The other *viennoiserie*-style pastries are equally good. I am partial though, to the *croissants ordinaires, pain au chocolat* and *croissants aux amandes*. For a savoury crepe, try the *galette*. Small personal quiches and sandwiches are available too. But oh, for the hands of a baker! Have an espresso while you wait, and take breakfast along on the road to anywhere. The supplies do not last through the day, so get there early.
• *House Specialties: Croissants* (arrive before noon!), savoury crepes (*galettes*), crepes, *viennoiserie*.

JK Bakery

Established: 1994 • Owners: John & Helen Kirchpfennig
1514 Railway Avenue (Aspen Industrial Park), Canmore
Phone: 678•4232
Monday–Friday 8:00 am–5:00 pm, Saturday 8:00 am–4:00 pm
V, MC, AE, Debit, $

THIS bakery does many things, but does its breads the best. Try the multi-grain, Volcorn or Norwegian loaves, or the *ciabatta* buns. If you like sweets, you may enjoy the European-style classic desserts like creamhorns and Florentines, fruit flans and strudel, Linzertorte and elaborate cakes.
• *House Specialties*: Multi-grain, European-style rustic breads, and pastries.
• *Also Available*: Rimrock Hotel, Banff Springs Hotel, and others.

Rocky Mountain Bagel Company

Established: 1995 • Owners: Shanyn Young & Darren Fischer
830 Main Street, Canmore
Phone: 678•9978
Monday–Sunday 6:30 am–6:00 pm
V, MC, Debit, $

IT is a hopping lunch spot, but it also sells bagels by the oddest amounts: a baker's dozen I comprehend, but why are a dozen on Wednesday less cash than any other day of the week? And what about "Last night's"? Even a cup of Oso Negro coffee and a bagel doesn't de-fog my brain and no one behind the counter appears to know either, when I ask! Baked goods from scratch, preferably toasted, with some nice lox and cream cheese, or that nice **Valbella Meats/Valbella's Deli & Café** cold cut I saw dangling from someone else's toasted bagel. Or maybe a pizza bagel. Or a good cinnamon raisin. Maybe I should buy that baker's dozen and have it all.
• *House Specialties*: Bagels (in odd amounts).

Sweet Madeira

Established: 1986 • Owner: Cecilia Lortscher
109, 112 Kananaskis Way, Canmore
Phone: 609•9957
Hours by Appointment
Cheque, $

CECILIA's cookies are very good indeed, and I am grateful, because a fine cookie maker is a rare bird. She is a talented, self-taught baker of Portuguese extraction, with an unerring eye, and a hand for textures. The bakery (in its current location since 2002) does little retail business, focusing on custom and contract baking. Cecilia uses certified-organic flours and grains, including *spelt* and rolled oats in her long list of cookies, loaves, quick breads and squares. Macaroons and cranberry pistachio biscotti are made with rice flour, thus are gluten-free, a difficult thing indeed to do well. The oatmeal rum and raisin cookies are like my grandmother Sarah's, with exactly the right texture, the macaroons remind my inner little girl of afternoons spent hunting meringues at age 9, and the brownies are fudgy, dense, chocolate. Oh well done, Cecilia!

- *House Specialties*: Biscotti, brownies, cookies, loaves, quick breads.
- *Also Available*: **Mountain Mercato Specialty Food Market**, Canmore.

BOOZE

Grizzly Paw Brewing Company
Established: 1996 • Owner: Niall Fraser
622 Main Street (Policeman's Creek Landing), Canmore
Phone: 678•9983
Monday–Sunday 11:00 am–1:00 am
V, MC, Debit, $

I T is a pub, but one that makes its own beer, available on tap at the bar and across the alley in kegs and bottles. You can also buy beer-infused BBQ sauce and a honey wheat hot sauce. How much do you like beer? Try Pale ale, IPA, Mooseknuckle Oatmeal stout, Rutting Elk Red, Grumpy Bear Honey Wheat ale, raspberry Beavertail, or eat a float (drink a float?) made with **MacKay's Ice Cream** (produced in neighbouring Cochrane). At Christmas, a seasonal Cranberry ale surfaces, and a Jack O'Lantern pumpkin ale smiles at Hallowe'en. Take a tour of the brewery, buy a tasting round of the house brews. Eat, and drink beer! Then cross the pedestrian walk to The Paw Shop to buy beverages for home consumption.

- *House Specialties*: Handcrafted beer, non-alcoholic ginger beer and black cherry cola.
- *Also Available*: The Paw Shop, Bay 5, 626 Main Street, in Canmore, **Bin 905** and local liquor stores, and on the menu at River Café,
  www.grizzlypaw.com

CHAINS (BIG & SMALL)

Sobeys/IGA
2, 950 Railway Avenue, Canmore
Phone: 678•6326
Monday–Sunday 8:00 am–10:00 pm
Pharmacy: 678•6394
Monday–Friday 9:00 am–9:00 pm, Saturday & Sunday 9:00 am–6:00 pm
V, MC, AE, Debit, $
[see Chains (Big & Small) for main entry on p. 49]

EUROPEAN

Mountain Mercato Specialty Food Market
Established: 2005 • Owner: Raegan Fodor
102, 817 Main Street, Canmore
Phone: 609•6631
Monday–Thursday 9:00 am–6:00 pm, Friday 9:00 am–7:00 pm
Saturday 10:00 am–7:00 pm, Sunday 10:00 am–6:00 pm
V, MC, AE, Debit, $

THIS pleasing space has changed hands several times in the past few years as Canmore has grown. Under its current owner, a front deli case showcases fresh pasta and sauces (*pomodoro, Calabrese, panna con funghi*) made at **Mercato** (no relation) in Calgary. House-made red pepper dip and bruschetta share space with a variety of olives, cold cuts and cheeses, with a handful of tables and cushion-strewn benches for in-house noshes and coffee (choose among several bean blends). Baked goods from **Sweet Madeira** in glass jars sitting next to a choice of good espressos have the rapt attention of shoppers intent on tasting those very cookies. Go past the counter, and find metal shelving loaded with a variety of olive oils, most of it very good extra virgin, some of it exceptional. A shelf of balsamic vinegars leaves no doubt that this shop likes things Italian. Good things include: Callipo tuna packed in olive oil, Uncle Luigi's olive oil, another **Mercato** (Calgary) specialty, South African spice blends, Maldon salt, Vancouver's Raincoast Crisps, and **Highwood Crossing Farm Ltd.'s** cold-pressed canola oil. The selection gives Bow Valley cooks an evolving pantry that is improving in breadth and scope. Service can be a bit thin, as in many Bow Valley (and Calgary!) retail shops, so be patient and polite. It takes time to grow a business.
• *House Specialties*: Olive oils, deli, takeout, pasta and sauces, *panini*.
www.mountainmercato.com

KITCHENWARE

The Colourful Cook
Established: 1993 • Owners: Claire Breeze & Alex Souvairan
103–104, 721–8 Street, Canmore
Phone: 678•3922
Monday–Saturday 10:00 am–6:00 pm, Sunday 11:00 am–5:00 pm
V, MC, Debit, $

THIS excellent shop is knee-deep in good stuff. The current owners (since 2003) stock a knife collection—Kasumi, Wüstof Trident, Global—that is as good as any in Calgary, supported by a selection of good sharpening tools and good cutting surfaces. Cooks needing pots will do well with Emile Henri, and the linens and hand tools are top-line and extensive. For dinnerware, hunt through the Trattoria brand collection, all in white, for a clean tabletop look. Some electricals—Cuisinart and Krups or Gaggia—in a full line. A new direction is spice blends, honey, jams and preserves. A carefully chosen collection of kitchen books is also worth a boo!

- *House Specialties*: Kitchenware, knives, pots, pans, books, smallwares, linens, electrical appliances.
- *Also Available*: **Pots 'n' Peppers**, 212–1 Street West, Cochrane.
  www.colourfulcook.ca

MEAT & GAME

Griesser Spoon Custom Catering • Railway Deli

Established: 2002 • Owners: Roland & Harry Griesser
Unit 101, 702 Bow Valley Trail, Canmore
Phone: 678•3637
Monday–Sunday 9:00 am–7:00 pm
V, MC, AE, Debit, $

AUSTRIAN brothers Roland and Harry Griesser relocated from **Valbella Meats/Valbella's Deli & Café** in 2007, and are well-established in the Railway Deli. Multiple arms of one business—restaurant, deli and catering— are all housed in a bright, centrally located space.

A strong focus on HMRs, a well-stocked deli case and refrigeration/freezer supply of nearly anything you need to eat well makes this stop more than worthwhile. Meats are from **Paolini's Sausage & Meats** in Calgary. Ready to heat-and-eat choices include the robust and the subtle—try pear and ginger soup, roasted garlic and onion soup, or mouth-fillingly meaty goulash. Game is a popular choice. Sample the bison stew or elk ragout with hand-made noodles. An in-house bakery produces pastries worth noshing—cookies, almond *croissants*, and hazelnut strudel. Yum! The butchery window gives access to custom meat-cutting. If you want a bigger cut than any on display, ask, and get a mountain-size cut-to-order steak to go. The business has been catering since 2002. They service off-premise events, and offer in-home catering, with cooking on-site. A popular choice is the roast beef or game BBQ. A mobile Alpine-style hut/kiosk attends Canmore's annual folk festival and other civic festivals.

- *House Specialties*: Catering, baked goods, HMRs, BBQ-ready and marinated meats, red meat, especially lamb skewers, beef and game.
- *Also Available*: Mobile Alpine hut-style food kiosk at Canmore Folk and other civic festivals.
  www.griesserspoon.com • www.railwaydeli.com

Valbella Meats • Valbella's Deli & Cafe

Established: 1978 • Owners: Walter & Lonnie von Rotz
104B Elk Run Boulevard, Canmore
Phone: 678•9989 (Deli) and 678•4109 (Wholesale)
Monday–Friday 8:00 am–6:00 pm, Saturday 9:00 am–5:00 pm
V, MC, Debit, $

THIS award-winning smokehouse was founded by Walter von Rotz, and recently celebrated its third decade. After a stint with the Greisser Brothers in charge of the front end, this wonderful shop has recently renovated and returned to the control of its founder.

Von Rotz chanced through Canmore in 1978 and was struck by the town's similarity—in elevation and dry climate—to his hometown near the St. Moritz highlands. The result is a highly regarded shop that makes and sells world-class sausages, smoked meats, *pâtés* and other delicacies in traditional Old World, low-tech style melded with state-of-the-art European equipment, and a commitment to no MSG or additives. Standouts include: a triple-gold-medal-winning ham and garlic sausage, *landjaeger*, the hiker's favorite—a chewy air-dried, meaty mini salami, succulent smoked sausage flavoured with sautéed leek and cabbage, *chimneysticks* smoked over birchwood in the old-fashioned smokehouse located in the warren of rooms in the rear of the building, Moroccan lamb sausage flavoured with sun-dried tomato and mint, and venison salami.

Von Rotz—a belt and suspenders type of guy—proudly shows off his Swiss and German-made machinery. Each costly machine has duplicates and parts somewhere in Valbella's cavernous interior. He grins at the buffalo chopper, a terrifying six-bladed meat cutter. "Faster than a Porsche," von Rotz says fondly, patting its stainless steel casing. "I never had any doubts that sausage-making wasn't what I wanted to do."

The extraordinary output of the smokehouse extends to fish, so do not overlook the cold-smoked steelhead and char. Behind the counter, find personalized meat cutting, with exclusively natural beef from Prairie Heritage Beef in Grande Prairie.

There is also a wide selection of HMRs, either "heat and eat" or "cook and eat": marinated meats, chili, stews and ragus of game, soups, turduckens, duck, ribs, and sauerkraut with onions and bacon. Von Rotz's favourite dessert is the Swiss hazelnut roll, but I tend to buy the chocolate, apricot and almond *croissants*. I want to take more than just a memory with me each time I leave this fabulous shop. The crumbs are my path back next time.

• *House Specialties*: Smoked meats, sausages, HMRs.
• *Also Available*: Meats and processed meats at many meat markets and delis in and around Calgary.

www.valbellagourmetfoods.ca

ORGANICS

Nutter's Bulk & Natural Foods

Established: 1982 • Manager: Sarah Merkel
900 Railway Avenue, Canmore
Phone: 678•3335
Monday–Friday 9:00 am–8:00 pm, Saturday 9:00 am–7:00 pm
Sunday 11:00 am–6:00 pm
V, MC, AE, Debit, $

I like Nutters. This Medicine Hat-based chain has spread into many western Canadian towns. It fills its niche admirably, and is astonishingly bigger inside than it appears from the exterior. Organic grains and flours in a considerable variety are in bulk bins: *spelt*, millet, flax, rices, cormeal in a variety of textures—from coarse to fine, rye, wheat, oats, *kamut, quinoa*. It makes baking easier for those with dietary difficulties. So too with the nut selection, the cereals, the herbs and spices (from Organic Connections), the pastas in a variety of types. Local growers and producers get their due too: **Highwood Crossing Farm Ltd.** cold-pressed oils, **Prairie Mill Bread Company** breads, Rocky Mountain Flatbreads (made in Canmore), High Country bison (frozen in a variety of cuts), game from **Winter's Turkey** and **Sunworks Farm** meats and sausages, **Fairwinds Farm** cheeses and yoghurts. Produce is well cared for, and wheatgrass trays are waiting for smoothies. Gardeners will welcome heirloom varieties of Stellar Seeds from Sorrento. There are rows of environmentally friendly cleaning products, pet food and body care products, baby care products, herbals and books too.
- *House Specialties*: Organic dry goods in bulk, organic produce and meats, gluten-free products, local foods.
- *Also Available*: Unit 9, 900 Village Lane, Okotoks as well as other locations across Canada.

www.nutters.com

PERSONAL CHEFS & CATERERS

Backcountry Bistro

Established: 2003 • Owner: Kelly Mager
Phone: 609•5580 • E-mail: kelly@backcountrybistro.com
Hours by Appointment
Cheque, $

KELLY Mager is not much for tea parties in elegant surroundings, despite time spent in Victoria—home of tea parties fit for the Queen. She began in her late teens as a backcountry mining camp cook for gold exploration companies in northern British Columbia, and prefers the backcountry, so consider your venue before you ask about her "mountain chef" catering services. Mountain catering requires great stamina and versatility. In the winter, Mager skis each day, then comes in and cooks for her guests. She can fit you out with dehydrated fare for a Wapta traverse, or fresh fare for a helicopter-serviced hut in the backcountry. She likes to present a different genre each night. Try her East Indian feast, or ask for a Greek night.

Alternatively, book the unique team approach: Mager as chef, and her partner, fully-certified mountain guide, Marco De la Salle of Great Divide Mountaineering guide services, for summer or winter trips, like backcountry skiing at the unique and beautiful Battle Abbey Lodge, a 10-minute heli flight from Golden, British Columbia, or Fairy Meadows, British Columbia. An Alpine Club hut with a history, Fairy Meadows has glorious scenery—glaciers and granite spires. No running water, no running cyberlines, no internet, no TV, no radio, no phones except for an emergency satellite phone. That is the good life.

- *House Specialties*: Mountain catering for skiers and hikers, ski touring, mountaineering trips and traverses, featuring fresh and house-made dehydrated foods.
- *Also Available*: One-month winter stints at *Olive Olio Bistro*, in Cadboro Bay, Victoria, British Columbia.

www.greatdividemountaineering.com

Culinary Adventures Catering

Established: 2004 • Owner: Suzy Rowan
E-mail: suzyrowan@hotmail.com
Phone: 678•0128
Hours by Appointment
Cheque, $

ALTHOUGH you can find Suzy Rowan on the ground of the Bow Valley, catering private in-home parties throughout the Bow Corridor, her private passion is in heading for the hills. Hire her as a backcountry outfitter, and she will provide food—some dehydrated—for campers, expeditioners, climbers, backcountry adventurers. If seeing the backcountry is your idea of how to get around Alberta, do it with good grub. Fly into Mount Assiniboine Lodge by helicopter from Canmore. Pack your cutlery, backcountry stove and fuel, sleeping bag and book in to the Alpine Club Naiset Huts. Rowan's prices are based on food, hut fees, and helicopter transport. Expect to pack her comestibles into your own coolers. Nor does she supply heat sources, pots or pans. It is strictly BYOG (bring your own gear). Her home-baked goods are excellent (ask about chocolate mousse cake or mango cheesecake), and she can provide appetizers, snacks, main courses, breakfast granola bars or loaves and breakfast burritos.

- *House Specialties*: Indonesian ginger chicken, vegetarian mushroom artichoke lasagna.

COCHRANE

BAKERIES

Bernie's Bavarian Bakery
Established: 1998 • Owner: Bernard Fortner
136 Railway Avenue, Cochrane
Phone: 932•9066
Tuesday–Friday 8:30 am–5:30 pm, Saturday 9:00 am–3:00 pm
$, Cheque

THIS bakery is a find. It is also hard to find, tucked away in a little hidey-hole in Cochrane. The organic whole-grain flours—rye, *spelt, kamut,* whole wheat—used at Bernie's Bavarian Bakery are from Nunweiler Flour, a family-owned mill in Alsask, Saskatchewan. Baker Bernie makes sourdough starter to leaven his rye loaves, and he does not add shortenings or oils, eggs or dairy products to his breads. Several wheat-free and yeast-free varieties are available on Wednesdays or Fridays. Wheat-free standouts are finely textured and crusty kings grain—made with 80 percent *kamut* and 20 percent *spelt*—and roasted onion, made with equal proportions of *spelt* and *kamut*. Other choices include *spelt* bread (wheat-free and yeast-free), pretzel sticks, buns, baguettes and a variety of cookies, tarts, cakes and sweets, some wheat-free. Personally, I prefer the breads. Advance order breads one day ahead, and three days in advance for cakes for special occasion.

• *House Specialties*: Wheat-free and yeast-free organic breads and sweets.

CHAINS (BIG & SMALL)

Canada Safeway
304–5 Avenue West, Cochrane
Phone: 851•1290
Monday–Sunday 8:00 am–10:00 pm
Pharmacy: 851•1279
Monday–Friday 9:00 am–9:00 pm
Saturday 9:00 am–6:00 pm, Sunday 10:00 am–6:00 pm
Gas Bar: 851•1290 ext. 6
Monday–Saturday 6:00 am–10:00 pm, Sunday 7:00 am–10:00 pm
Liquor Store: 932•8941
Monday–Sunday 10:00 am–10:00 pm
V, MC, AE, Debit, $
[see Chains (Big & Small) for main entry on p. 43]

Cochrane Valley IGA

609–1 Street West, Cochrane
Phone: 932•3222
Monday–Friday 8:00 am–9:00 pm, Saturday & Sunday 8:00 am–8:00 pm
V, MC, AE, Debit, $
[see Chains (Big & Small) for main entry on p. 49]

CHOCOLATE & SWEETS

MacKay's Ice Cream

Established: 1948 • Owners: Robyn & Rhona MacKay
220–1 Street West, Cochrane
Phone: 932•2455
mid-May–mid-September: Monday–Sunday 10:00 am–10:00 pm
mid-September–early-May: Monday–Sunday 10:00 am–6:00 pm
V, MC, Debit, $

EATING ice cream can be a chance to taste history. Cochrane's ice cream emporium, MacKay's, is in its second generation of vending top-line traditional and more modern flavours. In 1983, sisters Robyn and Rhona took over from their father, founder Jimmy MacKay, who made ice cream in the old Red & White general store after he returned home from World War II with his Scottish bride.

Advance order an ice cream cake, buy a liter tub, or slurp back a cone. Stake out space on an old-timey porch bench, and listen to the pace of small-town life; a record 4,500 cones sold one sunny Sunday is the sound of happiness in summertime. It's all about mouth feel, and that depends on whipping cream and air. Whether you lean to maple walnut, Alberta-grown Saskatoon berry, or Philippine *halo-halo*, a pair of double scoops will set you back less than a sawbuck ($10), and the rubbernecking is free.

• *House Specialties*: Premium ice creams.
• *Also Available*: **Bon Ton Meat Market, Buttercream Bake Shoppe, Calgary Farmer's Market, Heaslip Venture Meats Ltd., The Liberated Cook, Planet Organic Market, Second to None Meats** in Calgary, **Nutter's Bulk & Natural Foods** and **Railway Deli** in Canmore, and **Bison Mountain Bistro & General Store** in Banff.
www.mackaysicecream.com

COFFEE & TEA

Cochrane Coffee Traders

Established: 1991 • Owners: Jeff & Danielle Genung
114–2 Avenue West, Cochrane
Phone: 932•1695
Monday 6:00 am–9:30 pm, Wednesday–Friday 6:00 am–6:00 pm
Thursday 6:00 am–10:00 pm
Saturday 7:00 am–6:00 pm, Sunday 9:00 am–6:00 pm
Cheque, $

GET your fair trade and organic beans, roasted at the wholesale location, sold at retail here. While here, stop and sit: enjoy house-baked muffins and squares, baked goods, and choose loose-leaf teas—black, green, white, *rooibos* and *tisanes*—to take away. If you need home brewing tea and coffee equipment, a small collection is available. For beans to go, phone ahead and ask for home delivery to Calgary and Cochrane, available once a week.
• *House Specialties*: In-house roasting fair-trade and organic coffee beans.
• *Also Available*: 117 River Avenue, Cochrane (roasterie), **Amaranth Whole Foods Market**, **Community Natural Foods**, **Planet Organic Market**, **Second to None Meats**, **SPUD** and **Sunterra Quality Food Markets**.

Java Jamboree

Established: 2002 • Owner: Les Jaworski
9, 312–5 Avenue West (Cochrane Towne Square), Cochrane
Phone: 932•6240
Monday–Friday 7:00 am–9:00 pm
Saturday 8:00 am–6:00 pm, Sunday 9:00 am–6:00 pm
V, MC, AE, Debit, $

THIS is my favourite funky coffee bar, despite its location buried at the centre of a mall. Inside, comfy couches await, along with internet access, cool lighting, helpful staff, a gallery of art for sale on its walls (and Baltic amber jewelry too, in a glass case) and a style all of its own. While you wait for your coffee, admire the photos of latté art, and browse the shelves for Coppeneur chocolate, loose tea, teapots, and Moka coffee makers. This shop also sells a unique type of Indian coffee: monsoon beans are earthy, low-acid and spicy. "Monsooning" refers to a super-premium process of drying that reproduces the effects of the old sailing ships' environments as they carried beans in their hold to ports around the world. To accompany his beverages, Les brings in desserts from **Amandine Bakery & Pastry** and **Decadent Desserts Inc.**
• *House Specialties*: Indian shade-grown Malabar Gold monsoon beans from *Josuma Coffee Co.* in San Francisco.
• *Also Available*: Kawa, 1338–8 Street SW, Calgary.

FARMERS' MARKETS

Cochrane Farmers' Market*

Established: 2000 • Rotating Volunteer Manager
Highway 2A (Cochrane Ranche & Visitors' Centre), Cochrane
Phone: 932•4705 (June–September only)
June–early September: Saturday 9:00 am–1:00 pm
$ only

MAKE 'N' TAKE MEALS/HMRs

Twisted Basil Food Group Inc.

Established: 2006 • Owners: Leslie Thorson, Renée Christian,
Monique Miller & Kathleen Carter
208–3 Avenue West, Cochrane
Phone: 932•6727 or (877) 932•6727
Market & Deli: Monday–Friday 10:00 am–7:00 pm, Saturday 9:00 am–6:00 pm
V, MC, Debit, Cheque, $

BEGUN by four sisters, this multi-faceted business keeps all siblings deeply involved. The 5-year plan is growth—a foothold in south Calgary in 2008, then community corner stores in towns around the province. The current Cochrane store sets the tone—quaint, a little homespun, accessible without snob appeal, but deeply organic at its core.

Shop in person or online for groceries and ready-to eat fare. Selections includes a wide range of products—largely organic, locally-produced, and seasonal as available—including sausages from **Spolumbo's Fine Foods & Italian Deli**, and dairy products from **Vital Green Farms** and **Fairwinds Farm**. Fresh produce is supplied by **Blue Mountain Biodynamic Farms**, **Gull Valley Greenhouse**, **Lund's Organic Farm**, and **Poplar Bluff Farm**.

Some baked goods are from **Bernie's Bavarian Bakery**, **Byblos Bakery**, and **Lakeview Bakery** whereas others are baked in-house, including muffins, cookies and pies, made with *spelt* and *kamut*. "Knotty Twists," are yummy yeast-risen cinnamon twists. House-made "eat-more-healthy" bars are included as a treat inside each delivery bin, as an incentive and thank you for delivery clients.

Look for prepared foods and a growing range of HMRs for busy lifestyles. Choose á la carte ready-to-eat meals or meal kits of ingredients, chopped and measured to feed four. Ten ethnic selections include Thai, Indian, and Mexican dishes.

The sisters have their own community promise program (CPP) thru Family Community Services, providing a weekly meal to a different family in need or in transition.

For delivery of groceries and meals, order by Tuesday evening for deliveries later the same week. Deliveries to Canmore addresses are made on Wednesday evenings; deliveries to Airdrie, Bragg Creek, Calgary, and Cochrane are made on Thursday afternoons and evenings.

- *House Specialties*: Home delivery of organic local ingredients, HMR meals and prepared ingredient "kits," soups, baked goods, house-made canned preserves, organic canned goods, cubes of frozen smoothies— in non-dairy and dairy versions.

www.twistedbasil.com

KITCHENWARE

Pots 'n' Peppers

Established: 1995 • Owners: Clair Breeze & Alex Souvairan
212–1 Street West, Cochrane
Phone: 932•1175
Monday–Saturday 10:00 am–5:30 pm, Sunday noon–5:00 pm
V, MC, Debit, $

LARGER than its sister shop, **The Colourful Cook**, in Canmore, Pots 'n' Peppers is also a well-stocked shop. This location simply has more room to carry more specialty foods, and a wider range of knives, tableware, cookbooks, Le Creuset and Emile Henri stove and ovenware. A select range of electrical appliances includes Cuisinart, Bosch, Krups, and Gaggia. Dress your table in linen, sharpen your knife, choose good hand towels, browse a book.

- *Also Available*: **The Colourful Cook**, 103–104, 721–8 Street, Canmore.

www.potsnpeppers.ca

Food Flicks

IKE THE DUTCH MASTERS' PAINTINGS of ripe fruit and overripe game, food films are invariably about more than food. They are a wonderful medium for examining some of life's big things—love, sex, friendship, family, fidelity. Food films serve us our commonality. We all eat. We all love. We all dream. Along with a story, food movies tell us of ourselves. Here are my top ten favourites. Cook something special beforehand.

Babette's Feast (Babette's Gaestebud)

1 A woman chef with a secret past, a stunningly remote and austere location, and icy neighbours committed to self-denial. I love this story of generosity—how fabulous food, lovingly made by a talented chef, transforms neighbours and guests. Written and directed by Gabriel Axel, in 1987, based on a story by Karen Blixen, aka Isak Dinesen.

Big Night

2 It is more than the music and the re-creation of 1950s New Jersey that rings true for me in this story of siblings. What counts in this lovely movie is a chef's passion for authenticity, and the realization that life goes on. The best, and most tender scene is the final one, when the brothers share an omelet in the kitchen. *Big Night* was made in 1996, co-directed by Stanley Tucci, who plays one of the brothers.

Tampopo

3 Wildly funny, this campy 1986 movie made by Juzo Itami sends up "spaghetti Westerns." I loved the unlikely friendship, and I loved the café scenes of making and eating noodles. Be pre-armed with big bowls of noodles to slurp and share.

Eat Drink Man Woman

4 Ang Lee's story of a Chinese chef estranged from his children is visually and emotionally involving. His breath-taking kitchen scenes—the full pots, the flashing cleaver—remind me of meals I have cooked for my own family to tell them that I love them. The 1994 original completely outshines the 2001 remake, *Tortilla Soup*, directed by Maria Ripoll and Lulu Zezza.

Like Water For Chocolate

5 This slow-moving and erotic flick is a sexy Mexican portrait of love denied, invoking the power of food to make tangible our heart's true feelings. Don't watch it alone, for all the good reasons of *amore*. Directed in 1993 by Alfonso Arau, based on Laura Esquivel's novel.

Documentaries & TV Series

FOOD TV series worth finding on DVD include *Chef!* and *Pie in the Sky*, both good British comedies. Notable documentaries include: Debra Koons Garcia's *The Future of Food*; Craig Noble's *Tableland*; Nobel prize winner Al Gore's *An Inconvenient Truth*; *Fast Food Nation* by Richard Linklater, based on Eric Schlosser's book of the same title; Morgan Spurlock's *Supersize Me*; *The Gleaners and I* by Agnes Varda; and *Bad Seed: The Truth About Our Food*. Food pros might like *L'Invention de la Cuisine* by Paul Lacoste.

Mostly Martha (Bella Martha)

6 A tightly wound German woman chef is left holding the bag— her young niece—when her sister dies. For me, the true star of the show was the unflinching portrayal of a chef's obsession with her work. Sandra Nettelbeck's 2000 version is more believable than the 2007 remake, *No Reservations*, starring Catherine Zeta-Jones.

Moonstruck

7 Vintage Cher. Eating Italian. Nicolas Cage as an over-the-top opera-loving one-handed baker. Affairs, betrayal, keeping faith, mothers and sons. Oh, and falling in love. What's not to like? Uncork a good Barolo first. Made by Norman Jewison in 1987.

Stranger Than Fiction

8 This wacky flick reminds me of the redemptive power of freshly baked cookies, and that geeky guys can grow into sensitive friends and lovers. Directed in 2006 by Marc Forster, this story interweaves writing and baking with love and taxes. Ha! Real life.

Chocolat

9 It feels very much like a fairytale for grownups, lit by optimism—and unaccountable magic—despite the meanness of humanity. This portrayal of small-town France made me want to renew my passport, cross the ocean and eat chocolates. Made in 2000, directed by Lasse Hallström.

The Cook, The Thief, His Wife and Her Lover

10 Not very much fun but compelling all the same. I squirmed through this grim movie set in a dungeon-esque restaurant, but I loved the arresting colour-shifts as characters moved from room to room. All the characters were unlikeable, although I was captivated by the fabulous Helen Mirren's tense performance. Made in 1989, written and directed by Peter Greenaway.

The Lists

A business name in **bold** indicates the location of the business profile.

ASIAN

NORTHEAST
T&T Market

SOUTHEAST
Can Fung Oriental Foods & Fresh Meats
Hang Fung Foods
Hiêp Hòa Asian Foods
Loriz Pilipino Bakery & Convenience
  Store
Lucky Supermarket
Nha Trang Market
Shun Fat ("88") International Market
Tatak Pinoy Food Store

SOUTHWEST
Arirang Oriental Foods, Transocean
  Trading Co. Ltd.

NORTHWEST
Lambda Oriental Foods & Market
Tops 100 Supermarket

BAKERIES

CITY WIDE
Cakes For All Occasions

NORTHEAST
Amandine Bakery & Pastry
Byblos Bakery
City Bakery (Calgary) Ltd.
Latin American Empanadas
Lina's Italian Market & Cappuccino Bar
Melly's Bakery Café
Rolymie Bakery
Shaheen Grocery & Kabuli Naan
Urban Baker (The)

SOUTHEAST
Atlantic Pacific Fish Market & Bakery
Euro Pastry
Golden Happiness Bakery
Günther's Fine Baking Ltd.
Jing Jing Bakery
Ladybug Belgian Pâtisserie (A)

Loriz Pilipino Bakery & Convenience
  Store
Nectar Desserts
Pies Plus Café
Simple Simon Pies (Crossroads Market)

SOUTHWEST
Barel's Bakery & Nosh Ltd.
Bianky's Bakery
Brûlée Pâtisserie
Buttercream Bake Shoppe
COBS Bread
Crave Cookies & Cupcakes
Daily Bagel (at CFM)
Decadent Desserts Inc.
Glamorgan Bakery
Heritage Bakery & Deli
Ladybug Belgian Pâtisserie (A)
Lakeview Bakery
Manuel Latruwe Belgian Pâtisserie &
  Bread Shop
Montreal Bagels
Mueller's European Delicatessen Bakery &
  Imports Ltd.
Pearson's Berry Farm & Gordo's Foods
Rustic Sourdough Bakery
Simple Simon Pies
Tutti Frutti (at CFM)

NORTHWEST
COBS Bread
Crave Cookies & Cupcakes
Edelweiss Village
Lazy Loaf & Kettle
Maxima Bakery & Cake House [*see* **Lambda
  Oriental Foods & Market**]
Prairie Mill Bread Company
Wayne's Bagels

BOW VALLEY & BEYOND
Bernie's Bavarian Bakery, Canmore
Gourmet Croissant, Canmore
Griesser Spoon Custom Catering/Railway
  Deli, Canmore
JK Bakery, Canmore
Rocky Mountain Bagel Company, Canmore
Sugar Flowers & Elegant Cakes,
  Chestermere Lake

Sweet Madeira, Canmore
Wild Flour Artisan Bakery & Café, Banff

BOOZE

NORTHEAST
CSN Wine & Spirits
Merlo Vinoteca Inc.

SOUTHEAST
Big Rock Brewery
Willow Park Wines & Spirits

SOUTHWEST
Bin 905
Britannia Wine Merchants
Cellar Fine Wines & Spirits Inc. (The)
J Webb Wine Merchant/J Webb Market
    Wines
Metrovino
Richmond Hill Wines
Wild Rose Brewery
Willow Park Wines & Spirits
Wine Cellar South (The)

NORTHWEST
Kensington Wine Market

BOW VALLEY & BEYOND
Banff Wine Store, Banff
Bumbleberry Orchard & Fieldstone Fruit
    Wines, Strathmore
Chinook Honey Company/Chinook Arch
    Meadery, Okotoks
Grizzly Paw Brewing Company, Canmore

CHAINS (BIG & SMALL)

Calgary Co-op
Canada Safeway
Costco
Real Canadian Superstore (The)
Sobeys/IGA

SOUTHWEST
Sunterra Quality Food Markets
Sunterra Marché
Sunterra Market
Sunterra Marketplace/Sunterra Grocery
    Delivery
Sunterra Petit Marché/Sunterra
    Catering-Calgary
Sunterra Village Marché

BOW VALLEY & BEYOND
Calgary Co-op, Airdrie
Calgary, Co-op, Strathmore
Canada Safeway, Airdrie
Canada Safeway, Banff
Canada Safeway, Chestermere Lake
Canada Safeway, Cochrane
IGA, Cochrane Valley
IGA, Nanton
IGA, Strathmore
Real Canadian Superstore (The), Airdrie
Sobeys, High River
Sobeys, Okotoks
Sobeys/IGA, Canmore

CHEESE & DAIRY

NORTHEAST
Italian Store
Lina's Italian Market & Cappuccino Bar

SOUTHEAST
Say Cheese Fromagerie Inc.
Springbank Cheese Company

SOUTHWEST
Cookbook Company Cooks (The)
Janice Beaton Fine Cheese
Kalamata Grocery Store
Matterhorn Imports
Mercato
Springbank Cheese Company
Sylvan Star Cheese Farm
West End Produce & Mideast Grocery

NORTHWEST
Edelweiss Village
Janice Beaton Fine Cheese
Springbank Cheese Company

BOW VALLEY & BEYOND
Bison Mountain Bistro & General Store,
    Banff
Fairwinds Farm, Fort Macleod
Sylvan Star Cheese Farm
Vital Green Farms, Picture Butte

CHOCOLATE & SWEETS

NORTHEAST
Chocolaterie Bernard Callebaut

SOUTHEAST
Chocolaterie Bernard Callebaut

Les Truffes au Chocolat
Nectar Desserts
Olivier's Candies

SOUTHWEST
Biscotti by Susan D
Chocolaterie Bernard Callebaut
Community Natural Foods
Cookbook Company Cooks (The)
Diabetic Depot & Bakery
Fiasco Gelato
Jammin' It Jams & Jellies (at CFM)
Les Truffes au Chocolat
Lewis Chocolates & Candies
MacKay's Ice Cream Shop (at CFM)
Manon's Leonidas
My Favourite Ice Cream Shoppe
Tutti Frutti (at CFM)

NORTHWEST
Amato Gelato
Boca Loca Fine Mexican Foods
Chocolaterie Bernard Callebaut
Diabetic Depot & Bakery
Edelweiss Village
Fiasco Gelato

BOW VALLEY & BEYOND
Chinook Honey Company/Chinook Arch
Meadery, Okotoks
Chocolaterie Bernard Callebaut, Banff
MacKay's Ice Cream Shop, Cochrane

COFFEE & TEA

CITY WIDE
Big Mountain Coffee Roasters
tnik teas

NORTHEAST
Ten Ren Tea & Ginseng Co. (Calgary)
Ltd.

SOUTHEAST
Fratello Coffee Co.
Tea Affair
Tea Trader

SOUTHWEST
Blends Coffee Roasters
Bumpy's Café
Phil & Sebastian Coffee Co. (at CFM)
Steeps, The Urban Teahouse
TotaliTea, The Tea Boutique
Tutti Frutti (at CFM)

NORTHWEST
Cadence
Oolong Tea House
Planet Coffee Roasters
Roasterie (The)
Tea & Collection

BOW VALLEY & BEYOND
Cochrane Coffee Traders, Cochrane
Java Jamboree, Cochrane

COOKING SCHOOLS & CLASSES

CITY WIDE
Calgary Co-op
Inter-Course Chef Services
Sunterra Quality Food Markets

SOUTHEAST
Lee Valley Tools Ltd.
Willow Park Wines & Spirits

SOUTHWEST
Calgary Co-op (Midtown Market)
Cookbook Company Cooks (The)
Happy Cooker
Sunterra Village Marché
Talisman Centre

NORTHWEST
Antoinetta's Cooking School
Boca Loca Fine Mexican Foods
**SAIT Polytechnic Adult Continuing
Education**

BOW VALLEY & BEYOND
Fuze Finer Dining, Banff

CULINARY TOURS

CITY WIDE
Acquired Tastes Food Tours
Foodie Tootles, City Palate [*see* **Buffalo
Horn Ranch, The Cookbook
Company Cooks**]

SOUTHEAST
**International Avenue Business
Revitalization Zone**
"Around the World in 35 Blocks"
**Olympic Plaza Cultural District's First
Thursdays**

SOUTHWEST
Cookbook Company Cooks (The)

BOW VALLEY & BEYOND
Fuze Finer Dining

EAST INDIAN

NORTHEAST
A-1 Spice & Movie Centre
Al-Noor Halal Meat & Grocery
APNA Punjab Groceries & Movies
Bangla Bazaar
Bombay Sweet House
Central Halal Meat
Desi Bazaar
Lahore Foods & Halal Meats
OK Food & Produce
Sabzi Mandi Eastern & Western Groceries
Thumbs Up Foods

SOUTHEAST
Calgary Sweet House & Restaurant
Fairmount Spiceland
New Sunrise Spices & Halal Meat

SOUTHWEST
Raja Foods Grocery & Halal

NORTHWEST
Dalbrent Spice Rack

EUROPEAN

NORTHEAST
A Touch of Italy (ATOI)
Italian Store
Italian Supermarket Ltd.
Lina's Italian Market & Cappuccino Bar

SOUTHEAST
Atlantic Pacific Fish Market & Bakery
Bite Groceteria
DinoRosa's Italian Market
Dutch Cash & Carry
Euro Pastry
European Deli (Crossroads Market)
   [see Jan's Meats & Deli]
Hungarian Deli
Illichmann's Sausage Shop
Links Deli (Crossroads Market)
   [see Paolini's Sausage & Meats]
Old Fashioned Meat Products &
   Delicatessen

Paolini's Sausage & Meats
Polcan Meat Products & Delicatessen

SOUTHWEST
Cookbook Company Cooks (The)
Francesco's Italian Food Store & Deli
Heritage Bakery & Deli
Mercato
Mueller's European Delicatessen Bakery
   & Imports Ltd.

NORTHWEST
British Pantry
Edelweiss Village
Jan's Meats & Deli

BOW VALLEY & BEYOND
Mountain Mercato Specialty Food Market,
   Canmore

FARMERS' MARKETS

SOUTHEAST
Blackfoot Farmers' Market
Crossroads Market
Green Market*
South Fish Creek Recreation Association
   Farmers' Market

SOUTHWEST
Calgary Farmers' Market*

NORTHWEST
Bearspaw Farmers' Market*
Grassroots Northland Farmers' Market*
Hillhurst-Sunnyside Farmers' Market*

BOW VALLEY & BEYOND
Bison Courtyard, Banff [see Bison
   Mountain Bistro & General Store,
   Banff]
Black Diamond (Foothills Country)
   Market*
Brooks Farmers' Market*
Caroline Farmers' Market*
Claresholm Farmers' Market*
Cochrane Farmers' Market*
Didsbury & District Farmers' Market*
Drumheller Farmers' Market*
High River Farmers' Market
Innisfail Farmers' Market*
Millarville Farmers' Market*
Olds Farmers' Market*
Strathmore Farmers' Market*
Sundre Farmers' Market*
Sylvan Lake Farmers' Market*

FARMGATE SALES

SOUTHEAST
Bee Prepared Honey Farms, Calgary SE
Premium Organic Farms Inc., Calgary SE

BOW VALLEY & BEYOND

POINTS NORTH
Bles-Wold Dairy & Bles-Wold Yoghurt,
  Lacombe
Blue Mountain Biodynamic Farms,
  Carstairs
Buffalo Horn Ranch, Olds
Cakadu Heritage Lamb, Innisfail
DNA Gardens, Elnora
Edgar Farms, (Innisfail Growers), Innisfail
Jungle (The), [Innisfail Growers], Innisfail
Ladybug Organic Gardens/Bed &
  Breakfast, Blackfalds
Pearson's Berry Farm & Gordo's Foods,
  Bowden
Purple Ridge Farm, Airdrie
Staniforth Summerberry Farm, Eckville
Sylvan Star Cheese Farm, Sylvan Lake
TLC Farm Katahdins, Sundre
Twisted Willow Berry Farm, Delburne

POINTS EAST
Bumbleberry Orchard Ltd. & Fieldstone
  Fruit Wines, Strathmore
Serviceberry Farms, Strathmore
Spragg's Meat Shop, Rosemary
Sun Valley Farm, Drumheller

POINTS SOUTH
Bloomin' Inn, Pincher Creek
Broek Pork Acres, Coalhurst
Broxburn Vegetables & Café, Lethbridge
Chinook Honey Company/Chinook Arch
  Meadery, Okotoks
Driview Farms, Fort Macleod
Ewe-Nique Farms, Champion
Fairwinds Farm, Fort Macleod
Highwood Valley Ranch, High River
Kayben Farms, Okotoks
Paradise Hill Farm, Nanton
Room2Grow, Glenwood
Saskatoon Farm, DeWinton
Winter's Turkeys, Dalemead

FISHMONGERS

NORTHEAST
T&T Market

SOUTHEAST
Atlantic Pacific Fish Market & Bakery
Eastern Lake
Lucky Supermarket
North Sea Fish Market

SOUTHWEST
Boyd's Lobster Shop
North Sea Fish Market

NORTHWEST
Billingsgate Fresh Fish Specialists
King's Seafood Distributors [inside
  Lambda Oriental Foods & Market]

BOW VALLEY & BEYOND
Cunningham's Scotch Smoked Fish,
  Pincher Creek

GEMS

SOUTHWEST
Cookbook Company Cooks (The)

GREENGROCERS

CITYWIDE
Hotchkiss Herbs & Produce

NORTHEAST
Calgary Produce Market
Lina's Italian Market & Cappuccino Bar
T&T Market

SOUTHEAST
Chongo's Produce Market
Fairmount Spiceland
Market Produce
Shun Fat ("88") International Market
Hotchkiss Herbs & Produce
Premium Organic Farms Inc.

SOUTHWEST
Blush Lane (in CFM)
Boca Loca Fine Mexican Foods
Cherry Pit [see Calgary Farmers' Market]
Community Natural Foods
Cookbook Company Cooks (The)
Gull Valley Greenhouse (in CFM)

Habina's Harvest [*see* **Calgary Farmers' Market**]
Hotchkiss Herbs & Produce
Innisfail Growers [*see* **Edgar Farms, The Jungle, Calgary Farmers' Market, Bearspaw Farmers' Market**]
Lund's Organic Produce (in CFM)
Mercato
Planet Organic Market
Sunterra Quality Food Markets
Walker's Own (in CFM)

NORTHWEST
Boca Loca Fine Mexican Foods
Lambda Oriental Foods & Market
Tops 100 Supermarket

BOW VALLEY & BEYOND
Alexandra's Butterfly Garden, Black Diamond
Blue Mountain Biodynamic Farms, Carstairs
Broxburn Vegetables & Café, Lethbridge
Bumbleberry Orchard Ltd. & Fieldstone Fruit Wines, Strathmore
DNA Gardens, Elnora
Edgar Farms, (Innisfail Growers), Innisfail
Gull Valley Greenhouse, Gull Lake
Hotchkiss Herbs & Produce, Calgary SE
Jungle (The), [Innisfail Growers], Innisfail
Kayben Farms, Okotoks
Ladybug Organic Gardens/Bed & Breakfast, Blackfalds
Lund's Organic Produce, Innisfail
Paradise Hill Farm, Nanton
Pearson's Berry Farm & Gordo's Foods, Bowden
Poplar Bluff Organic Farm, Strathmore
Premium Organic Farms Inc., Calgary SE
Purple Ridge Farm, Airdrie
Room2Grow, Glenwood
Saskatoon Farm, DeWinton
Serviceberry Farms, Strathmore
Staniforth Summerberry Farm, Eckville
Sun Valley Farm, Drumheller
Twisted Willow Berry Farm, Delburne

HOME DELIVERY

CITY WIDE
Buffalo Horn Ranch
Calgary Co-op
Country Lane Farms Ltd.
Farm Fresh Organics Home Delivery Ltd.

Hotchkiss Herbs & Produce
Small Potatoes Urban Delivery (SPUD)
Sobey's/IGA
Sunterra Marketplace/Sunterra Grocery Delivery
tnik tea

SOUTHEAST
Lee Valley Tools Ltd.

SOUTHWEST
Baby Gourmet
Simple Simon Pies
Spoon Fed Soup
Sunterra Marketplace/Sunterra Grocery Delivery

BOW VALLEY & BEYOND
Cochrane Coffee Traders, Cochrane
Twisted Basil Food Group Inc., Cochrane

KITCHENWARE

NORTHEAST
A Touch of Italy (ATOI)
Dragons Den Knives
Geanel Restaurant Supplies Ltd.
Handles & More
Lina's Italian Market & Cappuccino Bar
Trail Appliances

SOUTHEAST
Brown's Food Service Equipment Sales
Compleat Cook (The)
Crown Restaurant Equipment
DinoRosa's Italian Market
Fratello Coffee Co.
Hendrix Foodservice Equipment & Supply Professionals
House of Knives
Ikea
Knifewear
Lee Valley Tools Ltd.
Mr. Cappuccino
Russell Food Equipment
Trail Appliances

SOUTHWEST
Art of Hardware (ah!)
Compleat Cook (The)
Cookbook Company Cooks (The)
Happy Cooker
Knifery (The)
Target Knives & Survival
Williams-Sonoma Canada Inc.

NORTHWEST
B & J Restaurant Supply Ltd.
Boca Loca Fine Mexican Foods
Compleat Cook (The)
Cutting Edge Cutlery
Happy Cooker
House of Knives

BOW VALLEY & BEYOND
A Touch of Italy (ATOI), Okotoks
Colourful Cook (The), Canmore
Fuze Finer Dining, Banff
Pots 'n' Peppers, Cochrane
Provenance, Black Diamond

LATIN, CARIBBEAN & AFRICAN

NORTHEAST
De Chosen African Market
Joycee's Caribbean Foods
TK's African Products Inc.

SOUTHEAST
Atlantic Pacific Fish Market & Bakery
El Bombazo Latino Market
Jubba-Nile Supermarket
La Tiendona
Lloyd's Patty Plus
Mayfair Foods

SOUTHWEST
Boca Loca Fine Mexican Foods
Cookbook Company Cooks (The)
Haifa Delicatessen & Caterers/Kavin's
   Kosher Meats

NORTHWEST
Boca Loca Fine Mexican Foods

LOCAL PRODUCERS

BOOZE
Big Rock Brewery, Calgary SE
Bumbleberry Orchard Ltd. & Fieldstone
   Fruit Wines, Strathmore
Chinook Honey Company/Chinook Arch
   Meadery, Okotoks
Grizzly Paw Brewing Company, Canmore
Wild Rose Brewery, Calgary SW

CHEESE & DAIRY
Bles-Wold Dairy & Bles-Wold Yoghurt,
   Lacombe
Fairwinds Farm, Fort Macleod

Sylvan Star Cheese Farm, Sylvan Lake,
   Calgary SW
Vital Green Farms, Picture Butte

CHOCOLATE & SWEETS
Biscotti by Susan D, Calgary SW
Bee Prepared Honey Farms, Calgary SE
Chinook Honey Company/Chinook Arch
   Meadery, Okotoks

FISHMONGERS
Cunningham's Scotch Smoked Fish,
   Pincher Creek

GREENGROCERS
Alexandra's Butterfly Garden, Black
   Diamond
Blue Mountain Biodynamic Farms,
   Carstairs
Broxburn Vegetables & Café, Lethbridge
Bumbleberry Orchard Ltd. & Fieldstone
   Fruit Wines, Strathmore
DNA Gardens, Elnora
Edgar Farms, [Innisfail Growers], Innisfail
Gull Valley Greenhouse, Gull Lake (in
   CFM)
Hotchkiss Herbs & Produce, Calgary SE
Jungle (The), [Innisfail Growers], Innisfail
Kayben Farms, Okotoks
Ladybug Organic Gardens/Bed &
   Breakfast, Blackfalds
Lund's Organic Produce, Innisfail (in
   CFM)
Paradise Hill Farm, Nanton
Pearson's Berry Farm & Gordo's Foods,
   Bowden
Poplar Bluff Organic Farm, Strathmore
Premium Organic Farms Inc., Calgary SE
Purple Ridge Farm, Airdrie
Room2Grow, Glenwood
Saskatoon Farm, DeWinton
Serviceberry Farms, Strathmore
Staniforth Summerberry Farm, Eckville
Sun Valley Farm, Drumheller
Twisted Willow Berry Farm, Delburne

MEAT & GAME
Bloomin' Inn, Pincher Creek
Broek Pork Acres, Coalhurst
Buffalo Horn Ranch, Olds
Cakadu Heritage Lamb, Innisfail
Canadian Rocky Mountain Ranch,
   DeWinton
Carmen Creek Gourmet Meats, Calgary
   SW
Country Lane Farms Ltd., Strathmore

Diamond Willow Organics Ltd., Pincher
  Creek
Driview Farms, Fort Macleod
Elbow Falls Wapiti, Priddis
Ewe-Nique Farms, Champion
Grazin' Acres, Two Hills (in CFM)
Highwood Valley Ranch, High River
Hoven Farms, Eckville (in CFM)
Old Country Sausage Shop, Raymond
Premium Organic Farms Inc., Calgary SE
Room2Grow, Glenwood
Saskatoon Farm, DeWinton
Spragg's Meat Shop, Rosemary
Sunworks Farm, Armena
TLC Farm Katahdins, Sundre
Valta Bison, Valhalla Centre
Wapiti Ways, Calgary NW
Winter's Turkeys, Dalemead

OTHERS

Brassica Mustard, Calgary NE
Grainworks Inc., Vulcan
Hamilton's Barley Flour, Olds
Highwood Crossing Farm Ltd.,
  Aldersyde
Soft Path Cuisine, Calgary NW
Zora's Lemonade Ltd., Calgary SW

MAKE 'n' TAKE MEALS/HMRs

CITY WIDE

Baby Gourmet
Dashing Dishes Inc.

NORTHEAST

Cedars Deli
Italian Store
Lina's Italian Market & Cappuccino Bar
Main Dish (The)

SOUTHWEST

Copper Pot Creations
Infuse Catering/Forage Foods
Mercato
Mise En Place
Planet Organic Market
Red Tree
Stock & Sauce Co. (in CFM)
Sunterra Quality Food Markets

NORTHWEST

Bon Ton Meat Market
Cedars Deli
Liberated Cook (The)
Italian Store
Planet Organic Market

BOW VALLEY & BEYOND

Bison Mountain Bistro & General Store
Griesser Spoon Custom Catering/Railway
  Deli
Route 40 Soup Company, Turner Valley
Twisted Basil Food Group Inc., Cochrane
Valbella Meats/Valbella's Deli & Café,
  Canmore

MEAT & GAME

CITY WIDE

Buffalo Horn Ranch
Calgary Co-op
Canada Safeway
Country Lane Farms Ltd.

NORTHEAST

Almadina Grocery
Al-Noor Halal Meat & Grocery
APNA Desi Meat Market
Bangla Bazaar
Calgary Meats & Deli
Central Halal Meat
Chahine Supermarket
Chinook Edge Lamb & Goat
Costco
Hage's Mideast Foods & Halal Meats
Horizon Meats
Lahore Foods & Halal Meats
Mann Brothers Meat Shop
Rocky's Meats & Delicatessen
T&T Market

SOUTHEAST

Better Butcher
Chinook Edge Lamb & Goat
Costco
European Deli (Crossroads Market)
  [*see* **Jan's Meats & Deli**]
Green Cedars
Heaslip Venture Meats Ltd.
Hungarian Deli
Illichmann's Sausage Shop
Links Deli (Crossroads Market) [*see*
  Paolini's Sausage & Meats]
Market Produce
New Sunrise Spices & Halal Meat
**Old Fashioned Meat Products &
  Delicatessen**
Paolini's Sausage & Meats
Polcan Meat Products & Delicatessen
Premium Organic Farms Inc.
Pyramids Halal Products & Wholesale/
  Retail Mideast Market
Regina's Fine Meats

Spolumbo's Fine Foods & Italian Deli
Valta Bison
Vin Khon BBQ [*see* **Shun Fat ("88")**
International Market]

SOUTHWEST
Barel's Bakery & Nosh Ltd.
Carmen Creek Gourmet Meats
Cookbook Company Cooks (The)
Grazin' Acres (at CFM)
Haifa Delicatessen & Caterers/Kavin's
   Kosher Meats
Hoven Farms (at CFM)
MacEwan's Meats
Missing Link Extraordinary Sausage
Mueller's European Delicatessen Bakery &
   Imports Ltd.
Old Country Sausage Shop
Planet Organic Market
Second to None Meats
Sunterra Quality Food Markets
Sunworks Farm (at CFM)
Valta Bison (at CFM)

NORTHWEST
Amaranth Whole Foods Market
Bon Ton Meat Market
Costco
Edelweiss Village
Fat Kee [*see* **Lambda Oriental Foods &**
   Market]
Gour-Mart Meat Shop
Jan's Meats & Deli
Master Meats
Second to None Meats
Wai's BBQ Centre [*see* **Tops 100**
   Supermarket]
Wapiti Ways

BOW VALLEY & BEYOND
Bloomin' Inn, Pincher Creek
Buffalo Horn Ranch, Olds
The Butcher Shoppe, (The) Airdrie
Cakadu Heritage Lamb, Innisfail
Canadian Rocky Mountain Ranch,
   DeWinton
Country Lane Farms Ltd., Strathmore
Diamond Willow Organics Ltd., Pincher
   Creek
Driview Farms, Fort Macleod
Elbow Falls Wapiti, Priddis
Grazin' Acres, Two Hills
Ewe-Nique Farms, Champion
Griesser Spoon Custom Catering/Railway
   Deli, Canmore
Highwood Valley Ranch, High River

Hoven Farms, Eckville
Old Country Sausage Shop, Raymond
Spragg's Meat Shop, Rosemary
TLC Farm Katahdins, Sundre
Valbella Meats/Valbella's Deli & Café,
   Canmore
Winter's Turkeys, Dalemead

MIDDLE EASTERN

NORTHEAST
Almadina Grocery
Calgary Produce Market
Cedars Deli
Chahine Supermarket
Hage's Mideast Foods & Halal Meats
Shaheen Grocery & Kabuli Naan
Village Pita Bakery & Mediterranean
   Food Store

SOUTHEAST
Green Cedars
New Sunrise Spices & Halal Meat
Pyramids Halal Products & Wholesale/
   Retail Mideast Market
SOMAR Mediterranean Market

SOUTHWEST
Atlas Specialty Supermarket & Persian
   Cuisine
Haifa Delicatessen & Caterers/Kavin's
   Kosher Meats
Kalamata Grocery Store
Luxor Emporium & Café
Shaganappi Grocery
West End Produce & Mideast Grocery

NORTHWEST
A & A Foods & Deli
Dalbrent Spice Rack

ORGANICS

CITYWIDE
Calgary Co-op
Canada Safeway
Farm Fresh Organics Home Delivery Ltd.
Hotchkiss Herbs & Produce
Real Canadian Superstore (The)
Small Potatoes Urban Delivery (SPUD)

SOUTHWEST
Blush Lane (at CFM)
Community Natural Foods

Grazin' Acres (at CFM)
Hoven Farms (at CFM)
Lakeview Bakery
Lund's Organic Produce (at CFM)
Planet Organic Market
Sunterra Quality Food Markets
Sunworks Farm [x-ref CFM]

NORTHWEST
Amaranth Whole Foods Market
Planet Organic Market
Prairie Mill Bread Company
Sunnyside Market
Urban Baker (The)

BOW VALLEY & BEYOND
Bernie's Bavarian Bakery, Cochrane
Diamond Willow Organics, Ltd., Pincher
   Creek
Fairwinds Farm, Fort Macleod
Grainworks Inc., Vulcan
Grazin' Acres, Two Hills
Hamilton's Barley Flour, Olds
Highwood Crossing Farm Ltd., Aldersyde
Ladybug Organic Gardens/Bed &
   Breakfast, Blackfalds
Nutter's Bulk & Natural Foods, Canmore
Nutter's Bulk & Natural Foods, Okotoks
Poplar Bluff Organic Farm, Strathmore
Route 40 Soup Company, Turner Valley
Sweet Madeira, Canmore
Twisted Basil Food Group Inc., Cochrane
Vital Green Farms, Picture Butte
Wild Flour Artisan Bakery & Café, Banff
Winter's Turkeys, Dalemead

PERSONAL CHEFS & CATERERS

CITY WIDE
Dine In Personal Chef Service
Inter-Course Chef Services
Judy Wood Cuisine
King Brisket Boy
Los Sabores de México/Flavours of
   Mexico Ltd.
Manna Catering Services
Meta4 Foods
Pennache
Saffron Personal Chef Services
Savour the Flavours
Sunterra Petit Marché/Sunterra Catering-
   Calgary
Suppertime Solutions Personal Chef

NORTHEAST
Darryl Bennett, Chef for Hire
EthniCity Catering
Main Dish (The)

SOUTHEAST
Great Events Group
La Table du Chatelain Cuisine &
   Catering
See Catering/Catering Inc./A Gourmet
   Affair
Spolumbo's Fine Foods & Italian Deli

SOUTHWEST
Barel's Bakery & Nosh Ltd.
Copper Pot Creations
Devour Catering Inc.
**Haifa Delicatessen & Caterers/Kavin's
   Kosher Meats**
Indulge Catering
Infuse Catering/Forage Foods
Red Tree
Sunterra Petit Marché/Sunterra Catering-
   Calgary

NORTHWEST
Lazy Loaf & Kettle
Liberated Cook (The)
Red Tree

BOW VALLEY & BEYOND
Backcountry Bistro, Canmore
Culinary Adventures Catering, Canmore
Griesser Spoon Custom Catering/Railway
   Deli, Canmore
Homestead Chef (The), Carstairs

FOOD ORGANIZATIONS

Alberta Food Processors Association
   (AFPA)
Calgary Drop-In & Rehab Centre
Calgary Horticultural Society
Calgary Inter-Faith Food Bank Society
Calgary Meals on Wheels
Community Kitchen Program of
   Calgary
Dine Alberta
Feed the Hungry
Growing Food Security in Alberta
   (GFSA)
Inn from the Cold Society
L'Arche Cakewalk
Slow Food Calgary

FOOD FLICKS

Babette's Feast (Babette's Gaestebud)
Big Night
Tampopo
Eat Drink Man Woman
Like Water For Chocolate
Mostly Martha (Bella Martha)
Moonstruck
Stranger Than Fiction
Chocolat
The Cook, The Thief, His Wife and Her
    Lover

BOW VALLEY & BEYOND

POINTS NORTH

AIRDRIE
Chains (Big & Small):
Calgary Co-op
Canada Safeway
Real Canadian Superstore (The)
Farmgate Sales, Greengrocers:
Purple Ridge Farm
Farmgate Sales, Meat & Game:
Butcher Shoppe (The)

ARMENA
Local Producers, Meat & Game:
Sunworks Farm

BLACKFALDS
Farmgate Sales, Greengrocers:
Ladybug Organic Gardens/Bed &
    Breakfast

BOWDEN
Local Producers, Greengrocers:
Pearson's Berry Farm & Gordo's Foods

CAROLINE
Farmers' Markets:
Caroline Farmers' Market*

CARSTAIRS
Farmgate Sales, Greengrocers:
Blue Mountain Biodynamic Farms
Personal Chefs & Caterers:
Homestead Chef (The)

DELBURNE
Farmgate Sales, Greengrocers:
Twisted Willow Berry Farm

DIDSBURY
Farmers' Markets:
Didsbury & District Farmers' Market*

ECKVILLE
Farmgate Sales, Greengrocers:
Staniforth Summerberry Farm
Local Producers, Meat & Game:
Hoven Farms (at CFM)

ELNORA
Farmgate Sales, Greengrocers
DNA Gardens

GULL LAKE
Local Producers, Greengrocers:
Gull Valley Greenhouse (at CFM)

INNISFAIL
Farmers' Markets:
Innisfail Farmers' Market*
Farmgate Sales, Meat & Game:
Cakadu Heritage Lamb
Farmgate Sales, Greengrocers:
Edgar Farms, (Innisfail Growers)
Jungle (The), (Innisfail Growers)
Local Producers, Greengrocers:
Lund's Organic Produce (at CFM)

LACOMBE
Farmgate Sales, Cheese & Dairy:
Bles-Wold Dairy & Bles-Wold Yoghurt

OLDS
Farmers' Markets:
Olds Farmers' Market*
Farmgate Sales, Meat & Game:
Buffalo Horn Ranch
Local Producers, Organics:
Hamilton's Barley Flour

SUNDRE
Farmers' Markets:
Sundre Farmers' Market*
Farmgate Sales, Meat & Game:
TLC Farm Katahdins

SYLVAN LAKE
Farmgate Sales, Cheese & Dairy:
Sylvan Star Cheese Farm
Farmers' Markets:
Sylvan Lake Farmers' Market*

TWO HILLS
Local Producers, Meat & Game:
Grazin' Acres (at CFM)

VALHALLA CENTRE
Local Producers, Meat & Game:
Valta Bison

POINTS EAST

BROOKS
Farmers' Markets:
Brooks Farmers' Market*

CHESTERMERE LAKE
Bakeries:
Sugar Flowers & Elegant Cakes
Chains (Big & Small):
Canada Safeway

DALEMEAD
Farmgate Sales, Meat & Game:
Winter's Turkeys

DRUMHELLER
Farmers' Markets:
Drumheller Farmers' Market*
Farmgate Sales, Greengrocers:
Sun Valley Farm

ROSEMARY
Farmgate, Meat & Game:
Spragg's Meat Shop

STRATHMORE
Booze:
Bumbleberry Orchard Ltd. & Fieldstone
  Fruit Wines
Chains (Big & Small):
Calgary Co-op
IGA
Farmers' Markets:
Strathmore Farmers' Market*
Farmgate Sales, Greengrocers:
Serviceberry Farms
Local Producers, Greengrocers:
Bumbleberry Orchard Ltd. & Fieldstone
  Fruit Wines, Strathmore
Poplar Bluff Organic Farm
Local Producers, Meat & Game:
Country Lane Farms Ltd.

POINTS SOUTH

ALDERSYDE
Local Producers, Others:
Highwood Crossing Farm Ltd.

BLACK DIAMOND
Farmers' Markets:
Black Diamond (Foothills Country)
  Market*
Kitchenware:
Provenance
Local Producers, Greengrocers:
Alexandra's Butterfly Garden

CHAMPION
Farmgate Sales, Meat & Game:
Ewe-Nique Farms

CLARESHOLM
Farmers' Markets:
Claresholm Farmers' Market*

COALHURST
Farmgate Sales, Meat & Game:
Broek Pork Acres

DEWINTON
Farmgate Sales, Greengrocers:
Saskatoon Farm
Local Producers, Meat & Game:
Canadian Rocky Mountain Ranch

FORT MACLEOD
Farmgate Sales, Meat & Game:
Driview Farms
Farmgate Sales, Cheese & Dairy:
Fairwinds Farm

GLENWOOD
Farmgate Sales, Greengrocers
Room2Grow

HIGH RIVER
Chains (Big & Small):
Sobeys
Farmers' Markets:
High River Farmers' Market
Farmgate Sales, Meat & Game:
Highwood Valley Ranch

LETHBRIDGE
Farmgate Sales, Greengrocers:
Broxburn Vegetables & Café

MILLARVILLE
Farmers' Markets:
Millarville Farmers' Market*

NANTON
Chains (Big & Small):
IGA
Farmgate Sales, Greengrocers:
Paradise Hill Farm

OKOTOKS
Chains (Big & Small):
Sobeys
Farmgate Sales, Booze, Chocolates & Sweets:
Chinook Honey Company/Chinook
  Arch Meadery
Farmgate Sales, Greengrocers:
Kayben Farms
Kitcheware:
A Touch of Italy (ATOI), Okotoks
Organics:
Nutter's Bulk & Natural Foods

PICTURE BUTTE
Local Producers, Cheese & Dairy:
Vital Green Farms

PINCHER CREEK
Farmgate Sales, Meat & Game:
Bloomin' Inn
Local Producers, Fishmongers:
Cunningham's Scotch Smoked Fish
Local Producers, Meat & Game:
Diamond Willow Organics Ltd.

PRIDDIS
Local Producers, Meat & Game:
Elbow Falls Wapiti

RAYMOND
Local Producers, Meat & Game:
Old Country Sausage Shop

TURNER VALLEY
Make 'n' Take Meals/HMRs:
Route 40 Soup Company

VULCAN
Local Producers, Organics:
Grainworks Inc.

POINTS WEST

BANFF
Bakeries:
Wild Flour Artisan Bakery & Café
Booze:
Banff Wine Store
Cheese:
Bison Mountain Bistro & General Store
Cooking Schools & Classes:
Fuze Finer Dining
Chains (Big & Small):
Canada Safeway, Banff
Chocolate & Sweets:
Chocolaterie Bernard Callebaut

CANMORE
Bakeries:
Gourmet Croissant
JK Bakery
Rocky Mountain Bagel Company
Sweet Madeira
Booze:
Grizzly Paw Brewing Company
Chains (Big & Small):
Sobeys/IGA
European:
Mountain Mercato Specialty Food
  Market
Kitchenware:
Colourful Cook (The)
Meat & Game:
Griesser Spoon Custom Catering/
  Railway Deli
Valbella Meats/Valbella's Deli & Cafe
Organics:
Nutter's Bulk & Natural Foods
Personal Chefs & Caterers:
Backcountry Bistro
Culinary Adventures Catering

COCHRANE
Bakeries:
Bernie's Bavarian Bakery
Chains (Big & Small):
Canada Safeway
IGA, Cochrane Valley
Chocolate & Sweets:
MacKay's Ice Cream
Coffee & Tea:
Cochrane Coffee Traders
Java Jamboree
Farmers Markets:
Cochrane Farmers' Market*
Make 'n' Take Meals/HMRs:
Twisted Basil Food Group Inc.
Kitchenware:
Pots 'n' Peppers

CALGARY FARMERS' MARKET

Blush Lane
Buttercream Bake Shoppe
Cherry Pit [*see* **Calgary Farmers' Market**]
Cookbook Company Cooks (The)
Daily Bagel
Francesco's Italian Food Store & Deli
Grazin' Acres
Gull Valley Greenhouse
Habina's Harvest [*see* **Calgary Farmers' Market**]
Hoven Farms
Innisfail Growers [*see* **Edgar Farms, The Jungle, Calgary Farmers' Market, Bearspaw Farmers' Market**]
J.Webb Market Wines
Jammin' It Jams & Jellies
Jungle (The), (Innisfail Growers)
Ladybug Belgian Pâtisserie (A)
Lund's Organic Produce
MacKay's Ice Cream Shop, Canmore
Missing Link Extraordinary Sausage
North Sea Fish Market
Old Country Sausage Shop
Pearson's Berry Farm & Gordo's Foods
Phil & Sebastian Coffee Co.
Rustic Sourdough Bakery
Simple Simon Pies
Stock & Sauce Co.
Sunworks Farm
Sylvan Star Cheese Farm
TotaliTea, The Tea Boutique
Tutti Frutti
Valta Bison
Vital Green Farms (with Sunworks Farm)
Walker's Own
Wapiti Ways
Wild Rose Brewery
Wish in a Dish (*see* **Simple Simon Pies**)

Index of Business Names

Gour-Mart Meat Shop, 179
Gourmet Croissant, Canmore, 258
Grainworks Inc., Vulcan, 156
Grassroots Northland Farmers' Market*, 105
Grazin' Acres, Two Hills, 152
Great Events Group, 204
Green Cedars, 186
Green Market*, 102
Griesser Spoon Custom Catering/Railway Deli, Canmore, 262
Grizzly Paw Brewing Company, Canmore, 260
Growing Food Security in Alberta (GFSA), 217
Gull Valley Greenhouse, Gull Lake, 146
Günther's Fine Baking Ltd., 14

H
Habina's Harvest [see Calgary Farmers' Market], 103
Hage's Mideast Foods & Halal Meats
Haifa Delicatessen & Caterers • Kavin's Kosher Meats, 207
Hamilton's Barley Flour, Olds, 156
Handles & More, 125
Hang Fung Foods, 8
Happy Cooker NW, 136
Happy Cooker SW, 133
Heaslip Venture Meats Ltd., 169
Hendrix Foodservice Equipment & Supply Professionals, 128
Heritage Bakery & Deli, 24
Hiêp Hòa Asian Foods, 4
High River Farmers' Market, High River, 246
Highwood Crossing Farm Ltd., Aldersyde, 157
Highwood Valley Ranch, High River, 247
Hillhurst-Sunnyside Farmers' Market*, 105
Homestead Chef (The), Carstairs, 226
Horizon Meats, 167
Hotchkiss Herbs & Produce, 147
House of Knives NW, 136
House of Knives SE, 129
Hoven Farms, Eckville, 152
Hungarian Deli, 170

I
IGA, Cochrane Valley, Cochrane,267
IGA, Nanton, 249
IGA, Strathmore, 240
Ikea, 129
Illichmann's Sausage Shop, 170
Indulge Catering, 207
Infuse Catering • Forage Foods, 208

Inn from the Cold Society, 218
Innisfail Farmers' Market*, Innisfail, 229
Innisfail Growers [see Edgar Farms, The Jungle, Calgary Farmers' Market, Bearspaw Farmer's Market], 103–4, 230–1
Inter-Course Chef Services, 198
International Avenue Business Revitalization Zone (BRZ) "Around The World in 35 Blocks", 83
Italian Store, 93
Italian Supermarket Ltd., 94

J
J Webb Wine Merchant/J Webb Market Wines, 35
Jammin' It Jams & Jellies, 64
Jan's Meats & Deli, 180
Janice Beaton Fine Cheese NW, 57
Janice Beaton Fine Cheese SW, 56
Java Jamboree, Cochrane, 268
Jing Jing Bakery, 14
JK Bakery, Canmore, 259
Joycee's Caribbean Foods, 138
Jubba-Nile Supermarket, 139
Judy Wood Cuisine, 199
Jungle (The), [Innisfail Growers], Innisfail, 231

K
Kalamata Grocery Store, 187
Kayben Farms, Okotoks, 251
Kensington Wine Market, 38
King Brisket Boy, 199
King's Seafood Distributors [inside Lambda Oriental Foods & Market], 7, 114
Knifery (The), 133
Knifewear, 129

L
La Table Du Chatelain Cuisine & Catering, 204
La Tiendona, 139
Ladybug Belgian Pâtisserie (A), 24
Ladybug Organic Gardens & Bed & Breakfast, Blackfalds, 224
Lahore Foods & Halal Meats, 88
Lakeview Bakery, 25
Lambda Oriental Foods & Market, 7
L'Arche Cakewalk, 219
Latin American Empanadas, 11
Lazy Loaf & Kettle, 29
Lee Valley Tools Ltd., 130
Les Truffes au Chocolat SE, 61
Les Truffes au Chocolat SW, 65

Glossary of Ingredients

A

adobo – Mexican or Filipino chili-based spicy meat sauce or stew.

affineur – French specialist in aging and storing cheeses.

ajwain – Indian seed, related to caraway and cumin, tasting of thyme.

akami – Middle Eastern cheese.

akawie – Middle Eastern soft unripened cows' milk cheese.

aloo gobi – Indian curried potatoes and cauliflower.

aloo moong – Indian curried potatoes and lentils.

aloo mutter – Indian curried potatoes and peas.

amuse-bouche – French "mouth amusement" or appetizer.

ancho – Latin American or Spanish dried rusty red chile, slightly sweet and fruity, called *poblano* when fresh.

andouille – French spicy smoked Cajun pork sausage.

annatto – tropical rust-red seeds, sold in paste or seed form, widely used for colouring cheeses, a primary ingredient in *cochinita pibil*.

apitherapy – medicinal products derived from honey bee-pollen, propolis, royal jelly.

Appenzeller – Swiss spicy cow's milk cheese, wine-and-cider-washed rind, with pea-to-cherry-sized interior holes.

aquaculture – fish farming.

arabica – species of high quality coffee beans grown in tropics and sub-tropics. Also *Coffea arabia*.

arancini – Italian "orange," little balls made of leftover risotto, usually deep-fried.

arborio – Italian short-grain rice commonly used in making risotto.

asado – Filipino soy-simmered meat sauce or filling.

asafoetida – Indian pungent curry spice, mostly sold ground.

assadeira – Portuguese ceramic casserole.

atta – Indian whole wheat flour primarily used for *chapattis*, *parathas* and *roti*.

azuki – Asian small red sweet dried beans. Also *adzuki*.

B

baba – French sweet Polish rum-soused dessert made from yeasted dough, baked in individual mould.

baba ganouj – Middle Eastern pureed eggplant dip seasoned with olive oil, *tahini*, mint and pomegranate.

babka – Russian or Polish dessert made from rich yeasted egg dough with peel and raisins.

baci – sweet Italian cookies called "kisses".

baklava – Middle Eastern pastry made with layered nuts and buttered filo, drenched in honey syrup after baking.

baladi – Middle Eastern soft unripened cows' milk cheese.

bamba – Israeli snack food.

banana leaf – flat leaf of banana plant used in Africa, southern Mexico, the Yucatan and Gulf states as a wrapper for steamed food.

baraka – Asian herb used in seed form in Turkish, Indian, Russian and Persian food. Also *Nigella sativa, black caraway, black onion seed, Roman coriander* and *kalonji*.

barista – Italian coffee maker who uses an espresso machine to foam milk and pull espresso shots.

basmati – Indian and Pakistani "queen of fragrance," long-grained aromatic rice.

bibingka – Filipino sweet festive cake of glutinous rice flour batter topped with coconut.

bigos – Polish hunter's stew.

biltong – Africaans beef jerky seasoned with vinegar and spices, similar to Swiss bündnerfleisch.

biodynamics – planting and growing philosophy invented by Rudolph Steiner.

biryani – Indian, Pakistani and Banglasdeshi rice dish.

bissli – Israeli snack food.

black tea – also *red tea*, rolled and fermented tea leaves that are heated and dried, makes assertive and astringent tea.

Bleu Bènèdictin – Canadian semi-soft cow's milk blue cheese made by Québécois Benedictine monks.

Bleuchâtel – Swiss cow's milk blue cheese made in a sweet and creamy style.

Bleu d'Auvergne – French sharply flavoured blue cows' milk cheese made in the centrally-located Auvergne district of France's Massif Central.

bocconcini – Italian small mozzarella cheese rounds in whey or water, sometimes made with buffalo milk, called *Mozzarella di Bufala*.

boeuf bourguignon – French Burgundian beef stew traditionally made with local wine.

boem – Serbian walnut and hazelnut torte.

boerewors – Africaans farmers' sausage.

bok choy – Chinese mild greens with white stalks and broad tender green leaves. Also *pak choy*.

bomba – Spanish short-grained rice used in making *paella*.

boniato – Caribbean tuber related to the sweet potato, red-brown skin and creamy interior.

borek – Turkish or Hungarian strudel filled with meat, vegetables or cheese. Also *burek* or *boreka*.

boule – French "bowl" usually refers to bread made in the shape of a bowl.

braciole – meat-stuffed Italian pasta.

Bresse – mild French surface-ripened blue cheese made from cows' milk.

Brie de Meaux – French Appellation d'Origine Controlée (AOC) raw cows' milk surface-ripened cheese.

brioche – French buttery yeasted pastry baked in distinctive round with topknot.

Bûche de Noël – French Christmas log of rolled sponge cake filled with chocolate or mocha buttercream and traditionally decorated with meringue mushrooms.

bulgogi – Korean soy-marinated thinly sliced beef that is quickly grilled.

bündnerfleisch – Swiss air-dried beef.

burdock – Japanese root vegetable, brown skinned and white fleshed, up to 18" inches in length Also *gobo*.

burfi – Indian fudge, milk slowly cooked to thick texture and flavoured with coconut, nuts or seeds. Also *barfi*.

burramundi – Australian sport fish. Also giant sea perch.

burro banana – Mexican flat, box-shaped, lemon-tasting banana.

by-catch – Swimming species caught inadvertently when fishing for another species.

C

cajeta – Mexican caramel made from goats' milk. Also *dulce de leche*.

Calabrese – Italian in the Calabrian style, often referring to sausages or olives.

calamansi – Filipino sour orange-pulped green skinned citrus the size of a small lime Also *kalamansi* and *calamondin*.

callet – French small flat high-grade chocolate drop that does not require chopping.

Camellia sinensis – tea plant native to China, now growing in tropical and sub-tropical regions.

cannoli – Italian crisp pastry cone filled with sweetened ricotta or whipped cream.

Caprice des Dieux – French small oval double-cream cows' milk soft-rind cheese made in the northeastern district of Champagne-Ardenne.

carnaroli – short-grain Italian rice used for making risotto.

cassava – African and Caribbean starchy brown-skinned white-fleshed tuber that must be peeled and cooked, basis of tapioca. Also *yucca*.

challah – Jewish traditional braided yeast-risen egg bread.

chana dal – Indian yellow split hulled peas. Also *chana* and *channa*.

chapatti – Indian whole wheat unyeasted flatbread baked on a stovetop pan.

charlotte – French mould for baking with deep vertical flutes in its sides.

chayote – Aztec and Mayan pear-size fruit with pale green skin. Also *mirliton* and *christophene*.

chèvre – French fresh goat's milk cheese.

Chèvre Noir – French-Canadian goat's milk cheese made in a cheddar style.

chimneystick – air-dried sausage that acquires a black exterior from hanging in or near a chimney to dry and smoke.

chioggia – beet coloured alternately pink and white in concentric circles. Also *candy cane beet*.

chipotle – Latin smoked and dried version of *jalapeño* chile with brown skin and toasted hot chocolate taste, often canned in *adobo sauce*.

chocolatier – French chocolate maker.

chorizo – Mexican or Spanish spicy pork sausage.

choy – Chinese family of cabbages.

ciabatta – Italian "slipper" yeast-risen bread, open-textured, flat and indented, often salt-sprinkled.

collagen – protein found in meat tendons, softened with long cooking at low temperature.

comal – Latin American round, flat metal pan used for cooking tortillas.

cordon bleu – French ham and cheese filling often placed within pounded veal or chicken breast.

cotognata – Italian quince.

couscous – Middle Eastern tiny golden pellets of pasta.

couverture – French professional-quality high-sheen coating chocolate.

crema – Italian espresso's oil-rich foam topping.

crème fraîche – thickened tangy heavy cream, naturally occurring in unpasteurized cream, but pasteurized cream needs the addition of buttermilk to occur.

crêperie – a food establishment that makes and serves thin unleavened filled or folded pancakes.

croissant – French flaky crescent-shaped multi-layered yeasted pastry. Also *croissant ordinaire*.

croissant aux amandes – croissant filled with almond paste and topped with sliced almonds.

crustacean – shellfish with hard "crust-like" carapace, including lobster, crab and shrimp.

cuitlacoche – Mexican highly prized fungus that envelops corn's ear, expanding the kernels into a glossy exterior and shiny black interior, cut free of the ear and sold separately. Also corn smut.

curry powder – blend of spices used in dishes originating in southern India, can include coriander, cumin, mustard and fenugreek seeds, hot chilies, whole peppercorns and turmeric; cinnamon and cloves add Moghul character.

D

dace – a wide family of Eurasian, African and North American freshwater fish that includes carp and minnows.

debrazinger – German and European veal-based equivalent of high-quality hot dog.

debrecini – Hungarian sausage spiced with paprika.

deglet noor date – Middle Eastern soft sweet high-quality date.

dhokla – Gujarati Indian fast food dish based on *chana dal*.

dobosh torte – Austrian sponge cake of many layers interspersed with chocolate buttercream and topped with caramel glaze. Also *dobos torte*.

Dolcelatte – Italian very mild brand of Gorgonzola cheese made from one milking's curd.

dominosteine – German "domino stones," gingerbread layered with marzipan and jelly in chocolate.

donair – Middle Eastern fast food, ground beef on a vertical grill.

dragonfruit – Central and South American edible cactus, with lime-green spikes and pink flesh.

drumstick – Indian vegetable with hard shell over green flesh, cut into lengths and squeezed by hand to free its tender flesh after cooking. Also *horseradish tree*.

durian – Malaysian fruit infamous for its rank smell, looks like a spiked football and tastes like custard.

Du Village de Warwick – Canadian village in Quebec famous for its cheese.

dry aging – meat left refrigerated but uncovered after initial aging for an additional 21–28 days, allowing enzyme action to break down the muscle tissue.

dry wors – Africaans dry aged sausage of beef and mutton. Also *droe wors*.

E

edamame – Japanese green soybeans.

empanada – South American filled and folded savoury pie.

enoki – Japanese tiny white cultivated mushrooms most often eaten raw.

Ermite – French-Canadian "Hermit" semi-soft cows' milk blue cheese made by Québécois Benedictine monks.

epazote – Mexican herb often described as a wild form of oregano, a pungent carminative that reduces gas, thus a common addition to bean pots. Also Mexican tea.

F

falafel – Middle Eastern chickpea patties often served with *tzatziki* and pita.

fatayer – Middle Eastern triangular pastries filled with meat or vegetables.

focaccia – Italian flatbread with coarse, open structure and dimpled surface, usually flavoured with herbs and garlic.

fondue – Swiss dish of melted cheese and wine, suitable for dipping cubes of bread.

Fourme d'Ambert – French cows' milk blue cheese made in the southeastern region of the Rhône-Alpes.

forno – Italian oven.

frame – fish bones including the head and spine used for making *fumet*.

fromage – French for cheese.

Formaggi di Tartufo – Italian truffled sheep's milk Pecorino cheese.

freekeh – Mediterranean cooked green wheat as in freekeh couscous.

fufu – African starch dish made of *cassava*.

fumet – French fish stock.

G

gai choy – Asian greens of the *Brassica* family with broad, pungent leaves. Also *bamboo mustard* or *leaf mustard*.

gai lan – Asian greens of the *Brassica* family with mild stalks, pungent leaves and white flowers. Also *Chinese broccoli* or *Chinese kale*.

galangal – Thai spicy peppery rhizome, called Laos when dried. Also *Siamese* or *Thai ginger*.

galette – French rustic single-crust, open-face tart.

ganache – French blend of melted chocolate and heavy cream used for truffles, sauce and tart filling.

garam masala – North Indian seasoning blend similar to curry powder, can include cumin, coriander, hot chilies, cardamom, cinnamon, cloves, peppercorns, bay, mace, fennel, thyme and nutmeg.

gari – Japanese pickled ginger served with sushi.

gelato – Italian ice cream, plural form *gelati*.

ghee – Indian clarified butter wherein the milk solids are browned for additional flavour.

glace de viande – French meat glaze, made by reducing meat stock into thick glaze-like consistency.

gongfu – Chinese term for any skill developed through greatly detailed practice.

Gorgonzola Cremosa – Italian brand of mild, young cows' milk blue cheese.

Gorgonzola dolce – Italian mild, "sweet," young cow's milk blue cheese.

grain-finished – cattle or bison which are fed grain for the final 3 to 5 months of life, for a higher marbling and fat content.

gram – Indian flour made from dried chickpeas. Also *besan*.

green tea – steamed, dried and unfermented tea leaves, makes yellowish grassy tea.

griotte – French variety of sour cherries traditionally steeped in kirsch or brandy.

Gruyère – Swiss cows' milk hard rind cheese with strong fruity/nutty flavour.

guajillo chile – Latin American dried and very hot chile of burnished russet colour.

guava – fragrant tropical fruit from Central America and southern USA.

gulab jamun – Indian deep-fried round sweets steeped in syrup infused with *rose water*.

guvar – Indian cluster beans.

H

habanero – Latin American extremely hot small lantern-shaped capsicum chile.

hahualla – Chilean traditional flat bun.

Halal – Muslim blessing and prescribed method of animal slaughter.

halo-halo – Filipino "mixed" half-half fruit mixture.

halloumi – Middle Eastern semi-soft pressed sheep's milk cheese. Also *haloumi* or *halloom*.

halva – Middle Eastern sweet based on ground sesame seeds and nuts, enriched with dried fruits. Also *halwa*.

harissa – Algerian hot chile pepper paste.

hawaji – Middle Eastern cumin.

hoisin – Chinese sweet dark brown bean paste.

hominy – Native American corn kernels slaked with lye, sometimes ground into grits.

honig nuss – German honey nut, cookie made with ground almond dough.

honigkuchen – German honey cake, marzipan layered with gingerbread.

hummus – Middle Eastern puree of chickpeas and *tahini* served as a dip with pita.

hurka – Hungarian spreadable sausage made of pork liver, similar to liverwurst, sometimes including rice.

hygroscopic – substance which absorbs moisture from the atmosphere.

I

ibrik – Turkish long-handled lidless brass or copper coffee pot.

injera – Ethiopian unleavened flatbread made of *teff*.

Israeli couscous – large balls of bulgur and flour. Also *maftoul* or pearl couscous.

J

jaggery – Indian raw sugar made from palm tree sap or sugar cane juice. Also *palm sugar*.

jalabi – Indian sweet of swirls of lentil and sugar batter dropped through a narrow-mouthed funnel into hot oil in circular patterns, deep fried, then immersed in sugar syrup. Also *jilabi*.

jalapeño – Latin fat dark green bullet-shaped hot capsicum chile, named *morita* or *chipotle* when dried and smoked, sometimes packed in *adobo* sauce.

jicama – tropical tuber, ovoid-shaped, with juicy white flesh and thin brown skin.

K

kabanosy – Polish air-dried sausage.

kaffir lime leaf – Southeast Asian tree leaves, strongly aromatic of citrus, most fragrant when purchased frozen or fresh.

kaiser bacon – German or Austrian smoked cured bacon.

kaiserfleisch – Austrian or German "king's meat" or smoked pork.

kajmak – Balkan cream cheese.

kamut – ancient Egyptian wheat, large kernels, nutty flavour and high nutritional value.

karela – Indian bitter gourd vegetable with spiky exterior reminiscent of a lizard.

kasha – Polish, Russian, or Hungarian roasted buckwheat groats.

kashanka – Polish fresh sausage made with 80 percent *kasha*, pork and bacon.

kashkaval – Turkish, Balkan, Middle Eastern or Bulgarian sheep's milk cheese Also *kachekeval*.

kassler – German smoked pork neck, loin or rib.

kataifi – Middle Eastern "shredded wheat" pastry. Also *kadaifi*.

kefir – fermented milk drink originating in the Caucasus.

kefolitiri – Greek sheep's milk cheese used for saganaki. Also *kasseri*.

ketjap manis – Indonesian sweet soy sauce containing *jaggery*, garlic and star anise. Also *kecap manis*.

kheer – Indian sweet rice pudding cooked in milk with sugar, flavoured with cardamom, nuts and fruit.

kibbe – Middle Eastern miniature football-shaped portions of bulgur mixed with ground lamb or beef.

kimchee – Korean fermented condiment, often cabbage, carrots and turnips. Also *kimchi*.

kingfish – Bangladeshi fish.

kielbasa – Polish chunky smoked pork sausage. Also *kolbassa* or *kolbasa*.

knish – Jewish baked dumpling of dough wrapped around mashed potatoes.

kosher – Jewish "proper" or compliant with rabbinical laws for food preparation and combination.

kransjska – Polish sausage flavoured with paprika.

kuchen – German cake.

L

laban – Lebanese yogurt.

labneh – Lebanese drained yogurt cheese.

labkuchen – German soft gingerbread.

lachs schinken – German cold-smoked pork loin.

laddu – Indian multi-coloured granules of chickpea flour (called *bindi*) poached in sugar syrup and formed into balls.

landjaeger – Swiss and German chimney-smoked pork sausage.

lait cru – French "raw milk" referring to unpasteurized milk in raw-milk cheeses.

langka – Filipino huge pebbly-skinned sweet tropical fruit related to breadfruit. Also *jackfruit*.

lapin – French rabbit.

latke – Jewish grated potato pancake, similar to *roesti* or *roschti*.

leche flan – Spanish or Mexican sweet cream or milk tart.

Le Chevalier – Canadian triple cream cows' milk cheese.

le puy – French green lentils.

letcho – Hungarian air-dried pork sausage.

levain – French sourdough starter.

longanisa – Filipino sausage.

longan – Southeast Asian small fruit with brown peel over a translucent white fleshy ball and central black seed. Also *dragon eye*.

lutefisk – Scandinavian dried unsalted cod or its constituent dish made after soaking the fish for several days.

lychee – Asian tropical fruit with brown skin encasing a central pit surrounded by succulent translucent flesh. Also *litchi*.

M

mâche – French tender elongated dark green wild or cultivated leaves used in salad. Also *corn salad* or *lamb's lettuce*.

macapuno – Filipino young coconut.

madeleine – French sponge cake baked in a tiny fluted metal scallop-shaped shell.

mahleb – Middle eastern black cherry kernel ground and used in Mediterranean sweet breads Also *mahlab*.

maja blanka – Filipino coconut cake.

maltitol – sweetener made of fruit-derived alcohol.

mandolin – French hand-held vegetable slicer with removable blades.

Manchego – Spanish sheep's milk cheese from La Mancha.

mangosteen – Asian purple-brown-skinned fruit with inner segments.

marbling – fine white streaks of fat running through lean beef which increases tenderness, juiciness and flavour.

marché – French for market.

mariquetta – Chilean round bun.

masa harina – Latin American dried corn flour with slaked lime (mineral, not juice), similar to cornmeal, used for making tortillas. Also *masa*.

masala – Indian spice mixture.

masala roti – Indian flatbread seasoned with *garam masala*.

matcha – Japanese brilliantly coloured, powdered green tea, very bitter, astringent and strong.

matzo – Jewish Hanukkah unleavened flatbread.

mercato – Italian for market.

merguez – Spanish hot sausage.

merveilleux – French "marvelous" tart.

methi – Indian fresh fenugreek leaves.

mignardaise – French miniature sweets that conclude a meal.

mishiri – Pakistani coriander.

miso – Japanese fermented bean paste.

mithai – Indian bite-size sweets served for Eid, Diwali or family celebrations.

molcajete y tejolete – Mexican black basalt mortar and pestle for mixing and grinding.

molé – Mexican "mixture", the name of many sauces containing chilies.

molé poblano – Mexican sauce made of *poblano* and dark chocolate.

molinillo – Latin American "windmill" or wooden hand mixer.

mollusk – one- or two-shelled, soft-bodied spineless animal, including oyster, squid, snail, scallop, mussel and clam.

molochia – African leafy green vegetable similar to spinach.

monay putok – Filipino crusty egg bread.

Monterey Jack – American mild semi-soft cheese.

mooncake – Chinese large round almond-flavoured cookie eaten to celebrate the annual Moon Festival.

moong – Indian skinned and split yellow beans similar to split yellow peas.

Mozzarella di Bufala – Italian mild and tender buffalo milk cheese of small white balls.

musztarda chrzanowa – Polish mustard with horseradish.

N

naan – Indian leavened flatbread.

nabulsi – Middle Eastern semi-soft unripened cows' milk cheese containing black niger seeds.

nori – Japanese thin green-black squares of seaweed wrappers used in sushi-making.

O

Oka – Québécois Trappist monks' semi-soft washed rind cow's milk cheese.

oolong tea – tea made of partially fermented leaves.

orangette – French candied orange slice dipped in dark chocolate.

P

pabda – Bangladeshi fish.

paella – Spanish slow-cooked rice dish cooked in a shallow two-handed pan.

palascinta – Polish crepes filled with cottage cheese, similar to Jewish *blintzes*.

palmier – French puff pastry cookie shaped like palm leaf and sprinkled with sugar.

pain au chocolat – French sweet bread or croissant filled with a piece of chocolate.

pandan leaf – Filipino for screwpine leaf, used in Thai, Indonesian or Malaysian rice or baking for its green colour and floral aroma, considered a restorative to counter the lassitude induced by tropical heat. Also *pandanus*.

pan de coco – Filipino coconut bread.

paneer – Indian fresh cheese made by acidulating hot milk with lemon juice to induce curdling, then whey is discarded.

panini – Italian sandwich or bun, commonly means a grilled sandwich.

panettone – Italian tall cylindrical Christmas sweet egg bread filled with dried fruit, anise, chocolate or chestnut paste.

panna con funghi – Italian mushroom cream sauce.

panzerotti – Italian filled ravioli, usually deep-fried or baked.

pappadam – Indian lentil wafer.

pareve – Jewish term for neutral dish that contains neither dairy nor meat, thus can be served with either. Also *parve*.

pâté – French ground meat, seasoned and cooked, garnished with many other ingredients, often formed into loaf and served as appetizer with bread or crackers.

pâtisserie – French pastry shop.

pea tendril – tender edible tips of the pea plant. Also *dau miu*.

peda – Indian sweet similar to *burfi*, shaped into soft balls, indented and topped with pistachio.

petisa – Indian sweet made of chickpea flour, shortening, sugar and pistachios formed into squares, with a taste similar to peanut butter.

pfeffernusse – German pepper nut, spicy cookie seasoned with pepper.

pico de gallo – Spanish "rooster's beak," finely chopped fresh salsa.

pichi-pichi – Filipino steamed *cassava* cake, flavoured with coconut milk.

piloncillo – Mexican raw grainy cane sugar, sold in cones, used chopped or dissolved, also added to Mexican chocolate.

plantain – Caribbean and African vegetable; a larger, starchier cousin to the banana, always served cooked.

pletzel – Jewish flat buns.

plum kifli – Croatian or Serbian croissants filled with plum preserves.

poblano – Mexican tapered green fresh peppers, called *ancho* when dried, commonly used in *chiles rellenos*.

pomodoro – Italian tomato.

poolish – a semi-liquid fermented baking starter dough made from apples, grapes and sometimes yeast.

pomegranate molasses – Middle Eastern dark garnet sweet-tart syrup made from sweetened pomegranate juice.

preserved lemon – sliced lemons, soaked in lemon juice and olive oil with spices and salt until soft and pungent, used in Mediterranean cooking.

Prunus cerasus – species of sour cherry tree.

Q

quesadilla – Spanish turnover of tortilla and cheese, often fried or baked, sliced and served hot.

queso – Spanish cheese.

queso fresco – Mexican or Spanish white or fresh cheese, soft and creamy. Also *queso blanco*.

quinoa – Inca mild-tasting ancient grain, contains all 8 essential amino acids, tiny cream-coloured pellets.

R

raclette – Swiss cow's milk cheese, nutty and sweet flavoured, or a meal of cheese melted and scraped off the wheel, served with sausages, potatoes and pickled onions.

rahu – Bangladeshi fish.

rambutan – Malayan fruit, related to litchi, with external spikes on a red, orange, yellow or green skin and translucent flesh with one central seed.

rapini – Italian bitter greens. Also *broccoli rabe*.

ras gullah – Indian cheese balls made of high-fat milk *chenna*, bound with starch, kneaded into balls, then poached in sugar syrup.

ras malai – Indian cheese balls poached in milk syrup infused with rose or orange syrup with pistachio.

raute – Afghani sweet cake-like round eaten for breakfast and snacks.

rhûm – French rum.

Riopelle – Canadian triple cream raw-milk bloomy-rind cheese

robusta – low-altitude tropical and sub-tropical coffee beans, less costly and generally agreed to be lesser quality than *arabica* beans.

rooibos –South Africa's "red bush," grown in the Cedarberg Mountains north of Cape Town, used to make *tisane*.

roti – Indian whole wheat flat bread.

roschti – German and Swiss fried shredded or grated potato pancake similar to *latke*. Also *röesti*.

Roquefort – strongly flavoured blue cheese made of sheep's milk in southern France.

rose water – Middle Eastern and Indian distilled essence of rose petals.

rouladen – European rolled and stuffed meat or sponge cake. Also *roulade*.

rugala – Jewish crescent-shaped Hanukkah cookie filled with fruit, nuts, poppyseed paste or jam. Also *rugalach*.

S

sabzi mandi – Indian vegetable market.

salsa verde – Latin or Mexican hot green chile sauce.

sambal manis – Indonesian spicy condiment.

sambal oelek – Indonesian hot chili paste. Also *sambal ulek*.

samosa – Indian deep-fried triangular pastry filled with spicy vegetables or meat.

sand pot – Asian slow-cooking method.

sand rose praliné – French sweet tart topped with praline.

sangre potato – Spanish red-skinned "blood" potato.

sapin-sapin – Filipino glutinous rice cake.

schinkenspeck – German ham or cured pork similar to proscuitto.

Scotch bonnet – hot fresh smoky conically-shaped chile—can be yellow, green, orange or red.

serrano – Latin American small, pointed hot chile, red or yellow when ripe, called chile seco when dried.

shabu-shabu – Japanese broth-based fondue.

shampita – Croatian, Serbian or Hungarian filo filled with meringue.

shar li hon – Chinese mustard greens.

shish taouk – Syrian marinated chicken skewers.

shiso leaf – Japanese perilla leaf, traditional vermifuge accompaniment to sushi, frequently dipped in tempura batter and deep-fried.

shwarma – Middle Eastern chicken thighs roasted on a vertical spit, carved and served in pita with *tzatziki*.

siopao – Filipino dumplings filled with pork or chicken.

soba – Japanese buckwheat noodles.

sofganiot— Israeli deep-fried jelly doughnut in yeast or cake style, filled with jam and dusted with powdered sugar. Also *sofganyot*.

sorbetto – Italian soft-textured non-dairy frozen sherbet or sorbet.

sorghum – cereal grass used world-wide as edible grain.

sosatie – Africaans-style kebab of raw marinated chicken or beef

souk – Moroccan market.

spanakopita – Mediterranean spinach and feta filo pie.

speculaas – Dutch ginger cookie left as a gift by Sinter Klaus on December fifth.

spelt – ancient southern European cereal grain similar to wheat, available as flour and flake.

St. Agur – French mild high-fat blue cheese.

stollen – German sweet-yeasted Christmas loaf containing dried fruit.

suduk – Hungarian smoked air-dried beef.

sui choy – Chinese mild, yellow and white tender crinkle-leaf cabbage. Also napa cabbage or Chinese cabbage.

sumac – Mediterranean shrub with sour lemony red berries, usually available ground.

T

tabbouleh – Middle Eastern salad of bulgur and parsley.

tagine – Middle Eastern stew or the conical-lidded dish in which it is cooked.

tahini – Middle Eastern sesame paste.

tamalera – Mexican tamale maker.

tamale – Mexican steamed corn-husk-wrapped dish of meat and vegetables.

tamari – Japanese soy sauce, sometimes wheat-free.

tamarind – sweet-tart brown fruit pod of Indian, African and Asian tree. Also *Indian date*.

tandoori paste – Indian red spice mixture used on meats, fish and vegetables for cooking in barrel-shaped tandoor oven.

taro – starchy tropical tuber with brown skin and grayish flesh.

tarte Tatin – French single crust apple tart customarily served inverted to display its caramelized fruit base.

tartuffo – Italian *gelato* flavoured with chocolate and hazelnut.

tawa – Indian flat pan for making *chapattis*.

tchotchke – Yiddish for trinket or knick-knack.

teff – Ethiopian tiny high-protein cereal grain traditionally used ground in making *injera*.

terroir – French grape-growing term referring to the influence of place—latitude and sunlight, elevation, temperature, geology and soil, water flow, and aspect.

tindoora – Indian small crisp gourds.

Tilsit – Dutch cow's milk cheese with irregular eyes and cracks, made in commercial and farmhouse versions.

tiropita – Mediterranean triangular cheese and filo pastry.

tisane – French infused beverage made from ingredients other than tea.

tobiko – Japanese flying fish roe used in sushi.

tocino – Filipino cured pork.

tohess speck – Austrian or German cured ham, brined, cold-smoked and aged.

tomatillo – Latin round green fruit similar to tomato, covered in a papery husk, soft, yellow and acidic when ripe.

toria – Indian long ridged tube-like vegetable with fluffy soft white interior.

tortilla – Latin American unleavened flatbread made of flour or *masa harina*.

tourtière – French-Canadian pork pie traditionally made for Christmas or Réveillon.

transitional – partway through the multi-year process of becoming organically certified.

tzatziki – Middle Eastern yogurt dip with grated cucumber, olive oil and garlic. Also *tsatsiki*.

tuile – French "tile," fragile almond cookie made with loose batter that is shaped over a rolling pin after baking to achieve traditional roof tile shape.

U

ube – Filipino purple yam, commonly used in Filipino baking and an ingredient in *yema*. Also *ube yema*.

udon – Japanese wheat noodle.

Umbriaco – Italian cow's milk wine-washed cheese made in Lombardy and similar to Asiago.

urad – Indian pulse that is cooked whole or split, or ground into flour. Also *urad dal, black gram* or *black lentil*.

V

vachekeval – Middle Eastern firm-textured cow's milk cheese similar to cheddar.

Vacherin Mont d'Or – notable Swiss cow's milk cheese with woodsy buttery flavour, leathery aroma and resin notes from bark rind, similar to French-made *Vacherin du Haut-Doubs*.

Valdeón – Spanish blue cheese with many small perforations, wrapped in sycamore leaves and made of goat's milk and cow's milk. Also *Queso de Valdeón*.

verdure – Italian vegetables. Also *verdura*.

verjus – French unripe "green juice" of grapes used in cooking to add acid to dishes.

vialone nano – Italian short-grained rice used for making risotto.

viennoiserie – elaborate Viennese-style sweet pastries.

vin santo – Italian sweet slightly oxidized white wine made of Malvasia and Trebbiano grapes.

W

wadi – Amritsari Punjabi lentil and soy chunk snack food.

wasabi – Japanese horseradish, accompaniment to sushi, sold in paste or dried ground form.

weisswurst – German mild white veal sausage.

Welsh onion – hollow stemmed bulb-less relative of common onion, used in China, Japan and Korea. Also *green onion, spring onion* or *scallion*.

wet aging – cuts of meat Cryovac'd after cutting, can be kept for up to 6 weeks, but the meat ceases aging after 30 days when enzyme action concludes.

white tea – made from first picked youngest leaves.

witloof – bitter yellow-white or red-white leaves in a tight elongated head. Also *Belgian endive.*

Y

ya choy – Chinese greens, members of the Brassica family with yellow flowers and slender, leafy fleshy green stalks Also *yu choy* and *yau choy.*

ya pear – golden-skinned round crunchy mild-flavoured Chinese pear apple.

yema – Filipino sweet of *ube*, sugar, coconut, egg and milk, shaped into balls.

yerba maté – Spanish South American *Ilex paragauriensis,* wild-growing evergreen member of the holly family, brewed into a stimulant traditionally sipped from a gourd, tastes bitter-sweet and alfalfa-like.

Z

zabaione – sauce of egg yolks whisked with sugar and Marsala over hot water to form foam served on berries, cake or alone. Also *zabaglione* and *sabayon.*

za'ataar – Middle Eastern herb that tastes like thyme, marjoram and oregano, may also mean an herb blend based on thyme, marjoram, sumac and sesame seeds. Also *za'atar* and *Syrian marjoram.*

Glossary Bibliography

Herbst, S.T. and Herbst, R. (2007). *The new food lover's companion, 4th ed.* Hauppauge, NY: Barron's.

Jenkins, S. (1996). *Cheese primer.* New York, NY: Workman.

Masui, K. and Yamada, T. (2000). *French cheeses: The visual guide to more than 350 cheeses from every region of France.* New York, NY: Dorling Kindersley.

Schneider, E. (2001). *Vegetables from amaranth to zucchini: The essential reference.* New York, NY: William Morrow.

The Last Word

WHEN dee initially invited me to write the afterword of the book, I responded that it wasn't, traditionally speaking, a role or function of the publisher to do so. Later, upon reflection, since the project was conceived as a joint venture between author and designer-publisher, then why not an afterword written by the other half of the partnership?

In some respects, the act of publishing, of overtly manifesting the whole process in a saleable book, is the epitome of self-confidence. It is a declaration that we have something to say and that it merits our sharing it by putting ink on paper—reproducing the message thousands of times, all with the implicit belief that as many people will be willing to purchase a copy of the book in order to access that same knowledge. Tall order indeed!

How does one approach the process of publishing a book, especially one about food—and remain congruent with stated and shared concerns for the wider environmental or ecological impacts of our work—when the footprint we would inevitably leave presented us with some serious dilemmas.

Any discussion about food eventually leads one to remember the connections between all things—air, water, soil, plants (including trees), animals, microorganisms, the weather and climate change. Having published a book, how do we repay our environmental dues?

For us, part of this project involved selecting a printer with an awareness of the environment, and through them we were able to choose a paper stock on which to print this book which did something significant about the triumvirate processes of reducing, reusing, and recycling. The Eco-Audit on page 306 provides a summary of what we were able to achieve in terms of print-production with a single, simple decision—change the paper stock!

We're also going further than any other local publisher—at least to my knowledge—in making the discount-upon-return offer to purchasers of this first edition of *Shop talk*. Bring back the old edition when the successive edition is published, and we'll give you a discount on the new book and make arrangements to recycle the old one. This offer is really an expression of the value and responsibility we feel for clearing up after ourselves—a principle instilled in me before ever I started school yet sadly one that many much larger corporations consistently fail to undertake.

Moving ever closer to the local, and a more immediate sphere of concern—because we can see it—was the question of what we could do for our region and community. Could the project benefit either, and if so, how?

We determined that there were at least three ways we could satisfy our need to make a constructive contribution towards Calgary and west-central Alberta. Perhaps the most obvious is to have showcased 350 businesses—at no cost to them—most of which are small, independent, family-owned enterprises. Some are successful, well established, and well known whereas others are more recent, less well established, and not as widely known—all factors which make their future viability uncertain. Not all businesses included in *Shop talk* were manifest with the same resources behind them on start-up. Our final selection of entries was as much based on obvious merit for some as it was for others on authorial judgement as deserving of a chance to grow and flourish—for which they need foot traffic!

We felt the inclusion of the section on Food Organizations was important to demonstrate our awareness that we have a shared responsibility towards feeding the hungry, under-privileged, and socially disadvantaged members of our community. We will be doing our bit by contributing a proportion of our profits from direct sales of the book to a recognizable charitable entity who have, as part of their own mandate, a commitment to feeding the hungry.

The third, possibly obvious, but certainly the most embedded means of making a contribution to our community, is manifest in the organization of the book. By presenting businesses within each of our major categories by city wide and city quadrant and, for the Bow Valley and beyond, by cardinal compass direction (which just happen to coincide with the most well-travelled highway routes into and out of the city), we hope readers will develop a more comprehensive geographical awareness of food shopping opportunities closer to home. In turn we hope this serves to reduce the distances driven to achieve personal objectives and fulfil family interests. Certainly we hope people will be in a position to more fully exploit any trip they make by motor vehicle and combine numerous reasons for leaving home into fewer, shorter, more time- and fuel-efficient trips.

As I rapidly exceed the originally allotted space for "The Last Word," I find I have much more to say on the subject of shopping for food. Thankfully there are others who are far more knowledgeable and erudite than I, such that I feel I can let myself off lightly by recommending among others, Michael Pollan's *The Ominivore's Dilemma* and *In Defense of Food*, and Raj Patel's *Stuffed and Starved*.

What I might still have room for though, are a few thoughts about why I felt this particular book was worthy of support and publication.

While there is much about the present organization of the world food industry that bears our collective closer examination and monitoring and, if even half of what I read is true, there are aspects of it which require a fundamental reconstruction, never mind a timely tweaking, I am also aware that alone, I cannot do very much about changing anything, other than bring what little global awareness I have about such things to influence the choices and decisions I make at home and in the local marketplace. The trade and transportation of foodstuffs has been a feature of our existence for hundreds of years, if not millennia. Dundee may have had a vibrant marmalade industry, but even as a child I knew oranges were not grown in Fife or on the slopes of the Sidlaw hills. The shipment of citrus fruits to Scotland was an addendum to an altogether darker trade. Times change and thankfully mostly for the better.

Here are a few parting thoughts you might consider taking with you to the grocery stores of your choice. Unless we grow it ourselves—and even here we might ponder the genetic origin of the seeds or exactly what is in the "organic" fertilizer we're spreading—without exception, everything we eat is based on trust, from what we read on the packaging labels declaring the ingredients and nutritional value thereof, to the governmental inspection agencies and everything else along the chain of activity between the raising or growing and its final port of arrival, our own buccal cavity!

While all of us can be more deliberate in our pursuit of the locally grown and raised, whether that be from sources less than 100 miles away or further afield, local is not necessarily synonymous with natural, organic, or fair trade—nor is it a guarantee of good or sustainable environmental practices on the part of the grower. All any of us can hope to become, I think, is a more curious, inquisitive, and therefore conscientious and well-informed consumer. To ask questions and learn as much as we can about our local producers—most frequently found in attendance at farmers' markets and of course at the farmgate—gives us a place to start.

It seems unlikely that worldwide trade in foodstuffs will experience radical or sudden change for want of a smaller carbon footprint in transportation practices. The kind of change we can hope for might be seen as radical, over time, if each of us were to make a series of more conscious and informed decisions. There are places all around the world where the domestic GNP, the balance of payments, and the livelihood of farming families are greatly dependent upon their own national exports and our imports of the same. We are a global village—and the atmosphere, fresh water, and tillable soil are resources that really belong—but only in trust—to us all. What any one of us does with these natural resources becomes an issue for all of us, regardless of the distance separating farmgate from plate. As much as we should be concerned about the impact of pesticides and herbicides on the future of honeybees in Alberta, we should be similarly concerned about their use on tea plantations in Sri Lanka. Our global village shares a planetary ecology!

Regardless of financial means, try always to purchase the best quality of foodstuffs you can afford. The more wholesome the nutritional value there is in whatever it is you do eat, the less of it you need. Look for what is local, fresh, and thus in season. Knowing where imported foodstuffs are coming from—provenance—and when they are in season based on their origins might assure some greater degree of freshness if only that the apple you're eating is from this last fall's crop, as opposed to the year before.

Learning how to cook—from scratch—and having fun doing so with your children and family pays dividends over the long term. We could do worse than seek to ensure both physical education as well as domestic science were attributed the same importance as literacy and numeracy in our schools. Happy and healthy children are more likely to achieve something closer to their full potential in both language arts and mathematics when well nourished.

We might consider practicing what I call moderate eclecticism, which means making a commitment to maintaining variety in our diet while remembering that almost everything we consume should be taken in moderation. The true measure of our moderation might be more successfully achieved in understanding the difference between sufficiency as opposed to excess. Ultimately it is a simple formula of energy intake versus energy expenditure measured in calories. This is true regardless of somatotype. In terms of maintaining variety in our diet, if we all made a greater effort to eat what was local and in season, we'd probably get enough of what we need but most of us simply replace what is missing from the cupboards and fridge with exactly that which we have eaten during the previous week—right down to the same brands. Over the long term, there might be a certain folly in the narrowing shopping practice of brand loyalty. Remember it's all based on trust.

Shop talk is one way I hope to make a small difference towards fostering some slightly different shopping practices among the citizenry of Calgary, the Bow Valley and beyond—at least when it comes to food.

Perhaps we'll bump into one another in the crowded aisle of a corner store, in a specialty outlet in a neighbourhood strip mall, or outdoors at one of the growing number of farmers' markets sometime over the summer. In the meantime, for the abundance and variety that we presently have available to us and can choose to enjoy, may we consume each morsel and mouthful with appropriate gratitude.

Jeremy Drought, Publisher
Last Impression Publishing
Calgary, Alberta
March 2008

About the Publisher

Last Impression Publishing Service was established in 1994 to provide a full spectrum of professional services to individuals and organizations with an interest in print media publishing. Services include: publishing and printing consultation, editorial, design, print brokering and management, marketing, publicity, and distribution support. To contact Last Impression and discuss your project or idea:

Phone: (403) 289·5718 • Fax: (403) 289·0157
E-mail: lastimpression@shaw.ca

Shop talk was published as a joint venture with the author. If you have an idea for a publication about which you are passionate, and would be interested in discussing its development on a joint venture basis, please contact Jeremy Drought at Last Impression Publishing Service for an initial, confidential consultation, with no associated cost or future obligation.

ENVIRONMENTAL BENEFITS STATEMENT

Last Impression Publishing Service saved the following resources by printing the pages of this book on chlorine free paper made with 100% post-consumer waste.

TREES	WATER	ENERGY	SOLID WASTE	GREENHOUSE GASES
126	45,956	88	5,901	11,072
FULLY GROWN	GALLONS	MILLION BTUs	POUNDS	POUNDS

Calculations based on research by Environmental Defense and the Paper Task Force. Manufactured at Friesens Corporation

The Last Impression

Everything we do has an impact upon the natural environment. The eco-audit above outlines what can be achieved simply by reducing, reusing, and recycling. It is a start but we would like to do more. Our hope is to make a positive and enduring impression upon our readers and also reduce the ecological impact of our activities. While we trust you will find the information contained in *Shop talk* invaluable, it will eventually become obsolete. Regardless of where you purchased your copy of *Shop talk*, if you purchase the second edition directly from the publisher then you can trade in your old first edition for the second at a discount, and we'll see to it that your old book is appropriately recycled. In the world of publishing, the last impression is always the most current, and we think there is no more current or forward thinking an offer than this!

About the Author

DEE HOBSBAWN-SMITH is partial to dark-roast coffee, eggplant, Riesling and cherries. A classically trained chef, caterer and restaurateur, dee's restaurant, Foodsmith, introduced regional cuisine to Calgarians in 1992–94. When she converted her lifelong love of words into a second career, her restaurant's Wolf stove was the subject of her first published article, in Calgary's *City Palate* in 1995.

An award-winning food writer, her weekly column, "The Curious Cook," appears in the *Calgary Herald*. Dee's work also appears in *City Palate*, *Western Living* and *Northwest Palate*, and other publications. *Shop talk* is her fourth book, and she is currently writing a book about western Canadian growers.

Dee serves on the steering committee of Slow Food Calgary and is a staunch advocate for local cuisine, chefs and growers. She enjoys helping others become competent and comfortable in their own kitchens.

When she has spare time, dee spends it renovating her slightly cranky old house, gardening, writing and reading poetry and prose, painting, cooking, and enjoying music, family and friends. She lives in Calgary with the youngest of her two sons and her pets, a miniature Schnauzer and a feisty Himalayan cat. She is learning to play guitar.

Previous Books by the Same Author

The Curious Cook at Home: Recipes and Secrets from an Adventurous Cook, 2004, North Vancouver, BC: Whitecap.

The Quick Gourmet: Fabulous Meals in Minutes, 1999, North Vancouver, BC: Whitecap.

Skinny Feasts: Deceptively Rich Cooking the Low Fat Way, 1997, North Vancouver, BC: Whitecap.

As a Co-Author

Double Dishing: Women Entertain, (with Chavich, C., Fortier, P., Miller, K., Norton, G., Robinson, S., Siebens, R., Webb, J. and Wood, J.), 2002, North Vancouver, BC: Whitecap.

Dishing: Calgary Women Cook, (with Chavich, C., Fortier, P., Harbrecht, R., Kelly, E., Miller, K., Norton, G., Robinson, S., Siebens, R., Webb, J., and Wood, J.), 2000, North Vancouver, BC: Whitecap.

You can visit the author at:
<http://curiouscook.net>

Feedback & Orders

THE author and publisher have made all reasonable efforts to ensure the information in *Shop talk* is both current and accurate at the time of publication.

Over time, the details of businesses change and, while we plan to publish a new edition biennially, should you discover in the interim, any errors, inaccuracies, or omissions (e-i-o's), we'd be most grateful to hear about them. You can communicate these by sending an e-mail entitled "Shop talk e-i-o's", referencing the business entry by name, the page number, and specific e-i-o to: <lastimpression@shaw.ca>.

All e-i-o submissions will be acknowledged and of them, those considered most grievous will be rewarded with an invitation to the filer to attend the next book launch at which time they will receive a complementary copy of the new edition. Thus remember please, to include your contact details.

IF you would like to order additional copies of *Shop talk*, you may do that by contacting the publisher:

Last Impression Publishing Service
930–30 Avenue NW, Calgary, Alberta T2K 0A1

Phone: (403) 289·5718 • Fax: (403) 289·0157
E-mail: lastimpression@shaw.ca

Price per copy: $23.95 + GST @ 5% = $1.20 + S&H @ $3.85 = $29.00
We'll accept payment by cheque, money order, or VISA.

Name: _____

Address: _____

_____

Phone: _____ Fax: _____

E-mail: _____

Check ONE Means of Payment: Cheque: ☐ Money Order: ☐ VISA: ☐

Card Name: _____

Number: ☐☐☐☐ ☐☐☐☐ ☐☐☐☐ ☐☐☐☐

Expiry: ☐☐ ☐☐ Security Code: ☐☐☐

Signature: _____

Discounts for volume sales are available.
Details are available from the publisher.